PRINCIPLES OF FIELD BIOLOGY AND ECOLOGY

To him who in the love of Nature holds
Communion with her visible forms, she speaks
A various language. . . .

William Cullen Bryant, "Thanatopsis"

PRINCIPLES OF
Field Biology & Ecology

ALLEN H. BENTON
Department of Biology
New York State College for Teachers
Albany, New York

WILLIAM E. WERNER, Jr.
Department of Biology
Blackburn College
Carlinville, Illinois

McGraw-Hill Book Company, Inc.
NEW YORK   TORONTO   LONDON
1958

PREFACE

Up to a century ago, most of the great biologists were field workers and were known as naturalists. Their studies were often based largely on field observations or on data collected by assiduous field work. The latter years of the nineteenth century and the early years of the twentieth century brought about the ascendancy of the laboratory aspects of biology—genetics, physiology, anatomy, and the like—and the naturalist passed into relative oblivion. Work in the field, with uncontrolled nature, was considered by many scientists to be hardly worthy of the true scientific biologist, who wanted controlled experiments. As a result, the laboratory sciences made tremendous strides, while advances in the knowledge of the life and habits of organisms were slow.

About the beginning of this century, events brought about a change in the importance of field biology. The rise of ecology, the increased need for conservation of natural resources and for management of wildlife, and the tremendous upsurge in popular interest in nature study have combined since that time to send thousands of workers into the field. Some are professionals; many are amateurs. Today fifty bird watchers crowd the city parks, where a half-century ago there was one. Amateur biologists may be found pursuing lizards over the deserts of Arizona, watching at a wren's nest in Illinois, and collecting marine plants and animals on Cape Cod. Conservation workers are counting deer herds in Michigan and evaluating grouse cover in New York. Ecologists are measuring the temperature and humidity of gopher burrows in Utah and counting plants on square meters of ground in every state of the union.

Field biology has become the biology of the people, the science of life as it exists everywhere, which everyone can study and everyone can enjoy. It is well that this is true; for as faith without works is dead, so are works without faith. Conservation, ecology, and all other phases of biological research depend for their existence upon the faith and support of an enlightened public. And the surest progenitor of this faith is a consuming interest in, and an adequate knowledge of, nature. It is the purpose of this book to contribute to the stimulation of such interest and to the dissemination of such knowledge of the principles and practices of the field aspects of biology.

As a textbook, this book is designed to meet the needs of the beginning ecology or field biology course. It is assumed that the student will have taken a minimum of six hours of introductory biology courses as a prerequisite. A workbook which complements the text in field and laboratory use is printed by the Burgess Publishing Company, Minneapolis.

It would be impossible to acknowledge all the individuals who have helped us in the preparation of the text. Our colleagues in the teaching of biology, particularly at the New York State College for Teachers at Albany, have assisted us from the outset. Portions of the manuscript have been read and criticized by John Belknap, Mabel French, Lucille Grace, Violet Larney, Paul C. Lemon, Ralph S. Palmer, Daniel Smiley, Lowell D. Uhler, and Alvin G. Whitney. For permission to use illustrations, we are indebted to the following persons and organizations: Richard Axtell, Victor Cahalane, Lloyd G. Ingles, Ralph S. Palmer, Olin S. Pettingill, Jr., Frank Pitelka, Thola Tabor Schenck, Minnie B. Scotland, N. Tinbergen, H. Wayne Trimm, Oxford University Press, New York, Charles Scribner's Sons, New York, National Park Service, New York State Conservation Department, and U.S. Soil Conservation Service.

Our students over the past ten years have been unwitting guinea pigs for much of the information which has found its way into the book, as well as for much which has been left out. Special thanks are due to our department heads, Dr. Paul C. Lemon and Dr. Minnie B. Scotland, for assistance of many kinds.

We are indebted to Blackburn College for secretarial help in the preparation of the manuscript.

Most important of all has been the patient forbearance of our wives, who have suffered through long periods of being "book widows" without complaint.

Allen H. Benton
William E. Werner, Jr.

CONTENTS

INTRODUCTION

The professional biologist of today is highly specialized, and there are thousands of specialized amateur biologists in addition. The well-trained biologist, whether amateur or professional, needs to understand the principles and scope of biology as a whole. This book is an attempt to synthesize some of the widely scattered information primarily concerned with the nonlaboratory aspects of biology and to indicate the importance of this information against the background of the whole field.

The first two chapters are background material, concerned with the history of field biology in America and its present status and importance. Chapter 3 gives the reader a general grounding in taxonomic theory and practice, so that he may better understand the techniques and problems involved in classification.

With the background of general information gleaned from these chapters, we are ready to consider some modern developments and trends in field biology. Ecology, which is discussed in Chap. 4, is one of the rapidly advancing frontiers of science. As we learn about organisms, we realize that any given species tends to occur in a particular type of habitat, and that certain species are usually found together. Bitterns (Fig. I-1) are found among cattails; red squirrels (Fig. I-2) associate with conifers; gray squirrels, with oaks and hickories. It is apparent that plants and animals group themselves into associations or communities, depending upon the environmental conditions in which they are most comfortable. The study of such communities, and of the interrelationships within the communities, is ecology.

The study of communities may lead us to wonder about the development of the different kinds of biological associations. Chapters 5 and 6 lead us into the study of that fascinating and ever-continuing process known as plant succession. Most of us do not live long enough, or in the right place, to see a full cycle of plant succession, but those who watch the reclamation by forest of an abandoned farm, or the growth of new timber after a forest fire, or the revegetation of the bed of a drained lake, are aware of the inexorable progress of this phenomenon. This is the terrestrial, or xerarch, succession. Even less obvious is the

Photo by E. G. Tabor

Fig. I-1. An American bittern, *Botaurus lentiginosus,* on its nest among the cattails.

aquatic, or hydrarch, succession. The life span of man is not long enough for him to observe the change from pond to bog, from bog to dry land.

Human beings tend to regard themselves as the center of things and to evaluate everything in terms of its effect upon human welfare. This natural feeling evidences itself in the tremendous interest in economic biology. Chapter 7 reviews the activities of field workers in economic biology, including game management, forestry, insect control, and other related subjects.

The individuals of a single species within a given area make up a population. In modern biology, the worker often thinks in terms of populations rather than individuals. The problems involved in the study of populations include counting and determining trends in numbers; marking out the range of the species; and finding the relative numbers of the two sexes (in the case of animals) and of the different age classes. Most animal species also have some kind of social organization, however temporary. Chapter 8 considers these and other problems of the study of populations.

Photo by Ralph S. Palmer

Fig. I-2. The red squirrel, *Tamiasciurus hudsonicus*, is usually found in association with coniferous trees.

Concurrent with the development of psychology, the field of animal behavior has shown rapid growth in recent years. Ethologists study the life of animals, their reactions to stimuli, their behavior in mating, feeding, and all the other daily activities. Some of the concepts and methods of these studies are discussed in Chap. 9.

With a background of knowledge about these aspects of field biology, we are ready to branch out into more specialized reading. As a guide to such reading, Chap. 10 discusses some of the important literature of field biology, with particular stress on the less technical, but accurate and authentic, works which have become so common in recent years. Emphasis is also placed on the techniques of exploring biological literature and accumulating facts about any biological problem. Extensive collateral reading at this point will provide a better basis on which to proceed to Chap. 11, which discusses the choice and conduct of a field problem and gives hints about the use of some tools of the field biologist.

Selected references at the end of each chapter provide clues to the student who wishes to read more about any of these subjects. In addition, the Appendix provides an extensive list of books and journals which are of special interest to the field biologist. A glossary of terms permits convenient reference to the meaning of unfamiliar words.

Our aim in this book has been to encourage the use of up-to-date information by the beginner or amateur in field biology, in order to increase his own enjoyment and the sum of human knowledge as well. The measure of our success will be the extent to which you, the reader, make use of the book which you are about to begin.

CHAPTER 1

WHAT, WHY, AND HOW

> The investigation of the life of animals is a concern
> of much trouble and difficulty, and is not to be attained
> but by the active and inquisitive.
>
> *Gilbert White*, "The Natural History of Selborne"

Biology, as we learned in high school, is the study of life. As living beings ourselves, we are naturally inclined toward the study of life in some of its many interesting aspects. We may want to know the names of all the animals and plants around our homes, so we study *taxonomy*, the naming of organisms. We may want to learn more about the way in which life's functions are carried on, so we study *physiology*, which deals with the functions of organs or parts of an organism. We may wonder how an organism gets along with its neighbors in the wild, so we study *ecology*, which concerns organisms in relation to their environment. We may also study *ethology*, animal behavior; *anatomy*, animal or plant structure; *genetics*, the study of heredity; or any of the other branches of biology. The study of life, in one aspect or another, has almost universal appeal.

Field biology may be defined as the study of life under natural conditions, or in its own habitat. As opposed to the strictly experimental disciplines of the laboratory, such as genetics and physiology, field biology is first observational and secondarily experimental. Instead of removing organisms from their native environments to study them in the laboratory, we go where they are and observe them there (Fig. 1-1). If we cannot perform the desired experiments or make the necessary observations under natural conditions, we try to duplicate natural conditions in the laboratory where certain factors can be controlled.

The profession of field biology, or its amateur status as a hobby, is an ancient and honorable one. Whether we begin with Noah, who must have had a sound knowledge of animals to select his breeding stock wisely, or with Aristotle, the first field biologist whose written

Photo by Allen H. Benton

Fig. 1-1. A class may learn facts about organisms which could be discovered in no other way than by actual field collection and study.

works have come down to us more or less intact, we will find a noteworthy line of men of many countries: Gilbert White, the gentle old vicar of Selborne; Jean Henri Fabre, the incomparable observer; Carl von Linné, who as Carolus Linnaeus became the great classifier; John Bartram, the Quaker naturalist; and many others from antiquity to the present (Peattie, 1936).

From the personal point of view, the aesthetic values of field biology are sufficient to justify its existence as a hobby, if not as a profession.

He who listens to the twilight song of the hermit thrush, or thrills to the lonely wail of the coyote, or watches the primeval courtship of the salamander, stores up riches of the mind which neither time nor circumstances can destroy. To some it is a source of gratification to search out the rarer wild flowers in their distant haunts. Others may find satisfaction in the pursuit of birds, and amateur observers have made great contributions to the study of these beautiful creatures. Even the sleek, sinuous beauty of the snakes and lizards has a peculiar

Photo by Allen H. Benton

Fig. 1-2. Workers of the U.S. Bureau of Entomology and Plant Quarantine spraying for insect control.

attraction for some of us. Were there no other value than the aesthetic in the study of nature, its pursuit would be amply justified.

Wherever we look, however, we see the beneficial results of field biology. Control of noxious insects (Fig. 1-2), for example, is now a billion-dollar business, to which each of us contributes through his taxes. Besides its direct effect on our pocketbooks, insect control has an equally important relationship to our very survival, for we must live on the products of our farms, where the front line of the battle between insects and man is formed. The development of new chemicals to combat insects is the work of the chemist, but the use of these chemicals is the duty of the field biologist. New insecticides to combat flies, mosquitoes, and other insect pests are fearfully effective, but what of their effects on other animals such as birds, mammals, and soil invertebrates? It is shortsighted indeed to poison a field for the purpose of killing grubs if the treatment either permits the poison to be ingested by livestock, and hence be transmitted into milk or meat, or kills the earthworms and other soil organisms which help to keep the soil fertile.

Often the field biologist can find biological controls which are effective against pests. A few years ago the pea aphid in parts of the East was controlled more effectively by the importation of millions of lady beetles than by chemicals. Other attempts at biological control by importation of predators have led to disaster, owing to a lack of careful study by competent biologists. The introduction of the mongoose to some of the West Indies to control rats has resulted in the near extermination of many native mammals and birds, while the rat and the mongoose flourish together. The story of the rabbit in Australia is another case in point. From a small original introduction, the population grew until it was estimated to be between one and three billion. Recently field biologists and pathologists have combined to study the introduction of a virus which kills rabbits but apparently does not affect other wildlife. This disease is transmitted by mosquitoes, and should be self-perpetuating. In early experiments, a 99.5 per cent kill of rabbits was secured in some areas. If this experiment succeeds, it will add another notable triumph to the annals of biological control. Anyone with an interest in control problems should read the account of the early experiments of this project (Herman, 1953).

Field Biology in Ecology. In the young science of ecology, the field biologist is undisputed king. Ecology is the more cultured off-spring of the old natural history; indeed, one well-known ecologist (Adams, 1917) has called ecology "the new natural history." Only by careful observation of nature and an intimate knowledge of the habits and characteristics of organisms can ecological data be gathered. Ecological experiments can be, and often are, performed in the laboratory, but correct interpretation depends on knowledge of the living organism in nature. Intelligent solution of the problems of forest culture, land clearance, range management, and many other areas depends upon a broad ecological study of the factors involved.

Field Biology in Taxonomy. Taxonomists, too, realize that study of the living organism may aid in classifying organisms sensibly. The old concept of the taxonomist as a rather musty character, tucked away in a corner surrounded by his bottles, jars, and trays of specimens, was usually unjustified. Certainly it cannot apply to most present-day practitioners of this science. Intelligent description, naming, and identification of animals or plants requires some under-standing of life histories and habits. But early taxonomists occasionally sat in their laboratories and named all the specimens they could secure,

Photo by William E. Werner, Jr.
Fig. 1-3. The mole, *Scalopus aquaticus*, whose huge forepaws, adapted for digging, led early biologists to believe that it was aquatic.

with little or no knowledge of the natural history of the animals and plants with which they dealt. For example, the scientific name of our common mole is *Scalopus aquaticus*. (*Scalopus* is derived from the Greek word for mole; *aquaticus* means "of the water.") This misnomer was given to it because the early European taxonomists mistook the streamlined body, strong shoulders, and scull-shaped forepaws (Fig. 1-3) as adaptations for swimming. In reality, the mole "swims" only through the soil, and is not in the least aquatic.

Such practices of the taxonomists also resulted in different names for different stages of the same species, or for different color phases, or for seasonal or sexual variations. The taxonomy of the American weasels, for example, has occasionally been confused because the males are much larger than females of the same species, averaging 15 per cent to 25 per cent larger and up to 50 per cent heavier (sexual dimorphism) (Fig. 1-4). Taxonomists thus concluded on several occasions that the two sexes represented separate species, or that the male of the small species and the female of a larger species really belonged to the same species. Many such mistakes were made because these workers had only a few specimens, from scattered localities, and had no knowledge of the species from their own field observations. These burdens of useless names are still being weeded out by modern taxonomists (Hall, 1951, pp. 72–80).

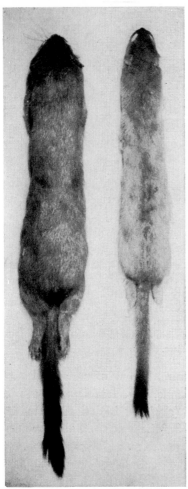

Photo by Allen H. Benton

Fig. 1-4. Male (left) and female of the New York weasel, *Mustela frenata noveboracensis*, showing sexual dimorphism in size.

One of the duties of the taxonomist which assumes great importance today is the discovery of new subspecies—populations which vary in some small manner from other populations of the same species (Fig. 1-5). These forms are of interest to the evolutionist because they represent evolution in action at an observable level (see p. 46). Unfortunately there have been some who sat with their trays of specimens, going over each one with millimeter rule and color guide to find new subspecies, rather than relying upon knowledge gained in field study. This has resulted, of course, in the erection of numerous so-called "millimeter races" and in the application of names to abnormal individuals, both plants and animals. Subsequent study often shows that these populations are not sufficiently distinct to warrant taxonomic recognition. A careful field study, by one who understands

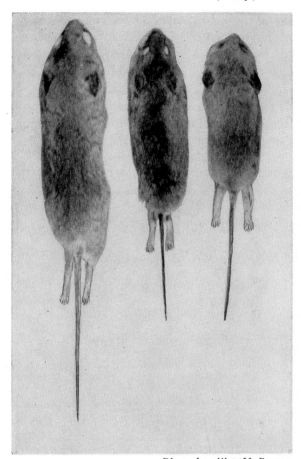

Photo by Allen H. Benton

Fig. 1-5. Three of the fifty-one described subspecies of the deer mouse, *Peromyscus maniculatus*. Left to right, *P. m. gracilis*, which occurs in northeastern United States and southeastern Canada; *P. m. bairdii*, which occurs from the upper Mississippi Valley to the Atlantic Coast; *P. m. gambelli*, which occurs from eastern Washington to Baja California.

their lives, should be performed before supposed subspecies are named rather than after, if this is possible.

An example of the kind of error which can be made is shown in the case of *Scalopus aquaticus anastasae*, a mole which was found on Anastasia Island, off the coast of Florida, and was described as a new form because of the golden color of its ventral surface. The name was accepted for many years until a field student of moles (Eadie, 1954) pointed out that this golden color is a seasonal characteristic, apparently due to glandular activity, and may be found on any individual of this species at the proper season.

Field Biology in Conservation. Conservation is one of the most acute and complex world problems of our generation. The conservation of our biological resources, and their use for the greatest

Photo by Ralph S. Palmer

Fig. 1-6. Thousands of acres of trees must be harvested each year to supply wood products. Forest conservation is thus a matter of growing concern to Americans.

good of the greatest number for the greatest possible length of time, must rest on a sound foundation of knowledge. Such knowledge can be gained only by field study. Our ancestors, in their understandable haste to clear the land and vanquish the wilderness, were led into excesses of destruction. The myth of inexhaustibility, though it should have been blasted by the events of the past century, still clings to the minds of many Americans, while plants and animals pass into extinction, topsoil washes down our rivers, the water table continues to fall, and virgin forests perish before the ax and the saw (Fig. 1-6). With advancing land utilization and increased numbers of sportsmen, many of our native game animals are in danger of extinction, following the dim trail of the Labrador duck and the passenger pigeon. Again the problems fall upon the shoulders of the field biologist. Good land practice must be reconciled with good wildlife conservation practice. Enough game must be produced to satisfy the growing army of hunters—and that in the face of increasing destruction of wildlife habitat. Sportsmen must have more and better information to prove to them that the protection of game is a necessity and not unjust government interference. Farmers must be convinced that game is a valuable crop, worthy of cultivation. Great strides have been made, and monographs, such as that of Bump et al. (1946) on the ruffed grouse, have been produced concerning some of our game species. The situation, however, is still acute, and many important studies remain to be carried on by state conservation departments and U.S. Fish and Wildlife Service workers. The place of predators in the scheme of nature must be much more fully and widely understood, or money will continue to be wasted in bounties which never work. A few thousand dollars spent on a careful investigation by a competent field biologist will permit sensible decisions on the need for predator control and the ways in which it can be attained. An excellent discussion of this many-faceted problem has been presented by Latham (1951).

Field Biology in Agriculture. Our farms today are producing many crops which were unknown a half century ago. Some of these, of course, are "manufactured" varieties, produced by genetical research. In a broad sense, the determination of desirable characteristics to be developed by geneticists was the work of field biologists. But even more direct is the influence of the introduction of new crops discovered by field workers of the U.S. Department of Agriculture and transported to this country to become important economic plants. Soybeans, kudzu, bird's-foot trefoil, and many others are recent additions to the farmers' operations, and have greatly increased the agricultural productivity of the nation.

THE FIELD BIOLOGIST'S SKILLS

In order to make these contributions to human knowledge and welfare, the field biologist must possess certain skills and use certain techniques. Let us now consider briefly the tools which he must acquire in the way of intellectual equipment and how he uses these tools in the pursuit of his studies.

The Scientific Method. The scientist in any field proceeds by a series of steps known as the scientific method. In its simplest form, this method consists of five steps, which may be listed in this way:

1. THE PROBLEM. A question or questions for which the answers are unknown. The formulation of the problem is often one of the most difficult steps in a study.

2. ACCUMULATION OF FACTS (DATA). Study of literature, field observations, asking questions.

3. FORMULATION OF A HYPOTHESIS. On the basis of data accumulated, a suggested answer to the problem may appear.

4. TESTING THE HYPOTHESIS. Experiments, observations, and continual checking of facts which bear on the suggested answer.

5. INTEGRATION AND INTERPRETATION OF DATA. If the evidence supports the hypothesis, it may be possible to reach a conclusion. A hypothesis may from the basis for a law in some cases. If data tend to disprove the hypothesis, we must return to Step 3 and start again.

In pursuing his studies in this manner, the field biologist must know many things. He must be able to identify the various species of plants and animals, often in the field. He must know how to evaluate their importance in the community, by means of counting and by studying their ecology, size, and distribution. He must be able to recognize unusual occurrences, which means that he must have adequate knowledge of animal behavior, seasonal phenomena in plants and animals, and other things which may affect the outcome of his study.

A Biological Study. As an example of the way in which a field biologist works, let us review an investigation which was carried out in accordance with the scientific method, using the various skills which we have mentioned.

1. THE PROBLEM. A serious infection of trees, the Dutch elm disease, threatened to destroy the native American elm population in parts of the eastern United States. This disease had caused the loss of millions of dollars' worth of shade trees and much timber. Certain bark beetles, when they emerged from pupation in diseased trees and flew away to feed, spread the disease by carrying the spores of the fungus to healthy elms. A method was devised to control the spread of the disease by spraying trees with the recently developed insecticide DDT, which

Photo by Allen H. Benton

Fig. 1-7. A DDT spray, applied twice during the spring and summer, was found to be effective in controlling the spread of Dutch elm disease.

killed the beetles before they could pierce the barks of healthy elms (Fig. 1-7). Complaints were received, however, that birds, fishes, and other animals were killed by the spray.

The operators of the spray program and the owners of the trees were anxious to save the elms, if possible. Nonetheless, popular opinion would not tolerate wholesale destruction of birds and mammals. A biologist was therefore assigned to the job of evaluating the toll of wildlife caused by spraying in this locality.

The specific problem faced by the biologist can be worded in these questions:

a. Does this operation kill birds and other wildlife?

b. Is the kill, if any, of wildlife sufficient to outweigh the value of the elms saved?

c. If so, can means be devised to reduce the kill without losing the value of the spraying?

2. ACCUMULATION OF DATA. DDT spray, in the concentration used in this program, had been shown in previous studies to be lethal to birds and mammals. Dead birds, mammals, and fishes had been found in the spray area soon after spraying but had not been analyzed to discover the cause of death. The local people believed that DDT was causing a great number of casualties. No accurate count of animals killed was available, however, and only the rather untrustworthy estimates of landowners gave any idea of the actual mortality.

The spraying was done twice each year, once in April–May and again in July. Reports indicated that mortality had been higher after the spring spray, but careful questioning elicited the fact that much of the mortality had occurred in areas which had been sprayed twice.

3. FORMULATION OF A HYPOTHESIS. With the accumulated data in mind, certain hypotheses could be stated:

a. DDT was responsible for some mortality of local wildlife.

b. The effect was most marked after the spring spraying.

c. Areas receiving heavy concentrations of spray, because of large numbers of elms or double doses of spray, were most seriously affected.

4. TESTING THE HYPOTHESIS. In order to test these hypotheses in a scientific manner and to secure additional data which might shed some light on the problem, a study area was chosen in the midst of a section heavily populated with elms which had been sprayed (Fig. 1-8). A check area of similar vegetation was chosen outside the sprayed section. Studies of the bird populations of these two areas were then made by standard methods, both before and after spraying. Bird nests were studied on both areas to determine nestling mortality. Dead birds and mammals were collected from both areas and analyzed for pres-

ence of DDT in the tissues. Observations were made to determine whether the spraying caused any variation from normal behavior.

5. INTERPRETATION OF DATA. Experimental and observational data, accumulated through two spray seasons, permitted the investigators to

Photo by Allen H. Benton

Fig. 1-8. A study area within the DDT-sprayed zone, where elms are abundant on both sides of the street.

reach definite conclusions and to make recommendations in regard to improvement in the spray program from the wildlife viewpoint. These data substantially supported the hypotheses stated in (3), and the following conclusions were drawn:

a. Chemical analysis of the carcasses of dead birds and mammals and observation of living birds indicated that DDT was causing some mortality.

b. Fewer dead birds were found after the summer than after the spring spraying.

c. Most mortality occurred in areas where elms were numerous.

d. Most of the birds killed in summer were young and nestling birds.

e. Adult populations were not significantly reduced following the summer spraying.

f. Most of the mortality in spring involved migrant birds, and occurred in late April and May.

From these conclusions, the investigator made the following recommendations:

a. Spraying should be as light as possible, consistent with adequate beetle control.

b. Spring spraying should be completed as early as possible, to avoid the peak of bird migration.

c. Summer spraying should be done after the peak of the nesting season is past, to avoid excessive mortality among nestlings.

d. Mortality among vertebrates other than birds was not widespread or heavy, and need not be considered a serious hazard.

Although the study did not prove conclusively that these measures would be effective in reducing wildlife mortality, it did produce data which could lead to immediate adjustments in the procedure of spraying (Blagbrough, 1952).

As for the techniques used by the field biologist who made these investigations, they may be summarized as follows:

1. Formulation of experimental procedure; setting up comparable areas for study.

2. Counting natural populations (in this case elm trees and birds).

3. Identification of various organisms, particularly trees and birds; finding bird nests.

4. Field study of the organisms involved, with particular reference to distribution, behavior, and the like.

These techniques and similar ones concerned with other groups of organisms are so generally useful to the field biologist that they can be used in almost any problem of wildlife research. They require ability to identify organisms, knowledge and understanding of the normal behavior and habits of animals, and the ability to formulate a field problem. These are among the important requirements for the field biologist, the *sine qua non* for the student of nature. The field biologist might well take for his slogan the one which hung on the wall of the famous Russian physiologist Pavlov: "Observation, and again observation."

REFERENCES CITED

ADAMS, CHARLES C. 1917. The new natural history: ecology. *Amer. Mus. J.*, 17:491–492.

BLAGBROUGH, HARRY. 1952. Reducing wildlife hazards in Dutch elm disease control. *J. Forestry*, 50:468–469.

BUMP, GARDINER, ET AL. 1947. "The Ruffed Grouse: Life History, Propagation, Management." New York State Conservation Department, Albany. xxxvi and 915 pp.

EADIE, W. ROBERT. 1954. Skin gland activity and pelage description in moles. *J. Mammal.*, 35:186–196.

HALL, E. RAYMOND. 1951. American weasels. *University of Kansas Publication, Museum of Natural History*, 4:1–466.

HERMAN, CARLTON M. 1953. A review of experiments in biological control of rabbits in Australia. *J. Wildl. Mgt.*, 17:482–486.

LATHAM, ROBERT. 1951. "The Ecology and Economics of Predator Management." Final Report, P.-R. Project 36-R. Pennsylvania Game Commission, Harrisburg, 96 pp.

PEATTIE, DONALD C. 1936. "Green Laurels: The Lives and Achievements of the Great Naturalists." Simon and Schuster, Inc., New York. xxiii and 368 pp.

SUGGESTED READING

BATES, MARSTON. 1950. "The Nature of Natural History." Charles Scribner's Sons, New York.

BEEBE, WILLIAM (ED.) 1944. "The Book of Naturalists." Alfred A. Knopf, Inc., New York.

CHAPTER 2

A BRIEF HISTORY OF
FIELD BIOLOGY IN AMERICA

It is the exclusive property of man, to contemplate and to reason on the great book of nature. She gradually unfolds herself to him, who with patience and perseverance, will search into her mysteries; and when the memory of the present and of past generations shall be obliterated, he shall enjoy the high privilege of living in the minds of his successors, as he has been advanced in the dignity of his nature, by the labours of those who went before him.

Carolus Linnaeus, "Species Plantarum"

Field biology has always been an important aspect of American cultural and intellectual life. Some of our most illustrious men have contributed to its development, and its course has had a profound effect on the history of our country. In a single chapter, it will be possible to follow only the main stream of accomplishment, with occasional brief excursions into some of the more interesting side branches. In general, we shall attempt to trace the development of ideas and movements, but in so doing it will be necessary to discuss the men who gave birth to the ideas and gave direction to the movements. Although much that is important has occurred in the past half-century, we shall, for the sake of perspective, end our survey with the beginning of the 1900s, so as to include the formation and early years of several great movements which had their origin around the turn of the century.

THE COLONIAL PERIOD

The years of colonization and expansion, from 1607 to 1775, saw the laying of the cornerstone of American field biology. The workers of those early days were scattered, in both space and time, and for the most part worked independently. These pioneer collectors and observers were in many cases only passing visitors to our shores, such as Peter Kalm, the Swedish botanist. Others, however, stayed for longer periods or were indigenous naturalists who spent their entire lives in America. It is with this latter group that we shall mainly concern ourselves.

The seventeenth-century American had little time or interest for the study of nature on the new continent. Some early travelers, like the redoubtable John Smith of Virginia, wrote books about their travels, in which they described some of the most interesting plants and animals, often with fanciful additions. The first biologist to do any work of significance in the colonies, however, was Thomas Harriot (1560–1621). Harriot was a friend of Sir Walter Raleigh, with whom he came to America in 1585. In "A Briefe and True Report of the New Found Land of Virginia," published in 1590, he described more than a hundred animals and many plants.

Other students of nature followed in small numbers through the seventeenth century. In 1637, King Charles I dispatched a young man named John Tradescant to collect plants and shells in Virginia. Tradescant's father was a botanist, and the surname is commemorated in the generic name of the spiderworts, *Tradescantia*. A few years later, in the 1660s, John Bannister, a friend of the English biologist John Ray, came to Virginia and collected biological materials. His paper on the plants of Virginia, published in 1886, was probably the first taxonomic paper produced in America. Bannister, a young man of great promise, was killed on a plant collecting expedition when he fell among the rocks at the falls of the Roanoke.

In New England, a few semiscientific works on biology were published during the seventeenth century. William Wood's "New England Prospect" and Thomas Morton's "New England Canaan" were more literary than scientific. At a somewhat higher level of biological accuracy were John Josselyn's "New England's Rarities" (1672) and

"Account of Two Voyages to New England" (1675). The century ended, however, with little important knowledge of American plants and animals having been published.

The pioneers, whether hunters, trappers or farmers, were vitally interested in the wild animals and vegetation which they had to conquer, but few of them were able to write, and even fewer cared to record the knowledge which they had accumulated. Until there was time for a cultured and leisurely class to develop, observations on nature were made available only through travel books or the occasional notes in the journal of a missionary, doctor, or other educated person.

The beginning of the eighteenth century, however, saw the influx into America of many Europeans of scientific bent. Some came to settle, but others came for the express purpose of discovering and collecting the rich natural wonders of America. To Virginia, about 1700, came John Mitchell, a biologist of some ability. He remained in Virginia until 1746, when he returned to England. His most important work was his "Dissertation upon the Elements of Botany and Zoology" (1738), but he also contributed specimens to European taxonomists. The beautiful little partridgeberry, *Mitchella repens*, bears his name.

John Clayton. Close upon Mitchell's heels came John Clayton (1685–1773), a botanist, who arrived in Virginia in 1705 to serve as a clerk. He worked long and faithfully in this capacity, and in his spare time collected plants and seeds for transmission to friends and acquaintances in Europe. As the years passed he became well known, and by mid-century he was corresponding with Linnaeus and other European biologists. The great "Flora Virginica" of Gronovius, published in 1739–1743, was based largely on the work of Clayton. The second edition, having a publication date of 1762, after the Linnaean system was established, is the basis of many botanical names which still stand. Clayton is remembered in the generic name of the spring beauty, *Claytonia*, named for him by his friend and coworker, Gronovius. Before his death in 1773, Clayton became a correspondent of Benjamin Franklin, Thomas Jefferson, and most of the other prominent scientists of his day. His manuscripts and specimens, unfortunately, were destroyed by fire during the Revolutionary War.

Cadwallader Colden. In 1710, Cadwallader Colden (1688–1776) arrived in Philadelphia from Europe. He had studied medicine in

London, and came to the New World to begin his career as a doctor. Being of a friendly and prepossessing personality, he became intimate with important New York politicians, and in 1718 moved there in expectation of a political appointment. This he received in 1720, when he became surveyor-general of the colony. He spent the rest of his life in public service, and in his spare time wrote numerous treatises on botany, medicine, mathematics, and philosophy. Colden's most important biological work was an extensive paper dealing with new American plants, which Linnaeus published in Sweden in 1749. Colden's daughter, Jane, was also a capable botanist.

Mark Catesby. In 1712 one of the great figures of American natural history landed in Virginia for a visit. He was Mark Catesby (1679–1749), who had studied natural history in England, and who immediately succumbed to the fascination of the New World. In 1719 he returned to England to secure financial backing for a natural history survey of the Southeast. He was successful in securing money, and in 1722 he was back in this country in what is now South Carolina. For four years he studied and collected in the Southeast and in the Bahamas. In 1726 he returned to England to write a report on his collections. This "Natural History of Carolina, Florida and the Bahama Islands" was published in three parts, from 1731 to 1748. Before his death, Catesby was recognized for his pioneer work by election to the Royal Society. Since his publications appeared before the work of Linnaeus, few of his scientific names of organisms are still in use today; but he is commemorated in the scientific name of the bullfrog, which Linnaeus named *Rana catesbiana* in his honor.

Many European travelers capitalized on their experiences by writing books upon their return to Europe. Much of our information about the status of American wildlife and plants at that time has been gleaned from the works of such travelers as Kalm,* Anbury,† Lahontan,‡ and Campbell.§ Other visitors made somewhat longer stays and contributed

---

* Kalm, Peter. 1770–1771. "Travels into North America." Trans. from Swedish by J. R. Forster. 2 vols. vol. 1, 414 pp.; vol. 2, 423 pp. London.

† Anbury, Thomas. 1789. "Travels through the Interior Part of America, in a Series of Letters." vol. 1. London.

‡ Lahontan, Louis Armand deLom D'Arce. 1703. "Some New Voyages to North America." London.

§ Campbell, P. 1793. "Travels in the Interior Inhabited Parts of North America in the Years 1791 and 1792." Edinburgh.

markedly to our knowledge of the flora and fauna. Outstanding among these were André Michaux and his son François, who together laid the foundation for American forestry. François's book on North American trees remains one of the great classics of botany.

In Charleston, South Carolina, Dr. Alexander Garden collected all manner of biological specimens from 1750 until the Revolutionary War. After the war he returned to England, but his biological career is commemorated in the name *Gardenia*, familiar to all lovers of flowers.

The Bartrams. Meanwhile, a completely untutored biologist was beginning a life work which would have a tremendous and permanent effect on American field biology. John Bartram (1699–1777) was described by classifier Carolus Linnaeus as "the greatest natural botanist in the world." Bartram was also interested in every other phase of natural history. A Quaker farmer, he became so obsessed with nature that he risked his life on travels to collect natural objects for European biologists and curio seekers. In 1728 he established a horticultural garden near Philadelphia, to which he brought all the new plants found in his travels. Through correspondence with the English botanist Peter Collinson, he was brought into contact with Linnaeus in Sweden, Gronovius in Holland, and other important European biologists. He corresponded extensively with Clayton and Colden, and was acquainted with Benjamin Franklin and George Washington. His garden on the Schuylkill River was a popular haunt of the scientifically inclined intellectuals of Philadelphia, and his influence may well have been important in the founding of the Academy of Natural Sciences of Philadelphia some thirty-five years after his death.

Photo by Popular Science Monthly, New York

Fig. 2-1. William Bartram, 1739–1823.

William Bartram (Fig. 2-1) was the only one of John Bartram's children to follow in his father's footsteps. He started his adult life as a trader but soon returned to his first love—exploring, collecting, and drawing natural objects. In 1791 he published an account of his travels in the Southern states. This book met with great acclaim in Europe, was translated into several languages, and brought Bartram before the eyes of the European biologists. A fine ornithologist as well as a botanist, he was of assistance to Alexander Wilson in his work on American birds. In honor of his friend, Wilson named the upland plover *Bartramia longicauda.*

Early Scientific Societies. By the beginning of the nineteenth century, exploratory work in the Eastern states was well under way. The number of active workers was increasing, although it was still pitifully small. Nonetheless, learned societies began to spring up in cultural centers, and these societies attracted new workers into the field. The first of these groups was the American Philosophical Society, organized in 1743 at Philadelphia. Since its early years under the aegis of such notable presidents as Benjamin Franklin and Thomas Jefferson, it has had steady growth and increasing influence. In 1812, the Academy of Natural Sciences of Philadelphia was formed. Led by such able men as Thomas Say, Thomas Nuttall, and Gerard Troost, it became, and remains today, an active force in the study of natural history. In 1817, the Lyceum of Natural History of New York was founded, and this organization still exists as the New York Academy of Sciences. Boston followed in 1830 with the formation of the Boston Society of Natural History.

THE ERA OF AUDUBON

Although the few learned societies of the early nineteenth century did much to advance the study of science, American field biology in this period was advanced largely by a group of the most ill-assorted and eccentric geniuses probably ever assembled in a single country at one time. Most of them came from abroad: a gay French dancing master turned trader; an eccentric cosmopolite of French ancestry, born in Turkey, and trained in Sicily; a poor Scottish weaver and poet, out to make his fortune in the new world. Among them, they scanned the whole field of natural history, and their contributions to science were so vast as to be almost unbelievable in this age of specialization. In those frontier days they ranged from the east coast to the

Mississippi, and occasionally joined expeditions to the Rockies or the west coast, collecting, observing, describing as they went. Three of these great naturalists, each of whom followed his own genius wherever it led him, seem to group naturally together.

John James Audubon. Certainly the best known of the towering figures in the field of natural history in that era was John James Audubon (Fig. 2-2). Born in 1785, the illegitimate son of a French sea captain and a Creole of Santo Domingo, he was legally adopted by his father and educated in France. In 1803 he was sent to America to work on his father's plantation in Pennsylvania. Much more interested in dancing, drawing, music, and sport than in the work of the plantation, he cut a dashing figure in the drawing rooms of the local aristocracy. When it became evident that he was not much of a plantation manager, he joined in a trading venture on the frontier in Kentucky. He took with him his young wife, Lucy Bakewell Audubon, who was to be the balance wheel of his existence for many difficult years. Audubon preferred to spend his time collecting and drawing birds

Fig. 2-2. John James Audubon, 1785–1851.

rather than tending his store, and bankruptcy followed wherever he went. Apparently he had no intention of capitalizing on his interests and talents until a chance meeting with Alexander Wilson, who was preparing his great work on American birds, crystallized his ideas and set him to work on a similar project. He began to travel widely, while his wife supported the family by teaching in Cincinnati. In 1823, Audubon felt that his work was ready for publication, but no American publisher would handle it. Undiscouraged, he sailed for England to find a sponsor there. An exhibition of his paintings in London met with overwhelming success. In a matter of days he secured a publisher and engraver as well as a host of influential friends. After a trip to France, he returned to America as a sort of public hero and elder statesman among naturalists. Always quite confident of his abilities and prospects, he was not noticeably affected by public adulation. He continued to work at his painting and writing; before his death he completed his "Ornithological Biography," which consisted of life-history studies of North American birds, and the paintings for "The Quadrupeds of North America," for which John Bachman did the text.

Alexander Wilson. The other giant of American ornithology was Audubon's opposite in many ways. Alexander Wilson (1776–1813) was born in Scotland to poor parents who apprenticed him to a weaver. A sensitive and poetic person by nature, Wilson was outraged by the treatment of the laborers of his day. His satirical lampoons of local industrialists caused him to be *persona non grata* in his own town, and he decided to try his luck in America. Although his education was largely self-administered, he succeeded in getting employment as a teacher, and eventually found his way to a school near the Bartram plantation at Philadelphia. Upon discovering Wilson's absorbed interest in birds, William Bartram and others of his circle persuaded Wilson to embark upon an ambitious project—nothing less than a monograph on North American ornithology. For a person without money, without literary or artistic training, and with no background whatever in scientific study, this might seem like a foolhardy venture; and so it appeared to most of the people who Wilson hoped would contribute to the support of such a study. Nonetheless, Wilson persevered, and succeeded in selling enough subscriptions to his work to be able to begin publication in 1809. It was a monumental opus, in nine volumes, but Wilson did not live to enjoy the fruits of his labors. He died in Philadelphia in 1813, before the last volumes of his life work appeared.

C. S. Rafinesque. While the birds were absorbing the attention of Audubon and Wilson, the rest of the biological world was not being neglected. One man, a genius of tremendous proportions, encompassed the whole field of biology (and many other fields as well), and threw away most of the results of his genius by careless work and personal eccentricities. Constantine Samuel Rafinesque-Schmaltz (1783–1840) was born of French and German parents in Turkey. Soon thereafter, his family moved to Italy, where young Constantine became interested in natural history and published his first work on botany. In 1802, after the death of his father, he came to America, and soon fell in with the Philadelphia naturalists, who had much influence on the direction of field biology in America. Because of his extensive knowledge of botany, Rafinesque hoped to secure the position of botanist for the Lewis and Clark Expedition, but failing to do so, he returned to Italy in 1805. Here he married, and two children were born. His son died at an early age, and a few years later his wife ran away with a traveling entertainer, taking their daughter with her. Rafinesque, heartbroken and embittered, gathered together his extensive notes and journals on American and European natural history, packed up his collections, and embarked again for America. Off Long Island his ship was wrecked and all his notes and collections were destroyed; Rafinesque was fortunate to escape with his life.

With this background it is perhaps a little easier to understand Rafinesque's later career. For several years he wandered over the United States, tutoring here and there, meeting other biologists, professional and amateur, and collecting and describing plants, fishes, mammals, insects, mollusks, and practically everything which came to his attention. In 1819 he was enabled, through a friend, to obtain the post of professor of natural history at Transylvania University, in Lexington, Kentucky. He was a popular and talented teacher, but his talents did not extend to getting along with others. Although these were the most productive years of his life, he antagonized many of his colleagues by careless work, descriptions based on hearsay, and attacks on the ability and character of those whom he disliked. In 1825, the president of Transylvania University dismissed him from his position, and Rafinesque again set out on his wanderings. After visiting other biologists and teachers, such as Amos Eaton at Troy, New York, John Torrey in New York City, and his old friends at Philadelphia, Rafinesque settled down in Philadelphia to attempt to make a living. An abortive banking scheme kept him in funds for a time. An offer of money for collecting materials for Cuvier in France was withdrawn when Cuvier died. Worn out by cancer, embittered by his misfortune, Rafinesque died in 1840, and only the vigilance of a friend saved his body from being sold to a medical school to pay for his back rent.

A number of other persons with an interest in natural history worked in the United States during this period. Manasseh Cutler (1745–1823) was the first to publish a systematic account of the plants of New England. A Congregational minister, Cutler was also a lawyer, physician, and scientist, and one of the early followers of the Linnaean system. In Pennsylvania another minister, Gotthilf Muhlenberg, published a catalogue of North American plants in 1813, listing 2,800 species. A genus of grasses, *Muhlenbergia*, is one of several scientific memorials of his name. Still another cleric, John Bachman, collaborated with Audubon in their great monograph "The Quadrupeds of North America," and was competent in other fields of natural history as well.

THE NEW HARMONY MOVEMENT

A very large proportion of the biologists of the early part of the nineteenth century were affected in one way or another by a remarkable social experiment which was carried on at this time. In 1824, Robert Owen, an English industrialist with a remarkable social conscience for one of his generation, purchased the village of Harmonie, Indiana, from the Rappites, a religious sect who were establishing a new community farther up the Ohio River. Here Owen planned to organize the world's first scientific community, which he called New Harmony. His plan was to gather one or two thousand people who wished to take part in his social experiment which promised security, culture, and an easy life in return for giving up family life and personal property.

Owen chose William Maclure, a geologist from Philadelphia, as director of education for New Harmony, and Maclure enthusiastically began to gather suitable personnel for his "university." The group sailed from Philadelphia to New Harmony in a small keelboat satirically dubbed the "Boat-load of Knowledge." Among the notables involved in this journey, two were field biologists of great ability.

Thomas Say. Thomas Say (1787–1834) had nearly the genius of Rafinesque but none of Rafinesque's eccentricity. The son of a physician, and great-grandson of John Bartram, he was fascinated by plants and animals from early youth. At the age of fifteen, unable to see any future in science, he took up an apprenticeship in his father's apothecary shop.

For some years Say and a few friends of similar scientific bent met occasionally at the shop of another apothecary, John Speakman, to discuss natural history. In 1812, Speakman suggested that they form a scientific society and have regular meetings. This proposal met with general favor and resulted in the formation of the Academy of Natural Sciences of Philadelphia. Say, who by now was in charge of the apothecary shop, gave so much time to the new Academy that his business went rapidly downhill and eventually failed. Say, no doubt with a sigh of relief at having been so easily relieved of his burdens, moved into the Academy museum and began to spend all his time in the pursuit of his studies.

In 1817, Say published a part of what was to have been a complete survey of North American insects. Before it was finished, however, he had taken up the study of mollusks and was well versed in other fields of natural history, so that this first great work remained incomplete. His extensive knowledge led to his employment, in 1819, as geologist with the Long expedition to the Rocky Mountains. The expedition traveled over much of the prairie between the Mississippi and the foothills of the Rockies, collecting hundreds of unknown species. As a well-known zoologist, Say was appointed, in 1822, to the chair of Natural History at the University of Pennsylvania. Here he remained until 1825, when his friend Maclure persuaded him to take part in the New Harmony movement as superintendent of literature. He retained this position until his death in 1834, producing voluminous works on insects and mollusks. It is said that Say described more species of animals than have been described by any other single American biologist.

Charles LeSueur. Charles Alexander LeSueur (1776–1843) was a French artist who became interested in natural history while on an expedition to Australia. In 1815 he came to America with William Maclure and settled in Philadelphia. His interest in science led him to the Academy of Natural Sciences, where he served as curator while teaching art for a living. After joining the New Harmony movement in 1825, he made numerous trips to the Mississippi Valley and the Southeast, specializing in the study of fishes. His studies and descriptions laid the groundwork for American ichthyology, and with that of Rafinesque, his work resulted in the discovery of most of the species of eastern fishes. When the New Harmony experiment failed, after Say's death, LeSueur returned to France, where he died in 1846.

Many other scientists visited and worked at New Harmony during its brief existence. Rafinesque visited there from time to time, and European visitors like Charles Lyell and Prince Maximilian du Weid stopped by in the course of their travels. With the demise of New

Harmony, there developed in American biology a vacuum which had no immediate prospect of being filled.

PIONEER BIOLOGY TEACHERS

Biology, however, had for some time been assuming an air of intellectual respectability by being taught in American colleges. In 1768 a course in botany was given at the College of Philadelphia, by Adam Kuhn, and the course was continued under William Bartram in 1782. The first natural history course in this country was given at Harvard by Dr. Benjamin Waterhouse, starting in 1788. Waterhouse was soon joined in the field of biology teaching by Benjamin S. Barton (Fig. 2-3) at the College of Philadelphia in 1789, Samuel L. Mitchill at Columbia University in 1792, and Thomas Cooper at Dickinson College in 1811. In most cases, these early teachers were chemists, physicists, geologists, or physicians, who were given the chair of natural history because they had the closest approach to biological training which was available at that time. Waterhouse was joined at Harvard in 1805 by William Peck,

Photo by Popular Science Monthly, New York

Fig. 2-3. Benjamin S. Barton, 1766–1815.

a zoologist of great promise. Peck, however, died in 1823, and was succeeded by Thomas Nuttall, who was appointed curator of botany. Nuttall was of a retiring nature and did not enjoy teaching, so he remained at Harvard for only a few years, after which he resigned to travel and study. Those who have read Richard Henry Dana's classic sea adventure, "Two Years before the Mast," may recall that the ship on which Dana was a sailor picked up Thomas Nuttall at Monterey, California, and gave him transportation back around the Horn to Boston. Nuttall's place at Harvard remained vacant for some years, although lectures in natural history were given in the meantime by T. W. Harris, a physician, librarian, and amateur entomologist. Meanwhile, Nuttall became famous for his treatises on botany and ornithology, before returning to England to live on the family estate which he had inherited.

In 1842, the professorship of natural history at Harvard was given to Asa Gray, whose works on botany had already placed him in the front rank of American scientists. During this same period Amos Eaton had given a series of lectures on natural history at Amherst College and had opened a school at Troy, New York, the forerunner of Rensselaer Polytechnic Institute, where he taught geology, chemistry, and natural history. Besides his classroom teaching, Eaton was a popular lecturer and tutored many interested amateurs in the sciences.

Fig. 2-4. Louis Agassiz, 1807–1873.

At Dickinson College in Pennsylvania, Spencer Fullerton Baird was employed to teach natural history, starting in 1846. Baird was the first to introduce field study of natural history into the American college curriculum, although he was only a short step ahead of another famous biologist who had already done much the same sort of thing in Europe.

Louis Agassiz. This European pioneer in biology teaching was Louis Agassiz (Fig. 2-4) (1807–1873) who, after receiving degrees from several universities in his native Switzerland and elsewhere in Europe, and writing several monographs on geology and natural history, came to Boston in 1846 to deliver a series of lectures. A noted authority and a fine lecturer, he soon became a famous figure in the intellectual circles of New England. In 1848, he accepted the position of professor of natural history at Harvard, and soon became the leading American proponent of natural history study. Students flocked to his classes, and his students and associates soon spread his knowledge and his methods over the entire country. His famous dictum, "Study nature, not books," has been the rallying cry of naturalists ever since. He did not hesitate, however, to produce books for people to study. Among his works are four volumes of a proposed ten-volume work on the natural history of the United States, which was never finished. He founded the first American biological station at Penikese Island, and undoubtedly had more influence on American biological thought and teaching in the last century than any other single person.

GOVERNMENT BIOLOGISTS

At about the time Agassiz came to America, a new trend in biology appeared—the entrance of government into biological research. In 1841, T. W. Harris wrote a "Report on Insects Injurious to Vegetation," the cost of which was partly defrayed by the state of Massachusetts. In New York, under the influence of Amos Eaton and other scientists, a series on the natural history of New York was published, with five volumes on zoology by James De-Kay and two on botany by John Torrey (Fig. 2-5), as well as others on geology, mineralogy, and agriculture. Although George Washington, in his annual message to Congress for 1796, had requested funds for the establishment of a national board of agriculture, it was not until 1853 that such a bureau was formed, within the framework of the U.S. Patent Office. In 1846 the Smithsonian Institution was established in Washington under government supervision, and in 1850 Spencer Fullerton Baird was employed as assistant secretary. Under his leadership, the museum there soon became the best in the entire country. In 1871 a national Fish Commission was formed, with Baird as its head. In connection with this work, Baird founded the marine biological station at Woods Hole, Massachusetts, which remains an important education and research center to the present time. Baird was a prodigious worker with a passion for accuracy, and his monumental works on mammals, birds, reptiles, and fishes are still used by biologists.

Photo by Popular Science Monthly, New York

Fig. 2-5. John Torrey, 1796–1873.

In spite of the study of insects by Say and other workers, little official notice had been taken of entomology. In the 1870s, however, an outbreak of migratory locusts brought about the establishment of a national Entomological Commission. C. V. Riley was the head of this commission, and continued active in this work until his death in 1895. By that time the Commission had advanced to a Division of Entomology in the Department of Agriculture, doing extensive field work all over the country.

These pioneer workers in governmental biology were so successful that in a short time state entomologists, botanists, and zoologists began to appear all over the country. In 1878, the states of New Hampshire and California formed state game commissions, and similar organizations soon appeared in other states. Meanwhile, the United States Fish Commission had been formed, and a forestry agent, Franklin Hough, had been appointed in the Department of Agriculture in 1876. The trend continued with the establishment of a Division of Economic Ornithology and Mammalogy in the Department of Agriculture in 1885. This division later became the Bureau of Biological Survey, which was combined with the Bureau of Fisheries in 1940 to become the present Fish and Wildlife Service. State experimental stations began with one in Connecticut in 1875, and the idea soon spread to other states.

THE RISE OF POPULAR NATURAL HISTORY

Meanwhile the work of colleges and private individuals continued to progress. Colleges staffed by the students of Louis Agassiz, or by like-minded biologists, began to teach more and better biology. The emergence of the theory of evolution in England gave impetus to biological study, both among the proponents and opponents of the theory. Manuals of biology for the use of amateurs began to appear, though most were too technical for the ordinary layman. David Starr Jordan published his "Manual of the Vertebrate Animals" in 1876, while Asa Gray's "Manual of Botany" and Elliott Coues's "Key to North American Birds" appeared earlier. Edward Drinker Cope and Spencer Fullerton Baird had laid the foundation for further study of reptiles, amphibians, mammals, and fishes. Monographs of most of the great natural groups of plants and animals had been completed. With the completion of the transcontinental railroad, almost every corner of the country had been explored, at least cursorily. Biology had become a field so vast and compartmentalized that the old days of the untrained naturalist were gone forever. The naturalist, in the sense in which the term is often used, had lost his place in professional biology. The closest approach to the old natural history was the field work of the U.S. Biological Survey (later the U.S. Fish and Wildlife Service) with such scientists as C. Hart Merriam (author of the life-zone theory), Vernon Bailey, and Bailey's talented wife, Merriam's sister Florence. Naturalists in the armed forces, such as Elliott Coues and Edgar Mearns, studied nature in the far places to which their duty took them.

Biology in many colleges was confined to the laboratory, where great challenges confronted the student of comparative anatomy, embryology, genetics, and evolution. Field biology had become temporarily a sort of stepchild of science, with undoubted economic significance and some public appeal, but the great days of natural history seemed to have passed.

THE NEW ERA OF FIELD BIOLOGY

In the last quarter of the nineteenth century, several great movements were born which were destined to bring about the rise of field biology, amateur and professional, to a new peak of popularity and importance. With a brief review of the early development of each of these movements, we must end our glance at the background of field biology.

The Conservation Movement. Americans have been brought up, since the settlement of the colonies, to regard nature as something that must be conquered. Forests were to be eliminated to make way for farms; wild animals to be destroyed if they stood in the way of progress; land to be exploited for what could be wrung from it, and then abandoned for the land over the next mountain. We ought not to blame the pioneers for the immense energy with which they compassed this destruction, for it was a product of the times and the circumstances. People believed the myth that resources are inexhaustible, that there will always be more land, more forests, more wildlife, more minerals.

With the later years of the nineteenth century, this myth was rudely shattered. The last mountain had been crossed, the last great forests felt the bite of the ax, the last individual of several species of wildlife had fallen before the fowler's gun or perished in the lonely confinement of a zoo. It was evident to professional men such as Franklin Hough and Gifford Pinchot that our forests were on the verge of complete destruction. The members of the newly formed American Ornithologists' Union were uncomfortably aware that the passenger pigeon and Labrador duck had passed beyond recall and that many other game birds and mammals might soon follow them down the road to oblivion. Families which had moved successively from New England to New York to the Midwest to the Pacific Coast found that there was no further frontier. It was obvious to the lovers of nature that the time had come to "gather at Armageddon and battle for the Lord."

Soon after 1900 the Audubon Society, headed by Frank Chapman, was engaged in a fierce battle with the despoilers of wildlife, to protect endangered species of birds, such as the egrets, from complete extinction. Foresters like Bernhard Fernow, Gifford Pinchot, and Henry Graves were urging the "long look ahead" and sustained-yield forestry. A few men who were in position to realize the problem were fighting the abuses involved in giving away the public domain, those millions of acres of public land distributed under the Homestead Act of 1862, the Timber and Stone Act of 1878, and other related legislation. The friends of conservation had succeeded in getting through Congress, in 1891, a bill to permit creation of forest reserves within the nationally owned forests. A commission appointed by Grover Cleveland in 1896 had examined the nation's forest resources and made recommendations on handling them, but Cleveland, a firm supporter of conservation measures, left office the next year, with most of the nation's resources still in danger.

The turn of the century saw a change in the affairs of conservation. In 1901, Theodore Roosevelt, an outdoorsman, hunter, and competent field biologist as well as politician, became President of the United States. In Gifford Pinchot, forester in the Department of Agriculture, C. Hart Merriam and T. S. Palmer of the Biological Survey, and Congressmen like John Lacey of Iowa, he had strong allies within the government. Conservation acts, one after another, began to pass into the law books. Acts forbidding the feather traffic, acts setting aside or authorizing the setting aside of vast areas for scientific or recreational purposes, acts affecting all the natural resources of the nation were passed. In May, 1908, Roosevelt convened a conference of governors at Washington, to consider problems of conservation. This was the birth of the conservation movement, which today is among the most important, fruitful, and forward-looking aspects of field biology. The forces of exploitation still constantly threaten, but they are now opposed by a large body of trained and educated conservationists, backed by a public which every year becomes more aware of the urgency of conservation needs.

The Nature-education Movement. Concurrent with the development of conservation, which was given impetus largely by governmental efforts, another movement was taking form with little or no governmental assistance. It was clear to many biologists that advances in the appreciation and understanding of nature would only be made by educating the citizens who hitherto had had no contact with biology. In the early 1900s, popular field guides began to appear, to aid in the identification of birds, butterflies, trees, ferns, and other flora and fauna. The Audubon Society, under Frank Chapman's able leadership, began to reach out into the public schools, where children in Junior Audubon Clubs learned about birds and eventually about other aspects of nature study. The Boy Scouts and similar groups, encouraged and guided by such able field biologists as Ernest Thompson Seton and Dan Beard, were exploiting the ingrained love of the out-of-doors, which is a part of American boyhood. At Cornell University, Liberty Hyde Bailey began the extension of nature study into the rural schools of New York State, and Anna Botsford Comstock embarked on a career of nature writing and illustration which brought this hobby to the attention of thousands.

These were only a few of the writers, speakers, and scientists who had a part in the development of the great nature-study movement. The varied approaches, the inclusion of both children and adults in these programs, resulted in a tremendous increase in appreciation of nature and in the number of amateurs engaged in bird study, botany, and similar pursuits. This in turn brought about an increase in the popular literature of biology (see Chap. 10). The crest of this wave of interest has perhaps not yet been reached; but nature study is certainly one of the major cultural trends of the twentieth century in America.

The Ecology Movement. As we have seen, the naturalists of the early pioneer days began to fade from the scene by the middle of the nineteenth century. Most of the more obvious organisms had been described, and biologists turned to the laboratory disciplines in great numbers. Advances in chemistry, medicine, and related fields paved the way for similar advances in physiology and other aspects of biology. The discovery of the basic facts of genetics, near the end of the nineteenth century, opened a new experimental field, and observational natural history fell behind. But as the old natural history died, the seeds of a new natural history were being planted. This was the science of ecology, the study of the environmental relations of organisms. Starting with the pioneer studies of Anton Koerner in Europe, S. A. Forbes, Chauncey Juday, and Edward Birge in the United States, ecology gained headway rapidly. Other leading educators, such as Charles Adams at Syracuse University, Victor Shelford at the University of Illinois, Frederic Clements and J. E. Weaver at the University of Nebraska, led students into the study of this new branch of biology. The old naturalists had laid the foundation, and on it modern ecologists have erected an imposing structure of ecological knowledge.

Today, field biologists are more numerous than ever before. Our knowledge of the lives and habits of wild animals, of the interrelationships of plants, animals, the soil, the climate, and other factors of the environment is increasing daily. We cannot say now what important advances will emerge during the next half century or what new trends in biology may open new vistas to the field biologist. We may be sure, however, that so long as men feel a kinship with nature and a desire to know more of her secrets, field biology will flourish both as a profession and as a hobby.

SUGGESTED READING

GOODE, GEORGE B. 1901. The beginnings of natural history in America. Annual Report for the year ending June 30, 1897. Board of Regents of the Smithsonian Institution, Washington. pp. 355–406.

KESSEL, EDWARD L. (ED.) 1955. "A Century of Progress in the Natural Sciences, 1853–1953." California Academy of Sciences, San Francisco.

LOCKWOOD, GEORGE B. 1905. "The New Harmony Movement." Appleton-Century-Crofts, Inc., New York.

MILNE, LORUS, AND MARGERY MILNE. 1952. "Famous Naturalists." Dodd, Mead & Company, Inc., New York.

PEATTIE, DONALD C. 1936. "Green Laurels: The Lives and Achievements of the Great Naturalists." Simon and Schuster, Inc., New York.

WEISS, HARRY B. 1931. "Thomas Say: Early American Naturalist." Charles C Thomas, Publisher, Springfield, Ill.

YOUMANS, WILLIAMS J. (ED.) 1896. "Pioneers of Science in America." Appleton-Century-Crofts, Inc., New York.

CHAPTER 3

TAXONOMIC PRINCIPLES

Without system, the field of nature would be a pathless wilderness.

Gilbert White, "The Natural History of Selborne"

One of the important branches of biological science is *taxonomy*, which deals with the process of naming organisms and arranging them into a usable classification. In the early development of any region, taxonomy is of primary importance, for plants and animals cannot be effectively studied until we at least have a name for them. It is not surprising, therefore, that most of the early naturalists mentioned in Chap. 2 were primarily taxonomists. In modern field biology, the taxonomist is still a person of great importance, for no one biologist can hope to learn to recognize all of the organisms with which he may come in contact. He must always expect to receive assistance from a specialist in the groups with which he himself is not familiar. The taxonomist is also busy with describing previously unknown forms, revising our system of taxonomic arrangement as new knowledge is gained, and writing monographs on the various natural groups which the field biologist may use in identifying organisms.

Our present system of classification has been so firmly fixed for so long a period that it seems very old and is taken as a matter of course by the beginning biologist. Actually, it is a comparatively recent development, and its details have been worked out and agreed upon within the present century. It is obvious that any system of classification, if it is to be workable, must include a different name for each species of organism. Each name must be clearly understood, universally accepted, and used. Names must be as permanent as the nature of organisms will allow, and rules concerning the classification system must be uniform throughout the world. The development of such a taxonomic system began about two centuries ago.

THE PRE-LINNAEAN PERIOD

Before the middle of the eighteenth century, plants and animals were known by local (vernacular) names, which varied from place to place. Scientists used Latin names, for Latin was the language of the learned, but there was no uniformity of usage. Communication was poor, scientists for the most part retiring and untraveled, and it was therefore virtually impossible to learn of scientific advances in other countries. Furthermore, as a result of rapidly expanding frontiers, an unwieldy nomenclature was developing.

So long as only a few forms were known, Latin names of two or three words would serve to identify a species. Names used in authoritative and widely known monographs might attain a fair degree of acceptance. But as explorations proceeded, more and more species were discovered. Botany and zoology were popular hobbies among the gentlefolk of those days, and many exploring expeditions took with them a collector or two, to bring back the curiosities of nature for some sponsor at home. In order to describe these species and set them off in an adequate manner from similar species which were already known, new names had to be invented. The only solution that the scholars could devise was to add Latin words which were descriptive of the new species to the existing name of a similar organism.

Suppose, for example, that a wild yellow rose existed in Europe which had been known for many years as *Rosa flava* (*Rosa*—rose, *flava*—yellow). Since this was the only yellow rose known to science, it would need no additional words to describe it to the satisfaction of any scientist. Let us suppose, however, that when exploring expeditions began to bring back organisms from unknown parts of the world, they brought back from the Far East two different kinds of yellow roses. One with hairy leaves might be called *Rosa flava, foliis hirsutis*, while the other, which had smooth leaves, could be named *Rosa flava, foliis glabris*. Meanwhile, the original flower, no longer the only yellow rose known to science, would have to be renamed—perhaps *Rosa flava, europea*. If, then, an expedition to Australia brought back three more yellow roses, all with hairy leaves but varying in size and shape of leaves, another modifying name would have to be added. In precisely this manner the names of organisms could, and did, proliferate, until many organisms had names like the one accorded to the common honeybee: *Apis pubescens, thorace subgriseo, abdomine fusco, pedibus posticis glabris utrinque margine ciliatis* (the downy bee with the thorax gray below, the abdomen fuscous, the hind legs hairless but with the margins ciliated). A fine mouthful indeed for the practicing taxonomist to commit to memory!

Linnaeus and Binominal Nomenclature. Obviously a system of this kind must eventually break down of its own weight. Workers in various countries were working toward the idea of a genus with several similar species grouped together. Bauhin in Switzerland and John Ray in England were groping toward a system which would permit a short simple name to be applied to each species. But the Gordian knot was finally cut by a young Swedish botanist, Karl von

Photo by Charles Knight and Company, Ltd., London.

Fig. 3-1. Carolus Linnaeus, 1707–1778.

Linné, later known by the name Carolus Linnaeus (Fig. 3-1). As an eager young student of natural history and medicine at the University of Upsala, he decided to devise a classification system for all organisms. Enlarging and improving upon the ideas of his predecessors, he finally formulated the system which still bears his name. In brief, his idea was to give to each species of plant and animal a name consisting of two Latin words—the name of the genus (generic name) and a trivial or species name. The first biologist to discover a previously undescribed species was to choose a name in accordance with the Linnaean system. This name, with a description of the organism, was to be published in a scientific journal or other publication where other workers might read it. The name thus selected, along with the name of the describer, would thenceforth be the only acceptable name for that species. Any worker who wished to know to what organism the name referred could, theoretically at least, find out by reading the description. In early days, all descriptions were written in Latin, but at present descriptions in other languages are acceptable in zoological taxonomy. Botanists still utilize Latin descriptions.

This system of *binominal nomenclature* was first used uniformly by Linnaeus in his "Species Plantarum" (1753), and for animals in "Systema Naturae," 10th edition (1758). These two dates are the birth dates of modern botanical and zoological nomenclature respectively. Names used before these dates have no standing in nomenclature, unless Linnaeus re-used them in these works.

The effects of this system can readily be appreciated. The name of the honeybee was reduced from the twelve words listed to *Apis mellifica* Linnaeus, and other names benefited in the same manner. The system met with general, though not immediate, acceptance among biologists, who could scarcely fail to appreciate the advantages of its simplicity. During his long lifetime (1707–1778) Linnaeus named and described thousands of species of plants and animals, which still bear his name.

Hierarchical Classification. The various forms of life thus described by Linnaeus were arranged by him in a hierarchical succession of larger and larger groups. Indeed, Linnaeus's contributions to an understanding of a natural arrangement of plant groups were nearly as important as his development of the binominal system. Species which seemed similar were placed in the same genus. Similar genera were placed together to make up a family. Families were grouped into orders, orders into classes, classes into phyla (singular, phylum). Modern usage is somewhat different from that of Linnaeus in the number and scope of these terms, but the principles of the system remain the same. The phyla were grouped into two kingdoms, plant and animal. To use the honeybee again as an example, its complete classification would be:

Kingdom: Animal
  Phylum: Arthropoda
    Class: Insecta
      Order: Hymenoptera
        Family: Apidae
          Genus: *Apis*
            Trivial name: *mellifica*

              Scientific name: *Apis mellifica* Linnaeus

Photos (a) and (c) by Allen H. Benton; photo (b) by R. S. Palmer

44

The Species Concept. Most of these taxonomic groupings are artificial concepts, set up for the convenience of taxonomists. The species, however, represents a natural unit. A species may be defined as a population of organisms, freely interbreeding, but not freely breeding with other similar groups, and resembling each other more closely than they resemble members of any other population. Mayr et al. (1953) based their definition of a species entirely on interbreeding, considering species as groups of organisms reproductively isolated from other such groups. This definition may be accepted with the understanding that this isolation often breaks down, and hybridization, especially in certain families, is common (Fig. 3-2). Simpson (1945) pointed out that our concept of a species is usually based on inferences drawn from a small sample of the actual population, and is, to that extent, a subjective concept based on a real morphological and genetical entity which is not generally observable as a whole. In a few unusual cases, we may be able to observe the entire existing population of a particular species. All the whooping cranes in existence, for example (except for a few in zoos), gather in winter at the Aransas Wildlife Refuge in Texas. Normally, however, we have to be satisfied with a small sample of the total number of a species.

It should be obvious that it is not always easy to decide what a species is. Some scientists will tell you that a species is what a competent taxonomist thinks it is. If we cannot settle on an adequate definition of a species, we can at least indicate the factors which a taxonomist will consider in deciding what a species is. First, of course, is morphological difference; that is, one species should not look exactly like any other species. Second is genetical difference; that is, different species are not expected to interbreed. Third is the geographical factor. A species generally, though not always, has a continuous geographical range, and very closely related species do not usually share the same range. There are, of course, exceptions to the last two of these criteria, and often the morphological differences which separate species are slight. But it is these criteria which must be considered when a taxonomist is required to decide whether an organism or group of organisms represents an undescribed species.

Fig. 3-2. Hybridism in the duck family. (*a*) A male pintail. (*b*) A male hybrid between mallard and pintail. (*c*) A male mallard.

The Subspecies Concept. As our knowledge of organisms has increased, it has been necessary to modify the hierarchical arrangement shown above by the addition of other groupings. Subphyla, superfamilies, subfamilies, and other groups have been added for the convenience of the taxonomist. These are of little importance to the non-taxonomist, except for the subspecies. The addition of this category has converted the binominal system of Linnaeus into an essentially trinominal system, although it may be said that some taxonomists do not approve of this trend. The subspecies was added because widespread species often show consistent regional variation in minor characteristics such as size, coloration, or habits, and such forms may be given a third, or subspecific, name. This recent trend in taxonomy is of importance to the field biologist, who may be called upon to evaluate the probable validity of subspecies on the basis of his knowledge of their natural history. It will be necessary, therefore, to give some further consideration to this concept.

Mayr et al. (1953) define subspecies as "geographically defined aggregates of local populations which differ taxonomically from other such subdivisions of a species." It will be noted that this definition has two requirements: geographical distinctness and taxonomic (morphological) distinctness. Genetical distinctness is not expected, since members of different subspecies which belong to the same species can interbreed freely if placed together. If there is no evidence of interbreeding, forms which are morphologically similar are at once suspected of representing distinct species. It is often impossible to prove that interbreeding will occur by placing the animals together in captivity, for they may not breed under artificial conditions. In nature, however, it is possible to deduce interbreeding by the discovery of *intergrades*—individuals which have either morphological characteristics midway between those of two subspecies, or some of the characteristics of both. When two subspecies meet over a large area, intergrades may be expected to occur throughout that area (Fig. 3-3). In the case illustrated by this figure, the two populations had originally been described as two species, but the presence of large numbers of intergrades where the two ranges come together indicates their subspecific status.

The subspecies concept, incidentally, has been most fully developed among zoologists, and has met with some resistance among botanists.

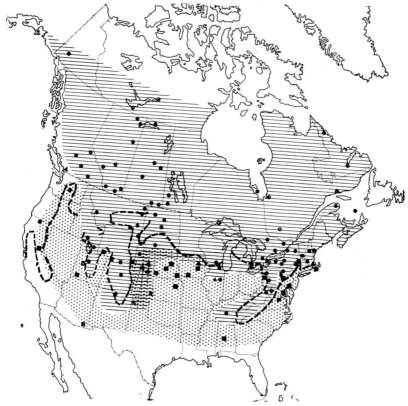

Map from Benton, J. Parasit., 41 (5): 493

Fig. 3-3. Subspeciation in a species of flea, *Epitedia wenmanni*. Large dots represent specimens of the northern subspecies *Epitedia wenmanni wenmanni*. Squares —specimens of the southern subspecies *Epitedia wenmanni testor*. Triangles— specimens intermediate between the two subspecies, known as intergrades. Note that such intergrades occur at various places along the line where the ranges of the two meet.

For this reason, the illustrations used to demonstrate the concept are all taken from the animal kingdom.

It has been pointed out that geographical separation is one of the characteristics of subspecies. This separation, however, may occur only in the most general terms. In parts of the Northeast, two subspecies of the deer mouse, *Peromyscus maniculatus* (Fig. 1-5), are separated only by virtue of the fact that one prefers grasslands and open fields while the other prefers forests. This has occurred, apparently, because a prairie population has worked its way eastward in cleared areas until it has invaded the territory of the other subspecies. The same phenomenon has occurred in the case of the Traill's flycatcher (Parkes, 1954). This latter case is further complicated by the fact that morphological differences between the two forms concerned are very small indeed. In life they can be readily distinguished by voice and habits, but study skins can be separated only with great difficulty.

Thus a subspecies may not be geographically isolated in the usual sense of the term. Mayr et al. (1953) elude this difficulty by the use of the term *microgeographical* to indicate that the two forms occur in different ecological niches. For practical purposes, however, two subspecies which occur over several hundred square miles of the same territory can hardly be said to show geographical isolation. It would be impossible to plot on a map of ordinary size the ranges of the two subspecies of deer mice or of Traill's flycatcher mentioned above. It seems simpler to say that these subspecies are ecologically separated rather than geographically separated. Another difficulty with the subspecies question is the effect of environment on color, size, and similar characteristics. If variations are not genetically fixed, the organism possessing them would not be considered taxonomically distinct, but this is not always easy to find out. No doubt there are many "subspecies" which have been described on the basis of variation due to environmental rather than genetical differences.

The Development of Codes. The work of the post-Linnaean taxonomists using the Linnaean system brought great progress in classifying the vast numbers of plants and animals. Complications arose, however, because of a lack of uniformity of usage and the absence of generally accepted rules. For example, a name which was later found to be unsuitable could be changed by a later worker. If our rose, *Rosa flava*, named after its yellow flowers, was found by a later worker to be based on an abnormal individual, the flowers of normal plants being red, he could rename it *Rosa rubra*. Changing of such names might also come about through national prejudices or personal dislikes, with no regard to suitability of the name. Furthermore, not all workers accepted the Linnaean system readily or with complete consistency, and among those who did there was no uniformity of method in adapting it to their own peculiar problems. Some workers developed personal rules of usage, but these differed in different countries and even within the same country. It began to appear that the ascent from chaos was only a temporary one.

By 1840, the need for a uniform code of usage was recognized to the extent that a committee was formed in England to draw up a suitable set of rules. The Stricklandian code, so named after the chairman of the committee, Hugh Strickland, was an outstanding accomplishment. The committee comprised representatives from many fields, including most of Britain's foremost biologists. The code which they produced was not universally accepted, but it succeeded in stimulating biologists in other countries to draw up different and better codes. By 1895 there were perhaps a half-dozen major codes in use, including the American Ornithologists' Union Code, the so-called International Code, the Dall Code, and the Stricklandian Code. The need of a genuine international code was obvious, and zoologists accepted one, written by an international committee, in 1901.

Botanists, meanwhile, were proceeding separately to establish a standard world nomenclature. The first International Botanical Congress met in Paris in 1867 and adopted a set of rules, mostly suggested by the Swiss botanist Alphonse de Candolle. This set of rules, usually known as the Paris Code, was generally accepted, but a group of American botanists did not find it to their liking and formulated a code of their own. The Vienna Congress of 1905 was expected to solve the difficulties between these opposing forces, but no satisfactory results were achieved. The stalemate continued until 1930, with American botanists more or less evenly divided between supporters of the International Code and users of the American Code. At last, in 1930, the Fifth International Botanical Congress at Cambridge, England, succeeded in bringing the major disagreements to a discussion and vote, and the American Code was abandoned.

The next logical step might seem to be a uniform code for both botanists and zoologists, but this may be long in coming. Because of the many differences between botanists and zoologists in nomenclatural usage, and because of the inevitable confusion which would result if either group accepted the usage of the other, most taxonomists are not anxious to make the change. As mentioned above, descriptions of plants are made in Latin, while any language may be used in describing new species of animals. In botany, tautonymy (the use of the same word for the generic and trivial names) is forbidden. In zoology, tautonymy is permissible, and names such as *Bison bison, Gallus gallus,* and *Turdus turdus* are quite acceptable. Many other small differences exist which would cause difficulties, although the general outlines of nomenclature are the same in both groups.

The international rules of nomenclature, whether botanical or zoological, are too lengthy to be included here, but some of the more important provisions are worthy of note. The basic principle of nomenclature is *priority*, that is, that the first name to be applied to a species must continue to be used so long as it is valid. This applies to all names used in Linnaeus's works of 1753 and 1758 for plants and animals respectively, or at any time since. In general, this has the effect of stabilizing the nomenclature and placing credit where credit is due. In certain cases, the retention of the rule of priority might cause more confusion than would result from ignoring it. In a group where the nomenclature has been well established for many years and where discovery of previously unknown publications brings forth many prior names, a drastic reshuffling of names would result. In such cases, the familiar names may be retained by a ruling of the International Committee on Nomenclature—a body set up to settle arguments about names and to interpret the rules in cases where they do not seem clear. Such a retained name is called a *nomen conservandum,* and once declared to be such it cannot be replaced on the basis of priority at any future date. Dozens of our plant genera would be given different names on the basis of strict priority but have been placed instead on the list of *nomina conservanda.*

Names of organisms are not completely stable, however. Revision of a group in the light of new knowledge may cause the transfer of species from one genus to another, the erection of new genera, or the reduction of genera which had been erected earlier. Regardless of changes in the generic name, the trivial name remains the same, except that the ending may be changed to bring it into agreement with the new generic name, if necessary. In rare cases the common name of a species may be more stable than the scientific name. For example, the common American robin was described by Linnaeus as *Turdus migratorius.* In the years since that time it has been known as *Merula migratoria,* then *Planesticus migratorius;* most recently the name has been *Turdus migratorius* again. It is this juggling about from genus to genus which makes taxonomic work confusing to the layman, but the eventual result is stabilization.

In order to have any nomenclatural standing, a name must meet with certain requirements. First, it must be printed in a publication which is placed on sale or is otherwise available to any interested person. It must be accompanied by an adequate description, so that the species thus described can be recognized in the future. A name without an accompanying description, or with one so inadequate that it is not evident what organism is being described, is a *nomen nudum*, and has no standing in nomenclature. For example, the weasel of the eastern United States was named *Putorius noveboracensis* by James DeKay in his volume on the mammals of New York. DeKay did not include any description; the name is therefore a *nomen nudum*. It was accidentally rescued from oblivion, however, by Emmons, who, in a similar work on the quadrupeds of Massachusetts, used the same name and gave an adequate description. This form has since been reduced to subspecific status, so that its present scientific name is *Mustela frenata noveboracensis* (Emmons). The parentheses around the name of the describer indicate that the species has been transferred to a different genus or that the name has been changed in some way since it was first used.

There are also well-established regulations, or suggestions, as to how scientific names are to be formed. Definite rules concern the grammatical structure of names, the spelling of derived words, and other matters primarily concerned with the technical points of etymology. Suggestions are given on the use of names derived from "barbaric languages" (other than Latin or Greek), the length of names, their suitability to the organism, and similar matters which are concerned with good taste and ease of use. In general, these matters are of little practical concern to the nontaxonomist. A detailed account of these and other important rules for zoological nomenclature may be found in the recent book by Mayr et al. (1953), and for botany in the work of Lawrence (1951).

The Use of Types. One of the important post-Linnaean concepts in taxonomy is the use of types. Every recent description of a new species includes the assignment of one specimen as the *type specimen* or *holotype*. This is a specimen which the describer considers typical, on which the actual description is based—usually a male in the case of an animal, but not necessarily so. Another specimen of the opposite sex (only in the case of animals, of course) is designated as the *allotype*, if such a specimen is available. Other specimens which may be available to the describer can be used in describing individual variation, range, and distribution, and these are designated as *paratypes*. If no type is designated in the original description (as is often the case with older descriptions), or if the type is lost or destroyed, a worker at any subsequent time can select one of the specimens used by the original describer as a *lectotype*, which takes the place of the type specimen.

If all this sounds a bit confusing, an explanation of the function of the type specimen may resolve the problem. The holotype provides a permanent reference point for future taxonomists. If any worker wishes to be absolutely certain as to what organism is referred to in a particular description, examination of the holotype will clear up the matter. If advances in knowledge show that several species were used in writing a particular description, the name used will apply to the species represented by the holotype, and new names can be given to such other species as may have been used. Use of this concept avoids a great deal of ambiguity and confusion for the taxonomist, though it may create some confusion when it is confronted for the first time.

Many other types of terms are now in use, but few are of importance to anyone but the taxonomist. The field biologist may, however, be interested in the *topotype*, a specimen taken at the same locality as the holotype but at a later date. Topotypes may be taken at any time, and there may be any number of them. Types used for larger categories (genus, family, etc.) refer only to groups and names, not to individual specimens. Thus the describer of a new genus selects a species as the "type" species of the genus. The word *genotype* has been much used in this connection, but in view of its long usage in genetics, in an entirely different sense, most modern taxonomists prefer to use "type of the genus." Similarly, a genus is designated as the type genus of a family.

The Taxonomic Key. Once the classification system became relatively stabilized, the knowledge of plants and animals increased rapidly. Thousands of new forms were described; monographs of groups were written; hundreds of workers in all parts of the scientific world needed means to identify the organisms in the groups of their interest.

One of the most useful tools of the biologist, in spite of some short-comings, is the taxonomic key which is used to identify known organisms. The taxonomic key is not an object used to open doors, although figuratively speaking it opens doors which might otherwise remain locked. In its simplest form, the key consists of a series of numbered couplets, each listing characteristics that the organism may

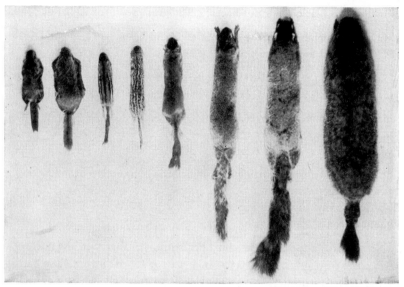

Photo by Allen H. Benton

Fig. 3-4. Squirrels (family Sciuridae) of the eastern United States. Left to right, southern flying squirrel, *Glaucomys volans;* northern flying squirrel, *Glaucomys sabrinus;* eastern chipmunk, *Tamias striatus;* thirteen-lined spermophile, *Citellus tridecimlineatus;* red squirrel, *Tamiasciurus hudsonicus;* gray squirrel, *Sciurus carolinensis;* fox squirrel, *Sciurus niger;* woodchuck, *Marmota monax.*

possess. The two parts of the couplet are mutually exclusive; the organism to be keyed cannot fit both parts. By successively choosing the correct part of the couplet and moving on to the couplet that the correct choice indicates numerically, one can trace an organism to its correct identification. The user will find that his facility with any key will gradually increase, and that there is much variation in keys; the principles of use, however, remain the same. As a simple example, a key to the members of the squirrel family in the northeastern part of the United States (Fig. 3-4) might run like this:

1. Length 18 inches or more.   (2)
1. Length under 15 inches.   (4)

2. Body stout, tail much shorter than body. (*Marmota monax*, wood-chuck)
2. Body relatively slender, tail about as long as body.   (3)

3. Gray above, white below, rusty on sides and head. (*Sciurus carolinensis*, gray squirrel)
3. Gray to black, tail rusty beneath. (*Sciurus niger*, fox squirrel)

4. Lateral membrane between front and hind limbs.   (5)
4. No lateral membrane present.   (6)

5. Length 10 to 12 inches. (*Glaucomys sabrinus*, northern flying squirrel)
5. Length 8 to 9.5 inches. (*Glaucomys volans*, southern flying squirrel)

6. Back prominently striped.   (7)
6. Back not prominently striped, red above, white below. (*Tamiascurus hudsonicus*, red squirrel)

7. Color olive green with many light stripes. (*Citellus tridecimlineatus*, thirteen-lined spermophile)
7. Color gray and reddish, with black and white stripes. (*Tamias striatus*, chipmunk)

Now let us suppose that you find a squirrel that you do not know. Using the key, you find that it is less than 15 inches long, so you go to the fourth couplet; it has no lateral membrane, so you go to the sixth couplet; its back is prominently striped, so you proceed to couplet 7; it is a gray and reddish animal with alternating black and white stripes. This brings you to the chipmunk, and you conclude that this is the name of your specimen.

To check the correctness of your keying, it is wise to compare the animal with more complete descriptions in some standard identification manual and with a photograph or drawing, if such can be obtained. Keys and identification manuals are available for almost any group of organisms (see Chap. 10). Some are highly technical and require advanced knowledge of biology. Others are mere picture books which in all too many cases are incomplete, inaccurate, and misleading. The field biologist will find it to his advantage to possess good manuals for the groups in which he is interested, and should familiarize himself thoroughly with the characteristics used in the keys, or in otherwise identifying the various species. Only in this manner can he become capable of intelligent field work.

Identification of organisms is a necessary means to an end, but it should not be considered an end in itself for the field biologist. Having achieved the ability to recognize the species with which he comes in contact, the average amateur, or occasional professional biologist, comes to a standstill. In so doing he sacrifices both enjoyment and usefulness, for much can be accomplished beyond this point if a few techniques are learned and a few principles understood. It will be our aim in the next few chapters to explore some of these principles and to review some important techniques.

REFERENCES CITED

LAWRENCE, G. H. M. 1951. "Taxonomy of Vascular Plants." The Macmillan Company, New York. xiii and 823 pp.

LINNAEUS, CAROLUS. 1753. "Species Plantarum." 1st ed. 2 vols. Stockholm.

———. 1758. "Systema Naturae." 10th ed. 2 vols. Stockholm.

MAYR, ERNST, E. GORTON LINSLEY, AND ROBERT L. USINGER. 1953. "Methods and Principles of Systematic Zoology." McGraw-Hill Book Company, Inc., New York. ix and 328 pp.

PARKES, KENNETH C. 1954. Traill's flycatcher in New York. *Wilson Bull.*, 66:89–92.

SIMPSON, G. G. 1945. The principles of classification and a classification of mammals. *Bull. Amer. Mus. Nat. Hist.*, 85:1–350.

SUGGESTED READING

CALMAN, W. T. 1949. "The Classification of Animals." John Wiley & Sons, Inc., New York.

CORE, EARL L. 1955. "Plant Taxonomy." Prentice-Hall, Inc., Englewood Cliffs, N. J.

DOUTT, J. K. 1955. Microgeographic races in mammals. *Syst. Zool.*, 4:179–185.

EDWARDS, J. G. 1954. A new approach to infraspecific categories. *Syst. Zool.*, 3:1–20.

JAEGER, EDMUND. 1955. "Source Book of Biological Names and Terms." 3d ed. Charles C Thomas, Publisher, Springfield, Ill.

SCHENK, E. T., AND J. H. McMASTERS. 1956. "Procedure in Taxonomy." 2d ed. Stanford University Press, Stanford, Calif.

CHAPTER 4

ECOLOGICAL PRINCIPLES

> Every reflective biologist must know that no living
> being is self-sufficient, or would be what it is, or would
> be at all, if it were not part of the natural world. . . .
> Living things are real things . . . but their reality is in
> their interrelations with the rest of nature, and not in
> themselves.
>
> *W. K. Brooks,* "Heredity and Variation:
> Logical and Biological"*

An important although limited approach to the study of ecology is
the community approach. Ecology is a broad field—the study of the
relations of organisms with their environment. Because of the wide
scope of this science, it has been divided into smaller fields, including
plant and animal ecology and marine and fresh-water ecology. The
study of communities approaches the whole field of ecology in a still
different manner. It permits the defining of an otherwise clumsily
broad topic, yet it does not exclude any group of organisms or any
kind of environment. The significance of this approach to ecology
is expressed by Clements and Shelford (1939), who state, "Ecology is
in large measure the science of community populations."

The word *community* is used in several ways, but in general, it
may be defined as all of the organisms that exist as interrelated members in a given area. The size of the community will depend upon the
degree of diversity of the environment in a geographical area and the

* 1906. *Proc. Amer. Phil. Soc.,* 45:70–76.

way in which this diversity affects the organisms present. Usually, one or more major environmental factors, such as amount of moisture, or type of substrate, will define the limitations of a community. A salt-water marsh, for example, can exist only where the substrate contains salty or brackish water. The plants and animals of a community may be considered separately for convenience, but even early ecologists such as Clements, Adams, Shelford, and others (see Chap. 2) recognized that plants and animals comprising communities are interdependent, forming a single unit.

FACTORS DETERMINING COMMUNITY TYPES

Certain environmental conditions are of prime importance in determining community types. Topography, soil, and various factors of the climate including rainfall, temperature, growing season, and wind are the more important general physical conditions that determine what types of plants may exist in a given locality. Of importance to animals is the presence or absence of certain plants in a community. Since animals ultimately depend upon plants for nourishment, plants are often an important environmental factor in determining the presence or absence of animal species in a given community. Other significant environmental factors are soil, temperature, moisture, and various physical conditions.

Plants. Plants may alter the physical conditions of the environment, or by themselves provide an environment. For example, certain plants may grow only where sunlight is limited, a condition provided frequently by a canopy of other plants. Trees shading a stream may allow certain animals, such as various species of fishes or amphibians, to survive and inhabit the stream because of the resulting cooler temperatures. Certain plants, such as the minute aquatic duck weeds, *Lemna* sp. (Fig. 4-1), may serve as a microcommunity for the tiny insects that mine or eat out the insides of this plant. Thus one worker (Scotland, 1934) found that two species of insects are obliged to live their lives with the thallus of *Lemna minor*. Many other animals are associated with these tiny plants, including occasional residents and their parasites.

General Topography. Within a given area there may be several different kinds of communities, depending on variation of the habitats.

Some areas obviously have greater variation of habitat than others. For example, hilly or mountainous regions are apt to have a wider variety of environmental conditions than flat areas. There is a greater opportunity for variation in moisture, light, and other factors. These environmental differences consequently produce different communities.

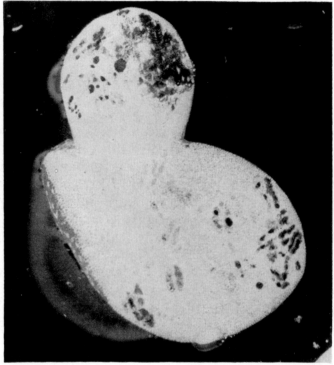

Photo by Minnie B. Scotland

Fig. 4-1. A single thallus of *Lemna minor*, a tiny flowering plant about ¼ inch in diameter, which represents one of the smallest of microcommunities. Note scars made by feeding of Lemna fly (*Lemnaphila scotlandae*) and egg on edge of leaf at bottom.

Variation in topography may produce not only minor community differences but major ones as well. Poorly drained areas will have different communities from well-drained areas. North-facing slopes of hills and sides of ravines will be cooler and therefore may possess slightly different communities of plants and animals than the south-facing sides.

Altitude. Elevation may produce great differences in community types. As one ascends a mountain, the temperature begins to go down, the amount of precipitation changes, and in general the environment becomes more rigorous. If a mountain is sufficiently high, these changes due to elevation will be great enough to cause the appearance of several different community types from the bottom to the top of the mountain.

Photo by Ralph S. Palmer

Fig. 4-2. Alpine tundra near the top of Mt. Katahdin, Maine.

High mountains may be so cold on top and may often have such a rigorous climate as to possess treeless vegetation in a region that is in a generally forested area (Fig. 4-2). Such a treeless area has a tundra community type. On Mount Washington, in New Hampshire, the tundra begins at elevations of between 4,500 and 5,700 feet, and continues to the top of this mountain, which is only 6,288 feet high (Griggs, 1946). In different latitudes and climates, the elevation at which the tundra commences will vary. In the Rocky Mountains, for example, it begins in Montana at about 8,000 feet, and in New Mexico at about 11,500 feet.

Just below the tundra on a mountain is a region of stunted trees, often called the *Krummholz* (Fig. 4-3). Here trees such as balsam fir or spruce invade the tundra area behind the abundant rocks in wet areas. They are not able to grow above the rocks, and are so bushy

Photo by Allen H. Benton

Fig. 4-3. *Krummholz* (stunted-tree) zone at top of Pitchoff Mountain, Adirondacks, New York.

that it is possible to walk on top of them. Where large rocks are absent, these trees are not found.

Below the *Krummholz* will be found a subalpine coniferous forest. Because of lower elevations, the temperatures are not so cold, nor are the winds so severe. In general, the climatic conditions, including increased moisture, are more favorable to growth of trees. This type of community will extend down the mountain until it is replaced by either a deciduous or another coniferous forest community. The

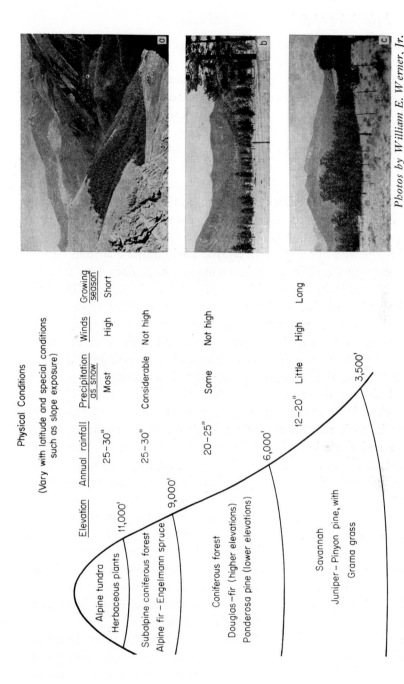

Physical Conditions

(Vary with latitude and special conditions such as slope exposure)

	Elevation	Annual rainfall	Precipitation as snow	Winds	Growing season
Alpine tundra		25–30"	Most	High	Short
Herbaceous plants	11,000'				
Subalpine coniferous forest		25–30"	Considerable	Not high	
Alpine fir – Engelmann spruce	9,000'				
Coniferous forest		20–25"	Some	Not high	
Douglas–fir (higher elevations)					
Ponderosa pine (lower elevations)	6,000'				
		12–20"	Little	High	Long
Savannah					
Juniper – Pinyon pine, with					
Grama grass	3,500'				

Photos by William E. Werner, Jr.

Fig. 4-4. Altitudinal zonation in western United States. (*a*) Alpine tundra and spruce-fir coniferous forest; here, in the Rocky Mountain National Park, Colo., timber line is at about 11,500 feet elevation; (*b*) pine coniferous forest; ponderosa pine, *Pinus ponderosa*, near Flagstaff, Ariz., at about 7,000 feet elevation; (*c*) pinyon pine, juniper savanna, near Flagstaff, Ariz., at about 5,000 feet elevation.

61

altitude at which this transition occurs will again be determined by latitude and general climatic conditions.

At still lower elevations, other communities will be found. The coniferous or deciduous forest replaces the subalpine coniferous forest where the elevations are such that temperatures are milder and moisture is abundant. If the mountains are in grassland area, the forest will finally give way to grasslands at their base as moisture decreases. In the Southwest, where mountains are in a desert region, one may ascend from desert through a savanna, coniferous forest, subalpine coniferous forest, and finally to tundra. All these community differences are primarily the result of change in temperature and moisture due to change in elevation (Fig. 4-4*a*, *b*, *c*).

Lake-bottom Topography. In aquatic environments, bottom topography may create differences in communities. A deep lake may be quite different in its communities from a shallow lake. A shallow lake has the major portion of its water set in motion by winds rather easily; therefore the water turns over from top to bottom during the summer, and warms fairly evenly. In deep lakes the bottom waters are never greatly warmed, and a *thermocline*, or area in which the temperature of the water drops rapidly in a vertical direction, is formed during the summer months (Figs. 6-7, 6-8). While the thermocline lasts, water does not circulate from top to bottom, resulting in such adverse conditions as depletion of nutrients at the surface and depletion of oxygen and accumulation of undesirable products at the bottom. During the winter, ice may form on shallow lakes, causing circulation to stop, and producing stagnation. Deep lakes will also freeze, but their large volume will contain sufficient oxygen to prevent stagnation. A shallow lake may support much more vegetation and in general be more productive, owing in part to the summer circulation. Another important factor is that in a shallow lake a larger percentage of shallow water permits more rooted aquatics to grow, which of course provides food for more animals. Depth of water also has its effect on the types of communities found in streams, often through the factors of oxygen and light.

Climate. The prime factor determining community types, however, is the climate. The climate controls rates of topography changes. It is instrumental in determining vegetation type and associated animal life in any area. It is involved in the control of the development of the soil and the rate of repopulation and development of communities in which life has been destroyed.

Climate controls rates of topography changes through rainfall, temperature, and wind. Increased rain ordinarily means increased erosion. Mountains wear down to plains, and bodies of water fill in or drain mainly as a result of erosion. The rate of erosion usually varies with the climate, other factors being equal. Wide seasonal changes of temperature producing alternate freezing and thawing, for example, cause greater erosion than more uniform temperatures where freezing and thawing are not involved. Similarly, presence or absence of strong prevailing winds will vary the amount of erosion by wind in any given area.

Plants are dependent on several factors of the climate, principal among which are rainfall, wind, temperature, and growing season. The first three are closely interrelated, for wind and temperature may control the amount of water evaporated from the soil and thus made unavailable to plants. Areas of high rainfall and relatively low evaporation rates, such as certain tropical regions, have a different vegetation from that of areas of low rainfall and high evaporation rates, such as deserts. The length of the frost-free part of the year (growing season) is frequently of importance in controlling the distribution of plants and hence community types, for some plants require a longer period for growth and reproduction than others. The plants present often determine what animals may be present, and thus the climate affects a whole community. (See the discussion of climax communities and biomes below.)

If the organisms of an area are destroyed, the rate at which they will grow back will be influenced by the amount of rain, light, wind, and other factors of the environment. Often, soil must be rebuilt by the plants, and this involves indirect control of the soil type by the climate. Eventually, the climate will determine the ultimate type of community evolving from this rebuilding process (see Chaps. 5 and 6).

TYPES OF COMMUNITIES

A major division of types of communities is between land (or terrestrial) communities and water (or aquatic) communities. Land communities include such varying habitats as areas recently denuded of

life, rocky areas, meadows or grasslands, and forests (Fig. 4-5). Slow
streams, fast streams, ponds, bogs, swamps, and lakes comprise some
of the broader types of aquatic communities (Fig. 4-6*a*, *b*).

The Microcommunity. Within each of these divisions may be
smaller communities, such as an oak-hickory forest, or the forest floor
litter of such a forest community. The latter is an example of a community type or microcommunity, and is in reality a specialized community dependent on the larger community of which it is a part.

Photo by Allen H. Benton

Fig. 4-5. A variety of natural communities and agricultural land in central New
York, ranging from bare ground (plowed field in foreground) to climax community (right background). A series of successional stages can be seen on the
distant hillside, where land once farmed is returning to a natural state.

Microcommunities are often convenient to study, owing to their
size and easier definition. One can study the community of plants and
animals of a fallen log in an oak-hickory forest, momentarily neglecting the total ecology of the forest community, although the forest
community is a part of the log community and vice versa. Similarly,
one could study the community of plants and animals in pebbles at the
edge of a lake, momentarily neglecting the total ecology of the lake
of which the smaller community is a part. Yet neither of these smaller
units could exist or be completely studied out of the context of their
natural surroundings. A log exposed to the sun in an open field would
not have the same inhabitants as one in a damp, shaded forest, and pebbles at the shore of a beach will encourage life vastly different from
life surrounding pebbles of a dry gravel bank far inland.

Photo (a) by A. H. Benton, photo (b) by William E. Werner, Jr.

Fig. 4-6. Aquatic communities of two major types. (*a*) A fast-stream community, near Albany, N.Y.; (*b*) a lake community, Higgins Lake, Michigan. Important environmental variables include water movement, oxygen content, and light.

Climax Communities. Geography and geology teach us that eventually mountains wear down to hills, and hills to plains. Deep lakes fill in and become shallow, passing then into ponds, swamps, and finally dry land. The type of soil may change because of the continual processing by the organisms living in and on it, from accumulation of organic matter, and from leaching or lack of leaching. These changes are part of a process called succession, which will be discussed later (see Chaps. 5 and 6).

Changes in topography are going on continually, but eventually a stable condition will be reached and there will be only one major community type in a region. The controlling element of this stable condition is the climate of the area, and theoretically, once the stable condition has been reached, only a change in climate would change the major community type of the area.

A community which is so stabilized that it does not change unless the climate changes is called a *climax* community. The term *climatic climax* is often used to describe the specific type of stabilization. Two evidences of a climax community are that the young produced are the same as the mature species in the area, and that the same species are present throughout the community. Exactly which species form the climax depends upon the original rocks, the other plant and animal species present, and such conditions as fire or other disturbances, in addition to chance. It is possible, for example, that the climate will support two different species that have a similar function in a community, but one species may become established first in a certain community and not allow another species to gain a foothold in the same location.

Minor variations in climate may also produce minor variations in climax communities. For instance, along the Hudson River Valley in New York State is found a climax type in which oak and hickory are dominant trees. That is, these trees are the controlling and characteristic species of the community. Slightly to the north, continuing west in New York, is the Mohawk River Valley, where the climax includes such dominants as beech, maple, birch, and basswood. Both types of climax communities are deciduous types as far as dominants go, although some conifers such as white pine and hemlock may be found in the area. The slight difference in climax type is due to a slight difference in climate.

It should also be noted here that dominant species are usually plants, although some animals may control the vegetation and thereby be dominants. Bison may have been dominants before their slaughter by the white man, since they may have helped to maintain the grasslands in the Midwest. Often man or his domesticated animals will determine the vegetation type of large areas.

Some areas within a climax region possess a different community type from the climax community because of marked physical differences in the environment. Such communities are relatively stable, for the geologic or other processess that cause the physical differences to disappear may take a long time to accomplish the change. These relatively permanent communities are those produced by such phenomena as north and south slopes, differences in drainage, periodic fires, etc. (Fig. 5-15). Such communities also reproduce themselves, but over hundreds or thousands of years may fail to do so, and are eventually replaced by the climax community of the larger area. These communities are usually smaller in area than the climax community.

Successional Communities. In many places, the major community type is not a climax community nor is it in any sense stable; it is characterized by continual shiftings of the constituent species, allowing a gradual evolution of the community. Such a community occurs in areas where the organisms have been disturbed, by man or nature, as in a region where life has been destroyed by fire or bulldozers. In these areas communities will grow back toward the climax community. Communities that are in the process of growing back are called successional communities (see Chaps. 5 and 6).

BIOMES

In order to create a simpler classification of the community types, various areas of similar vegetational types have been grouped together into classification known as *biomes,* or formations. The principal biomes include the tundra, coniferous forest (taiga), deciduous forest, grasslands, desert, and tropical rain forest (Fig. 4-7). Biomes are found in areas of relatively similar climatic conditions, and include roughly similar climax communities, although this does not mean that they include only the climax communities of the area. A biome includes *all* the communities of an area, successional and otherwise, and is there-

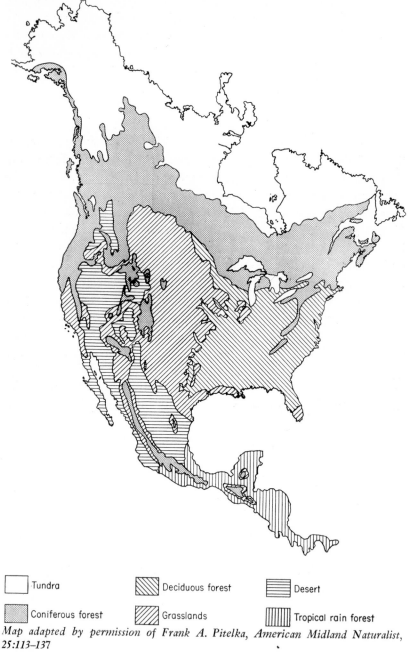

Tundra

Coniferous forest

Deciduous forest

Grasslands

Desert

Tropical rain forest

Map adapted by permission of Frank A. Pitelka, American Midland Naturalist, 25:113–137

Fig. 4-7. Biomes of North America.

fore not merely a climax term. For example, those parts of the prairie states bordering the Mississippi River are within the deciduous forest biome. That is, according to rainfall, temperature, and other climatic conditions, this area should support deciduous forests. Yet these forests have been nearly eliminated by the agricultural practices of man. Some areas bordering rivers and their tributaries, however, are still wooded. Such areas are not only moist and allow rapid invasion of trees, but

Photo by Ralph S. Palmer

Fig. 4-8. Close-up view of arctic tundra at Churchill, Manitoba. There is a profusion of plants in spite of thin soil.

are hilly and not so desirable for agriculture as the surrounding level areas. The deciduous forest biome, then, includes the areas in Illinois that are at present deciduous woodland, as well as some of the areas farmed by man, and therefore treeless. A vegetation map of Illinois made in 1926 (Brown and Yeager, 1943) shows prairie in a large portion of the state. This, too, has been removed by farming, and the land is now occupied by corn, soybeans, wheat, and other crops instead of prairie grasses. Hence, a great deal of the treeless region of Illinois belongs to the prairie biome.

Tundra. The tundra (Fig. 4-8) is characteristic of the severe, cold climates of the north and of high mountain tops. An important factor for plants of this biome is physiological drought produced by prolonged periods of frost and high winds favoring rapid evaporation. (Water is present but unobtainable by the plants for physical reasons.) Wet, boggy areas provide places where plants can grow, however, so that dwarf willows, birches, cranberries, as well as sedges, grasses, lichens, and mosses can be found in this area.

Arctic tundra animals include musk oxen, caribou, arctic wolves, arctic hares, arctic foxes, and lemmings. Many birds (Fig. 4-9), espe-

Photo by Ralph S. Palmer

Fig. 4-9. A representative breeding bird of the tundra, the Hudsonian curlew *Numenius phaeopus hudsonicus;* here incubating.

cially waterfowl, migrate to the tundra for the brief summer. A few birds, for example the ptarmigan, are permanent residents. Arctic mammals do not hibernate but live active lives under the snow during the long winter months. The tundra is also found at higher elevations on the mountain ranges of the United States, including the Sierra Nevadas, Rockies, and Appalachians. It is the area above the timber line, where trees cannot grow. The tundra of the far north is called arctic tundra; that of the high mountaintops, alpine tundra. They differ from each other perhaps more in endemic species than in true character.

Taiga. The northern coniferous forest, or taiga (Fig. 4-10*a, b*), has a climate not quite so severe as the tundra but still a northern climate, and is found as a band directly south of the tundra across North America. Rainfall is an important environmental factor too, being only

Photos by William E. Werner, Jr.

Fig. 4-10. The Coniferous forest biome. (*a*) The taiga in northern Michigan; (*b*) close-up view of the taiga in northern Michigan.

71

Photos by Ralph S. Palmer

Fig. 4-11. Representative mammals of the taiga. (*a*) Moose, *Alces americana*, a grazing and browsing mammal; (*b*) porcupine, *Erethizon dorsatum*, a tree-climbing herbivore; (*c*) least shrew, *Microsorex hoyi*, one of the smallest carnivorous mammals in existence.

moderate in this biome. Much of this biome is poorly drained, owing to the effects of recent glaciation, so that ponds, bogs, and lakes are common. However, this region is still relatively dry physiologically, and the topography is rough and very rocky. Vegetation in this biome includes such conifer dominants as larch, spruce, and fir, while deciduous trees such as paper birch, alder, and willow are also present in lesser numbers. The trees usually grow close together and, because they are of the type that can suc-cessfully stand close competition for light, moisture, space, and nutritive materials, are known as tolerant species. The soils are moist and acid. Sphagnum, a moss that tends to produce acid conditions, is common. Vernal-flowering plants, ground pines, and ferns are to be found growing in this biome, but soil acidity and lack of light as well as certain other environmental conditions probably act as restrictions on the presence of a wide variety of herbaceous plants. Representative mammals (Fig. 4-11*a*, *b*, *c*) include wolves, moose, foxes, otters, minks, weasels, squirrels, porcupines, and several smaller mammals

Photo by Ernest G. Tabor

Fig. 4-12. Goshawk *Accipiter gentilis*, a representative breeding bird of the taiga.

of the forest floor. Reptiles are few in species as are amphibians. Many species of birds (Fig. 4-12) spend the breeding season in this region.

The taiga extends from subarctic Canada into the United States along major mountain systems, the Rockies and the Sierra Nevadas. It is also to be found on a few of the higher mountain tops of the Appalachians. The species vary in these diverse locations, forming distinct communities, but the biome remains the same in general structure.

Deciduous Forest. The deciduous forest biome (Fig. 4-13) occurs where the climate is milder than that of the coniferous forest and where rainfall is abundant relative to the amount of evaporation. The area included in this biome in the United States varies widely in soil types and topography, with elevated regions such as the Appalachians, and river valleys such as the Mississippi. Sugar maples, beech, basswood, oaks, and hickories are common dominant types, with the first three more common in the more northern and usually wetter parts of the biome. In the higher regions and in the area south of the

Photo by Soil Conservation Service, U. S. D. A.

Fig. 4-13. The deciduous forest in Kentucky.

Appalachians some coniferous species may contribute to the list of dominants. This is true of white pine and hemlock in the North and such species as loblolly, pitch, and shortleaf pines in the South. The latter are often maintained as dominants by recurrent fires and not by the climate. The deciduous forest once also included the American chestnut, and saplings of this species, coming out of the stumps of the old trees killed by the chestnut blight, can still be found.

Along the Great Lakes, maple, beech, and basswood are frequently

Photos by Ralph S. Palmer

Fig. 4-14. Mammals of the deciduous forest biome. (*a*) White-tailed deer, *Odocoileus virginianus;* (*b*) flying squirrel, *Glaucomys volans;* (*c*) eastern cottontail, *Sylvilagus floridanus.*

the climax dominants, with hemlocks in the higher altitudes or cool, moist areas. Elsewhere, especially southward and westward along the Mississippi and its tributaries, oaks and hickories are dominant. In the deciduous climax communities, underbrush is usually heavy, often forming an understory of vegetation. Ferns, vernal-flowering plants, sedges, and mosses are also abundant. A complete canopy is usually formed by the trees, but the trees are not crowded as they are in the coniferous biome. Vertebrates (Fig. 4-14*a*, *b*, *c*) include such mammals as raccoons, opossums, foxes, deer, skunks, weasels, minks, bobcats, beavers, and muskrats. Snakes are fairly abundant, as are turtles, salamanders, and frogs (Fig. 4-15). Birds are common, and occur in great variety.

Photo by Ralph S. Palmer

Fig. 4-15. The wood frog (*Rana sylvatica*), a common amphibian of the deciduous-forest biome.

Grassland. The grassland formation (Fig. 4-16) is often divided into tall-grass prairie and short-grass plains climaxes. In such regions, rainfall is not sufficient for forests, and evaporation rates are high. Temperature extremes vary considerably throughout this region. Grasses of various kinds are the dominant plants. Tall-grass prairies— those next to the deciduous biome—receive more rainfall than the short-grass prairies. The former, being favorable for agriculture, are severely disturbed from their natural state. They are found in the midwestern United States and western Canada, just west of the Mississippi, and also extending as far east as Indiana.

Short-grass plains (Fig. 4-17) are the driest part of the grasslands

Photo by William E. Werner, Jr.
Fig. 4-16. The prairie biome: short-grass plains in Wyoming.

Photo by William E. Werner, Jr.
Fig. 4-17. Short-grass plains in Colorado.

biome, and extend in the Great Plains from Canada into the desert plains of the Southwest. They are bordered on the east by the tall-grass prairies and extend west to the Rocky Mountains. As the name implies, the dominant plants are short grasses in the short-grass plains and taller grasses in the tall-grass prairies. Natural animals of the grassland once included the bison, and one can still find pronghorn

Photo by Ralph S. Palmer

Fig. 4-18. The pronghorn antelope, *Antilocapra americana,* a typical resident of the prairie biome.

antelopes (Fig. 4-18), jack rabbits, ground squirrels, badgers, prairie dogs, prairie chickens, and coyotes. Many species of reptiles and amphibians occur in the prairie region. A few species are endemic to the plains, while others do not follow the biome regions in their distribution.

Desert. The desert biome (Fig. 4-19*a, b, c*) in the United States is chiefly the area of the North American Desert. It is interrupted in certain places by mountain ranges which possess other biomes. In the

Photos by William E. Werner, Jr.

Fig. 4-19. Three variations of the desert biome. (*a*) A "cool" desert in northern Nevada; (*b*) a "hot" desert, the Painted Desert in Arizona; (*c*) a "hot" desert in southern Nevada.

79

desert, precipitation is extremely low, and temperatures are high in the day and low at night, since there is no blanket of clouds or other phenomenon to buffer temperature changes. There are different desert climaxes in this biome just as in the others, but all are characterized by plants and animals that can survive long periods of drought. Sagebrush, creosote bush, Joshua tree, and saguaro are among the shrubby plants that are dominants in the various desert climax communities. Animals of the deserts must be able to survive both drought and heat, yet there are several species of vertebrates, such as kangaroo rats (Fig. 4-20), lizards, snakes, and the like (as well as invertebrates) that can

Photo by Ralph S. Palmer

Fig. 4-20. Kangaroo rat, *Dipodomys merriami*, a common mammal of the desert biome.

live in such situations. Plants must often complete their entire life cycle in a very brief season of a few weeks when there is sufficient rainfall to produce vegetative structures, flowers, and seed. Many of the animals avoid the intense heat of day and move about at night.

Tropical Rain Forest. Finally, the tropical rain forests present a distinct biome type. Found in Central and South America in this hemisphere, this formation is due to heavy rainfall and high temperatures, with mild winters. Seasonal variation in temperature is small. Such forests are characterized by tall, broad-leaved, nondeciduous trees forming a high canopy. Undergrowth is dense, at least in places, and the space under the trees is dark and humid. Climbing plants are carried to the tops of the tall trees, where they help make the solid canopy that shuts out a great deal of light. Tropical rain forests are found in the warmer climates only where there is

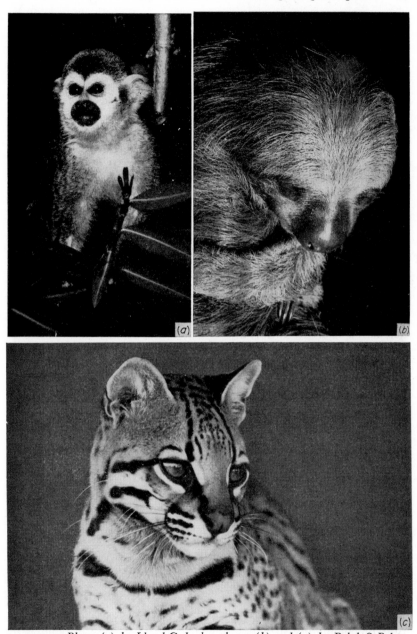

Photo (*a*) by Lloyd G. Ingles, photos (*b*) and (*c*) by Ralph S. Palmer
Fig. 4-21. Mammals of the rain forest. (*a*) Squirrel monkey, *Saimiri oerstedii;*
(*b*) three-toed sloth, *Bradypus griseus;* (*c*) ocelot, *Felis pardalis.*

abundant rainfall. As in the other biomes, variations may exist. Regions of high elevations will have cooler climates. Mountains may interrupt rain-bearing cloud formations and prevent areas within the tropical region from becoming rain forests. Thus Central America has tundra, grasslands, deserts, and deciduous forests, although in general it is within the rain-forest biome area.

Animals of the rain forests are not conspicuous. Many birds and mammals (Fig. 4-21*a*, *b*, *c*) live in the crowns of the trees high above the forest floor. Although such reptiles as snakes are common, they are not so abundant as is often imagined. Insects are tremendously abundant, however, and since many of them are carriers of disease, they make these forests dangerous to man.

TERRESTRIAL ECOLOGICAL METHODS

It is the task of the ecologist to study microcommunities, communities, or biomes in a thorough manner, noting all the environmental and biotic factors, or conditions, and taking both quantitative and qualitative data on them. These data are accumulated over an appropriate length of time and are then evaluated, and general principles are formulated, if possible. Often, in addition to the knowledge of natural history, the valuable tool of statistics is employed in interpreting and synthesizing the data.

Dominant Physical Factors. Frequently, some correlation between type of community and a single environmental factor, such as rainfall, can be made. For example, rainfall is apparently one of the chief conditions controlling the vegetational types of the world, although other factors such as temperature, topography, and prevailing winds also play an important part. On a smaller scale, environmental conditions are responsible for vegetation types, too, and at least indirectly for the types of animals present.

Indicators. Often, the variations of environmental conditions under which a particular type of plant community may exist coincide with the variations in which certain kinds of organisms may be able to survive. Thus, given a certain species, one may correctly predict the type of community in which it will be found. A case in point is the red-backed salamander, whose habits apparently link it closely with beech-maple forests. Therefore, an experienced collector can usually find this animal in such a forest. Such a species is termed an *indicator* of a particular type of community. However, other salamanders, such as the dusky salamander, can be found in the same type of forest in its more southern reaches but not in the northern extent of this community. Apparently some environmental factor other than vegetational type prevents its northern range from coinciding with the northern extent of the beech-maple forest community.

Study of Species or Communities. In addition to examining the physical factors of the environment in a community in a methodical manner, one must study the organisms carefully. Plants and animals must be considered individually as species to learn their life histories and thereby their requirements as to their physical and biotic environment. They must also be studied as species to learn their relationships to other populations and their importance in the community (Chap. 8). A single species, either plant or animal, may be studied thoroughly, noting all its plant and animal associations, such as parasites, food, social relationships with other species or within the species, its distribution geographically, its importance in a food chain, its taxonomic relationships, and many other relationships with its environment. Or, an entire community may be considered at once, in which case stress must be put upon the dynamics of the community and upon interrelationships of many species with each other and with the environment. In both types of studies, correct taxonomic determinations are of the utmost importance. Each type also demands a careful examination of the physical factors of the environment in which the study is conducted.

The amount of information collected in an ecological study may become voluminous. If a truly thorough investigation is to be made, every facet of the environment that may be of some significance to the organisms living in the communities must be examined with care. In order that no important factor be omitted, it is well to use some plan of organization. Such a plan will vary with the peculiarities of the local situation and with the aspect of the community being studied, but it will probably include the factors discussed below.

Limitations of Ecological Studies. The limitation of the extent of a community to be studied is often a major problem. If the area is large, it will be impossible to study every bit of it completely. There will be too many variable conditions to allow analysis of the collected information. Occasionally an ecological study will include all of the plants and animals of a community but will be restricted in scope by the physical area. More often an investigator will choose to emphasize one aspect of a community. Thus, the plants may dominate his interest, with lesser attention being given to animals, or certain groups of plants or animals will be thoroughly studied, such as all insects or a certain group of insects in the community. Occasionally, a single species will be studied exhaustively in relation to its community. In such a case, other species are noted only as they affect the species under consideration. Making such restrictions is not the most desirable practice. It would be much better if all the organisms and all the factors of their environment could be examined simultaneously. However, most investigators do not have time for such extensive studies. Furthermore, one person can scarcely hope to have intimate knowledge of all the organisms that may be found in a community.

Sampling Problems. Even with the subject of investigations narrowed down in some way, it is usually necessary to make sample observations. That is, small areas are selected within the study area for intense investigation. This raises problems of selecting such samples. Organisms are not randomly distributed over the face of the earth, nor is a species so distributed within its range. Often this irregularity in distribution is due to physical variations in the environment. The presence of a boulder in a certain spot, for example, may prevent a tree from growing at that location where it might otherwise have taken root. A similar situation exists in the animal kingdom. For example, the biologist does not look just anywhere for salamanders; he proceeds to flat rocks and logs lying on the ground or to other particular habitats where salamanders may be known to congregate. Over a wide area, such variations are perhaps of small consequence in the distribution of a species. But locally, they may cause great fluctuation in abundance of a species, and this fluctuation may have important local effects on other organisms. For certain population studies we want results to be useful over a wide area. Therefore, sample areas must be selected so as to minimize these wide local variations.

Quadrats. A common method of selecting sample study areas is the *quadrat* method. This method involves a systematic way of choosing areas (quadrats), and then the organisms and environment within the quadrat are studied intensively qualitatively and quantitatively. Sometimes areas within the quadrat will be further marked off. Thus, one practice in plant ecology is to use quadrats 10 meters square for woodland communities. All the trees in this area are noted, including the number of each species. Then, within one corner of the quadrat, another square is laid out, four meters square, in which all the shrubs are noted. Finally, within each corner of the 10-meter square, a one-meter quadrat is laid out, and in this the herbs are noted. In grass-lands where herbs are abundant and trees absent, these figures for quadrat size may be reduced. The quadrats themselves are usually laid out in a regular fashion, such as in parallel lines. Curtis (1956) recommends that 30 or more such quadrats should be made for any one type of community in order to avoid sampling errors due to local variations.

A useful device for implementing the laying out of such quadrats is a chain of known length, either to space the quadrats or to lay off each quadrat. Surveyors' instruments are also useful in lining up the quadrats. Quadrats may be used for quantitative work by zoologists as well, especially if the latter are concerned with invertebrates or small vertebrates. If the animals being studied can be easily seen, as is true of birds, regular observation at stated intervals may give some idea as to the numbers and kinds present. Animals such as birds can also be studied by the quadrat method over a period of time. This involves setting up a system of quadrats and then observing the animals within them at regular intervals. Not only may various kinds and numbers of birds be studied in this manner in relation to the environment, but also such matters as home range, territory, and time of activity can be noted.

Organisms that are found within the quadrats must be properly identified. In some cases, such as with insects where identification cannot usually be made on sight, this will mean collecting the organisms, carefully labeling them, and then making the proper identification in the laboratory. The more specific the classification, the more valuable the study will be. Naming the subspecies or variety is desirable but not always possible. Careful notes must be taken at the time of collection at the quadrat site if any importance is to be attached to the specimens collected. This will include data on the physical conditions of the environment as well as the other organisms, and exact location of collection (see Chap. 11 on note-taking).

With some types of ecological studies, quadrats are not feasible.

Usually this is because the organisms under study are wide ranging. Thus, while it is conceivable that meadow mouse populations could be studied with a quadrat system, a species such as the fox or any of the larger mammals could not be. For such animals, other sampling devices are utilized. The methods include ways of either collecting specimens or observing signs made by the animals.

Trapping. The most obvious way of determining the presence of wary animals is the use of traps. These include live traps, steel traps, snap traps (household mousetraps), and various types of pitfalls. Traps can be set in regular patterns or at likely looking places. One method is to use a group of traps set at regular points along a given straight line. Manville (1950) found that traps set in a straight line in wooded areas took a higher number of small mammals than several other patterns that he tried. Other systems of trapping in quadrats are also employed and have been described and evaluated by such workers as Blair (1941) and Bole (1939). Pitfalls made of cans sunken in the ground have been reported to take more animals, and frequently a greater variety of species, than other types of traps. Traps may be baited with food or with scent of animals. For some small mammals, no bait whatever is necessary if the traps are placed in runways. For certain larger mammals such as foxes and minks, scents are the best guarantee of a catch. An advantage of trapping is that it may afford a means of determining not only the kinds and numbers of animals in an area, but also the times of activity of these animals. Of course, determining the numbers of animals by use of traps is often presuming an attractiveness of certain bait and a wariness—or lack of it—to traps, on the part of the animals. Also, a great deal of trapping success depends upon the experience of the trapper.

Animal Signs. Presence of animals can be determined by other means as well. None of these methods to be described involves killing or removing the animal, and in that way these methods are superior to some kinds of trapping. On the other hand, positive identification of the animals may not be possible. The first of these observational methods involves the use of "scat" (feces) boxes. Small boxes set about a field attract small animals, which defecate in the boxes. A practiced zoologist can recognize the scat and can get an idea of population size from such signs. Other animals often leave scats where they can be found, and may thus show their presence in an area. Also, herbivorous animals frequently make characteristic "cuttings"—pieces of herbaceous vegetation, often grass, that have been chewed into short lengths by a mammal. Cuttings can be used to indicate presence of the animal as well as its abundance. Several kinds of mice make cuttings of characteristic lengths that reveal their presence. It is difficult, however, to use such signs as an indication of population, except in a rough way. Observation of animal burrowings and tracks (Fig. 4-22) is still another method of detecting the presence of animals in a given area, and may indicate their abundance as well. Hamilton (1939) made

Photo by Allen H. Benton

Fig. 4-22. Tracks, such as this one of a cottontail rabbit, are used to determine the inhabitants of an area.

a study of the activity of moles by pressing down their tunnels and noting when these tunnels were repaired.

Still another method involves bait removal. In this procedure, bait is set out in a pattern and then is inspected at regular time intervals in order to determine removal by animals. Activity of animals in the wild may also be recorded by a photoelectric device that records their passing. In all cases, familiarity with the animals being studied is of the utmost importance if reliable data are to be secured.

Other Sampling Methods. Some animals are considered rare by collectors, yet they are apparently part of the environment and may not really be rare but merely of such habits that they are not easily discovered. That such is the case is borne out by the fact that other animals are able to find them. There are several techniques employed for disclosing the presence of apparently rare animals. They depend on the collecting powers of predators. In one technique, stomachs are analyzed for food recently consumed. Often, identification may be made of species which serve as food items. The feces of animals (scats) may also be examined for traces of food remains. These may include bones, hair, insect exoskeletons, and other undigestible remains which give a clue to the food of the predator. Finally, owl pellets (Fig. 4-23*a*, *b*) may be examined. Owl pellets are undigestible remains—balls of hair and bones—regurgitated from the stomachs of these birds of prey. In many cases such techniques reveal species not often collected by man. For example, the small shrew *Cryptotis* has been found in owl pellets in areas where it was seldom, if ever, taken by traps.

Certain animals are not observed during the day and are not observable by scats or other signs; nor are they easily trapped. If such animals are nocturnal, they may be collected at night more easily than in the daytime. This is the case with many amphibians that are secretive or wary during the day but may be blinded at night by a bright headlight and thereby more easily collected. Certain snakes are also on the prowl at night and may be collected along the highway. These collecting methods are usually only qualitative and not useful in a quantitative way. One type of nocturnal collecting that may be more quantitative is that of trapping insects with lights or with sugar as bait. Such trapping can be not only quantitative but can indicate the time of emergence of the insects and their period of activity.

Similar studies of activities and abundance of various types of invertebrates can be made by observing tree stumps. A trail may be established through the woods in which specific stumps are used as observation points. At stated intervals through the night, the stumps may be observed and data on the conditions of the environment recorded. Various insects, snails, slugs, spiders, and other arthropods can be observed on the stumps, and their numbers, kinds, and time of appearance may be noted and correlated with environmental conditions.

Physical Conditions of the Air. In addition to sampling the organisms in a given area, as much of the environmental conditions as possible should be determined in the area sampled. Among the more common aspects of the physical environment studied by ecologists are the amount and quality of light, and various conditions of the air such as currents and their velocity, moisture content both absolute and relative, evaporation, and temperature. See the Appendix (p. 306) for a description of the devices for measuring these conditions.

(a)

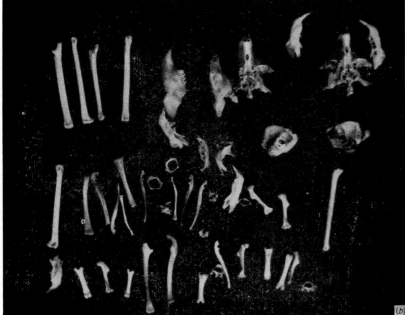

(b)

Photos by William E. Werner, Jr.

Fig. 4-23. (*a*) An entire owl pellet, a ball of fur and bones about two and one-half inches long; (*b*) bones from a single owl pellet. Notice the skulls and lower jaws. Such bones allow precise identification of food species.

Physical Conditions of the Soil. Another major environmental factor that must be considered in an ecological study is the soil. The pH, organic matter, mineral content, moisture, and temperature are all factors that may influence the presence or absence of organisms. Analysis of organic and mineral content of the soil is difficult and is best left to soil experts. Moisture, temperature, and pH of the soil, however, can be determined more easily. For measuring pH of soils, a specific amount of soil is mixed with distilled water, and then the solid matter is withdrawn. The resulting solution is then tested for pH. Temperatures of the soil are taken at varying depths. Determinations of moisture content can be made by weighing a soil sample, then drying it thoroughly in an oven, and weighing it again. The loss of weight indicates the amount of moisture that was present in the soil.

AQUATIC ECOLOGICAL METHODS

In aquatic situations, the same major problems are involved as in the terrestrial ones. Some method of providing representative samples of the flora and fauna must again be used. For certain purposes, quadrats can be utilized, for instance if the life on the bottom of a stream is to be surveyed. Here certain quadrats can be laid out and all organisms on the bottom within them can be studied, including rooted or microscopic plants as well as smaller animals. This will give quantitative and qualitative relationships. As in terrestrial situations, however, there are certain forms that do not allow themselves to be easily studied in this manner. In the aquatic situation such organisms include not only fast-moving vertebrates, but also the microscopic animals and plants that constitute the plankton.

Plankton Sampling. Plankton may be studied using the quadrat system, but usually other sampling methods are used. Furthermore, the third dimension of depth becomes a problem in considering plankton and in setting up quadrats. Therefore, instead of quadrats, samples of water are taken at various locations and depths in a body of water, whether it be in a stream, small pond, or lake. The samples can be taken at regular depths at specific points. Usually they are taken where variations are expected, in order to gain an idea of the total ecology of a body of water. The bottom may also be sampled in a similar manner for animals and plants and for the purpose of chemical analysis. From these samples, quantitative and qualitative analyses can be made not only for plankton but also for various chemical properties of the water.

Since bacteria may be difficult to collect, special techniques have been developed in concentrating them for study. One of these techniques involves "seeding" bacteria on glass slides left in the water. Bacteria will accumulate on the slides. The slides may then be stained for detailed examination, or the water collected may be treated with $Al(OH)_3$ to flocculate the bacteria and the water then filtered to remove them.

Larger plankton organisms are usually gathered in a fine mesh net towed through the water. The net has the effect of concentrating the minute organisms for easier study. However, the problem arises as to their natural density. If water from sampler tubes is centrifuged, plankton can also be concentrated, and the original concentration can be easily calculated. With plankton nets, devices have been designed to measure the amount of water flowing into a plankton net, thus enabling one to determine original concentrations. However, certain physical conditions make accurate determinations of this kind difficult.

Larger Organisms. For larger aquatic invertebrates and vertebrates, sampling may not be so exactly quantitative as with plankton, although methods have been devised to determine populations of fishes and other aquatics. This is usually done by tagging specimens, releasing them, and then retaking them at a later date. The Lincoln-Peterson index is an estimate of total population found by trapping, marking, and releasing animals, and then trapping again after a suitable time has passed to allow recombination of the marked and unmarked segments of the population. The index is equal to the number of marked animals released, divided by the proportion of marked to unmarked animals in the second trapping. (See Chap. 8 for a more detailed discussion.) This has been modified by later workers to improve the accuracy of the estimate (Bailey, 1952). This same method is used for certain large terrestrial animals, and was devised for studying bird populations from bird-banding techniques. Such a method, of course, can also give information on individual behavior, such as migration, home range, and length of life.

For less detailed population studies of a community where quantitative data are not desired, ordinary collecting methods will suffice. Nets

of various types are employed, and experience in such collection enables the collector to gain ideas as to the approximate numbers and
species present. The collector's knowledge of the habits of the organisms he is studying may be as important to accurate sampling as are
the refined techniques of estimating populations from the samples collected. For instance, the spawning or breeding seasons of certain fish,
amphibians, and reptiles may change their seasonal distributions, as
they move to particular areas, and may be taken advantage of in studying aquatic communities. Certain of these vertebrates—some turtles,
for example—evade ordinary collecting methods and must be gathered
with special traps. Some aquatic salamanders, such as the newt, have
been known to exhibit seasonal migrations from one pond to another
for food or for reproduction purposes. Such habits must also be known
if accurate community studies are to be made. Thus a knowledge of
natural history becomes a valuable if not an indispensable tool of the
ecological investigator.

Measurement of Physical Conditions. The physical environmental
conditions of streams, ponds, lakes, and bogs are as important in a community study as are the inhabitants of these areas. Two important
physical conditions of water are temperature and light. Devices to
measure light penetration are available, but color and turbidity of the
water often affects their accuracy. In shallow water, temperature is
easily taken with ordinary thermometers. In deeper water, however,
other devices are used (see Appendix, p. 309).

Other physical aspects of aquatic situations include bottom types
and water currents. Bottoms of deep bodies of water are studied by
means of random samples collected by various kinds of dredges (see
Appendix, p. 309) which take a vertical sample of the bottom without
disturbing any layering of deposits. Similar techniques can be used in
shallow streams and lakes as well. The velocity of streams can be
measured by using floating objects or calculation of volume of water
flowing past a given point. But care must be taken not to neglect
variations in current velocity near the bottom, sides, and surfaces due
to friction. Currents in lakes may also occur not only on the surface
but underneath, and these subsurface currents may be horizontal as
well as vertical.

Water Sampling. Water samplers (see Appendix, p. 309) are used to
collect samples of water at any desired depth for chemical analysis. A

core of water thus removed can be studied for oxygen content, dead and living organic matter (seston), color, alkalinity, turbidity, pH, free CO_2, and the like. Amounts of oxygen in water may be determined by quantitative volumetric chemical processes. Such a determination can easily be made as soon as the water samples are taken.

Buffers. An important chemical condition of water is the amount of buffer present. Buffers are chemicals that may prevent, within limits, a rapid shift of pH in either direction. It can be therefore easily understood why buffers may influence the life of a body of water. Buffers include weak acids and weak bases, such as calcium carbonate and magnesium carbonate. The amounts of certain buffer substances in water can be determined by using methyl orange and phenolphthalein as indicators. Total alkalinity, bicarbonate alkalinity, carbonate alkalinity, free carbon dioxide, and pH determinations are made in connection with the problem of the amount of ions in solution and of changes in pH. Methods of calculating the pH of the water are similar to those used in terrestrial situations. Chemical analysis may also be made in an effort to determine the presence of nitrites and other important chemical factors in the water. Hardness, or the amount of such salts as calcium, iron, silica, and magnesium, can also be determined rather easily, for example, by the use of standard soap solutions.

In all ecological studies, maps of various kinds may be of invaluable assistance and should not be overlooked as an aid to study of an area. Such maps include geological survey maps, which give such information as elevation (contour lines) and often general vegetational types, as well as accurate mapping on a large scale (Fig. 4-24). Soil maps are also available for many areas of the United States (see Appendix, p. 316).

Once data have been obtained, they must be sorted out and generalizations and summarizations made. Graphs are often convenient tools for summarizing and comparing different kinds of data. The use of statistical methods may often require the help of a statistician, but some simple methods may be utilized (see Chap. 8 and Appendix). It must be pointed out that the more inclusive the study is, the wider will be the generalizations that may be made. Therefore, many observations may well be made over a long period of time and at great frequency during this period, in order that sampling errors due to daily, seasonal, or yearly variations may not lead to false conclusions.

Map by U.S. Geological Survey

Fig. 4-24. Section of a topographic map. The contour lines represent intervals of equal elevation. Railroads, houses, roads, and other artifacts are represented by standard symbols. Natural features such as swamps, streams, and bodies of water are also indicated. Some modern topographic maps show wooded areas in green.

It must also be remembered that conditions that may prevail in the area examined may differ from conditions elsewhere, and conclusions should be made with this fact in mind.

REFERENCES CITED

Bailey, N. T. 1952. Improvements in interpretations of recapture data. *J. Animal Ecol.*, 21:120–127.

Blair, W. F. 1941. Techniques for study of mammal populations. *J. Mammal.*, 22:148–157.

Bole, B. P. 1939. The quadrat method of studying small mammal populations. *Scient. Publ. Cleveland Mus. Nat. Hist.*, 5:15–77.

Brown, L. G., and L. E. Yeager. 1943. Survey of the Illinois fur resource. *Bull. Ill. Nat. Hist. Survey*, 22: Art. 6.

Clements, F. E., and V. E. Shelford. 1939. "Bioecology." John Wiley & Sons, Inc., New York. 425 pp.

Curtis, J. T. 1956. "Plant Ecology Work Book." Burgess Publishing Company, Minneapolis. 86 pp.

Griggs, R. F. 1946. The timberlines of northern America and their interpretation. *Ecol.*, 27:275–289.

Hamilton, W. J., Jr. 1939. Activity of Brewer's mole, *Parascalops breweri*. *J. Mammal.*, 20:307–309.

Manville, R. H. 1950. A comparison of trapping methods. *J. Mammal.*, 31:377–383.

Scotland, M. B. 1934. The animals of the *Lemna* association. *Ecol.*, 15:290–294.

SUGGESTED READING

Allee, W. C., Alfred C. Emerson, Orlando Park, Thomas Park, and K. P. Schmidt. 1949. "Principles of Animal Ecology." W. B. Saunders Company, Philadelphia.

Anderson, R. M. 1948. "Methods of Collecting and Preserving Vertebrate Animals." National Museum of Canada, Bulletin 69, Ottawa.

Braun, E. Lucy. 1950. "Deciduous Forests of Eastern North America." The Blakiston Division, McGraw-Hill Book Company, Inc., New York.

Carpenter, J. Richard. 1940. The grassland biome. *Ecol. Monographs*, 10 (4):617–684.

Dice, Lee R. 1952. "Natural Communities." University of Michigan Press, Ann Arbor, Mich.

Elton, Charles S., and Richard S. Miller. 1954. The ecological survey of animal communities: with a practical system of classifying habitats by structural characters. *J. Ecol.*, 42 (2):460–496.

FAUTIN, REED W. 1946. Biotic communities of the northern desert shrub biome in western Utah. *Ecol. Monographs*, 16 (4):251–310.

HESSE, R., W. C. ALLEE, AND K. P. SCHMIDT. 1951. "Ecological Animal Geography." John Wiley & Sons, Inc., New York.

KIMBLE, GEORGE H. T., AND DOROTHY GOOD (EDS.) 1955. "Geography of the Northlands." John Wiley & Sons, Inc., New York.

LAGLER, KARL F. 1956. "Freshwater Fishery Biology." William C. Brown Company, Dubuque, Iowa.

OOSTING, HENRY J. 1956. "The Study of Plant Communities." W. H. Freeman and Co., San Francisco.

RICHARDS, PAUL W. 1952. "The Tropical Rain Forest." Cambridge University Press, New York.

SHELFORD, VICTOR E. 1926. "Naturalist's Guide to the Americas." The Williams & Wilkins Company, Baltimore.

———. 1937. "Animal Communities in Temperate America." University of Chicago Press, Chicago.

SHREVE, FORREST, and IRA L. WIGGINS. 1951. "Vegetation and Flora of the Sonoran Desert." vol. 1, Forrest Shreve. "Vegetation of the Sonoran Desert." Carnegie Institute of Washington, Publ. 591.

WEAVER, J. E. 1954. "North American Prairie." Johnsen Publishing Company, Lincoln, Nebr.

——— AND F. W. ALBERTSON. 1956. "Grasslands of the Great Plains." Johnsen Publishing Company, Lincoln, Nebr.

WELCH, PAUL S. 1948. "Limnological Methods." The Blakiston Division, McGraw-Hill Book Company, Inc., New York.

CHAPTER 5

TERRESTRIAL PLANT SUCCESSION

> For every wound the ointment of time.
> *Welsh proverb*

Although we speak of climax communities and think of them as large homogenous areas in which the biota is relatively uniform, such areas are frequently difficult to find under our conditions of civilization. For example, in the forested biomes one seldom sees a vast, uninterrupted area of trees. There may be occasional bodies of water, such as lakes, rivers, and streams; or open fields planted in crops; or extensive areas where fire has recently leveled a woodland to charred ruins (Fig. 5-1). Even in the West, where animals and plants tend to be in a more natural condition over large areas, there are still deviations from the climax community in areas of extensive rock outcrops, overgrazed range, or salt flats. Such regions may have few organisms or may include a community unlike that of the climax type for the region. These departures from the climax type are frequently observed, a fortunate occurrence for the ecologist and field biologist; for the existence of such areas, as well as their origin, development, and fate, provides us with an opportunity to understand the dynamics and construction of climax communities.

If a person could watch these islands of nonclimax communities over a period of time, he would see them change slowly in the direction of the climax community. In some cases this would be a lengthy process, not observable in a man's lifetime. In other instances the change might be completed in a few decades. Careful scrutiny would reveal that the process of change follows a definite pattern. The movement of gradual, orderly, and predictable changes in the composition of communities toward the climax type is known as *succession*. There is some tendency, at least in certain instances, for succession to occur in steps, by

Photo by Jack K. James, Soil Conservation Service, U.S.D.A.

Fig. 5-1. Burned-over forest in the Kaniksu National Forest, Washington. Even the organic humus of the forest floor has been reduced to ashes.

definite, easily detectable communities. It is obvious, of course, that there must be transition periods, even in such instances, with perhaps the major steps lasting longer than the transition periods.

Basic Concepts of Succession. Succession involves at least four basic concepts:

1. There is a dynamic shifting in the species composition of the community.

2. The species change is an orderly one, so that it may be predicted what community will follow an existing community.

3. The sequence of changes of the community types is directional, with each succeeding community type becoming more like the climax type, at least in physical characteristics.

4. The ultimate community type is the climax community.

As we travel along a highway, the variations of a climax community mentioned previously are easily visible. These are the major variations. Upon closer inspection of the areas that at first glance appear homogeneous, one will usually find smaller variations. Perhaps there will be a boulder covered with lichens and moss in the midst of a forest, or a huge tree rotting away on the forest floor. In time, these smaller variations, like the larger and more obvious ones, will be obliterated in an orderly manner; ecologists consider them situations in which minute examples of the phenomenon of succession may be demonstrated. Such small variations are present in every community. An area undergoing succession may therefore cover square miles or only a few square feet.

It was mentioned that rivers, lakes, ponds, and other aquatic areas relieve the monotony of climax communities, and it was intimated that these variations, too, were only temporary. In a process similar to that occurring on land, aquatic communities change until an end point is reached, that point usually being the terrestrial climax community. The way in which aquatic communities do so, however, is sufficiently distinct to warrant separate discussion in a later chapter (see Chap. 6). Suffice it to say here that succession is occurring everywhere, and the process is basically the same in aquatic and terrestrial situations.

If succession proceeds from an area devoid of organisms, which has not been changed physically by organisms, it is called *primary succession*. If, on the other hand, succession proceeds from a state in which there are other organisms still present, or if their effects are still evident, as in an organically enriched soil, it is called *secondary succession*. All of the communities which will be formed and destroyed until the climax community is reached are collectively termed a *sere*, and any one community of the sere is a *seral stage*. A primary-succession sere may, for example, commence with windblown sand and end with a prairie community. A secondary-succession sere may start with a plowed field where grasses had been growing and end also with a prairie community. The end point for both types of succession will be the climax community, whether it be desert, grassland, or forest. Only the origin of the two kinds of succession is different.

Speed of Succession. Upon reflection, it is obvious that if succession is occurring everywhere, and if such areas are so numerous as to be common, either these areas must take a long time in reaching the climax community, or new successional areas are constantly being created. Actually, the latter is usually the case. In the region around the Great Lakes, however, there are still some boulders left by the receding glaciers of 10,000 years ago. They may be covered only with lichens, the first stage of a primary succession, while other smaller rocks deposited at the same time by the glacier are well advanced in the seral stages, and are now buried under the duff and in the soil of the forest floor. In the same region, the meadows of an abandoned farm may be repopulated with a forest of a climax type within a hundred or two hundred years. On the prairies, an old wagon trail may be revegetated with grasses in a far shorter time. In the desert, a rock may remain bare for a longer period than would occur in a forested biome. Climate, the extent of variation from the climax, and other factors may alter the time it takes for succession to be completed; but in most cases succession is a relatively short-time phenomenon. It would seem that the frequency of its occurrence is in large part due to new areas undergoing a change which destroys the climax community. On an overall view, we see that any community, including a climax, is stable in only a limited sense. Actually, there are always within it some areas that are being destroyed and some that are undergoing an orderly growth back to the climax community.

AGENCIES OF CHANGE

To a large extent, the dynamic state of communities of plants and animals, including the climax, is due to the multiplicity of agencies of change acting within them and upon them. Some of these agencies are physical, such as wind and rain; but the organisms themselves bring about many of the changes that are involved in succession. Some of the changes are destructive, tearing down a community to a lower stage, or extinguishing life in an area altogether. Other changes are constructive. Both the constructive and destructive changes may be brought about either by biotic or physical factors, or both. The tendency is that as soon as destruction of a community occurs, forces begin to work to rebuild toward the climax state. Curiously enough, this rebuilding process (succession) occurs, in a sense, through a systematic destruction of one community as it is replaced by the next higher seral stage. The plants and animals, by their reactions upon the physical environment, such as in the accumulation of their wastes and dead remains, make the situation less favorable to themselves or more favorable to other organisms. In any case, certain species of a community are replaced by others until a new type of community is formed. In addition to these biotic factors, physical factors such as erosion by wind and water may help to bring about constructive successional changes in which certain members of one community are replaced by others.

Natural Catastrophes. Any physical phenomenon that will destroy life directly, or alter environmental conditions so that the old community cannot tolerate the new conditions, or allow new organisms to compete successfully with the old species, provides a situation in which succession may occur. Volcanic activity, earthquakes, fire, flood, drought, and severe storms may temporarily denude an area or cause the death of many of the inhabitants, including dominants. When volcanoes erupt, their ashes and molten lava may kill all organisms for miles around. Topsoil is buried, and bare rock formed by the cooling lava must then be invaded by organisms. Katmai Peninsula in Alaska is still completely free of vegetation as a result of the eruption of Katmai volcano in 1912 (Fig. 5-2). Earthquakes may not be so drastic in effect as volcanic action, but they often destroy life in small areas. Floods may destroy life on large areas and deposit soil, gravel, and debris over existing communities. Although such regions are left without the larger flora and fauna, reoccupation is comparatively rapid, since soil remains in place and often includes organic nutrients and seeds, spores, or other living material. Similarly, drought may kill many organisms of a community but may leave enough individuals to retain its essential structure. Fires and severe storms may also kill only certain members of a community, but they—and drought as well—may affect organisms such as trees which are dominant in the community. The changes through which the community will then go are successional, and eventually the climax is once again established. By definition, these successions, in which some effects of previous life are left for new communities to build upon, are secondary. In a sense, change of climate causes a successional change too, although in this instance a

Photo by Victor Cahalane, U.S. National Park Service

Fig. 5-2. The Valley of Ten Thousand Smokes, Katmai Peninsula, Alaska. The area in this photograph is still almost completely free of vegetation as a result of volcanic eruption in 1912.

longer period of time is involved. In the recent glaciation of North America, not only was there a change of climate but the land under the ice was completely wiped free of organisms, and we may still witness the last stages of succession proceeding as a result of this destruction.

Changes in the Earth's Surface. In a similar way, rising and sinking of land masses may create changes which are so subtle that we do not recognize them as successional. Although movements of land masses occur gradually, they do produce conditions that are involved in succession. Thus elevation increases or changes drainage, which will have its effect on communities through different moisture conditions and in increased erosion. If the elevation is pronounced, temperature changes due to altitude will also be effected. Depression of land would bring about the same types of changes in environment as elevation, but in reverse. Furthermore, elevation or depression may raise land out of the water or inundate areas. It is believed, for example, that the weight

Photo by William E. Werner, Jr.

Fig. 5-3. Some of the Thousand Islands in the St. Lawrence River. This land is said to be rising and may eventually cut off the Great Lakes from the sea.

of the glaciers on North America during recent geological history depressed the land so that an arm of the sea covered the area now occupied by Lake Ontario. Then, as the glacier receded to the north, the land was reelevated, a fresh-water lake was formed, and the St. Lawrence River was established as an outflow for the Great Lakes. But the land is still rising, and it is believed that eventually the region of the St. Lawrence River known as the Thousand Islands (Fig. 5-3) will be dry land. Thus, organisms in this region will have changed from marine to fresh-water and finally to terrestrial. A slow succession will have occurred, of which the elevation and depression of land is the causative agent.

Biological Agents. Man occasionally introduces a destructive organism by which the constitution of the climax community will be altered. The American chestnut was one of the dominant trees in the forest biome of eastern North America in the early days of this country. Then a fungus, the chestnut blight, was accidentally brought in, and in less than half a century the species was almost completely wiped out. Not only was the space formerly occupied by these trees left vacant, but their death and disappearance has changed the interrelationships of other organisms in the community. What happened in this instance has happened many times when an organism is introduced into a new area. The introduction of rabbits and prickly pear into Australia, or of goats on oceanic islands, has disrupted the climax communities of those places. Finally, man with his plow, ax, fire, and bulldozer alters communities and creates situations in which succession may proceed.

THE PROCESS OF SUCCESSION

First Physical Changes. As soon as the destructive forces have finished their action, the constructive processes of succession begin. Again, the agents of construction toward the climax community are both physical and biological. Let us take, for example, bare rocks such as those left after a glacier has receded, or after a volcano has erupted. At first, the only factors that may change the nature of the surface of the rocks are the elements. Rain and snow may now begin erosion. Rain as it falls through the atmosphere gathers carbon dioxide, and this in combination with water forms carbonic acid, which may aid in erosion. If a crack or fissure is formed, water in it may freeze, expand, and help to split the rock further. Stone particles carried by water act as abrasives and wear down the rocks, while they themselves are worn down by the contact. Wind, bearing small particles of sand, buffets against the rocks, helping to rub off small fragments. In parts of the western United States, the effects of wind erosion are pronounced, and softer rocks are worn away, leaving the harder ones standing out in relief (Fig. 5-4). Some of our most scenic national monuments feature this type of eroded rock.

Physical Effects of the First Organisms. In many biomes, however, such rocks do not long remain without a cover of organisms which will aid in the constructive processes. Spores of algae and fungi come through the air from surrounding areas, and soon algae or those sturdy

Photo by William E. Werner, Jr.

Fig. 5-4. Wind-eroded rock, with the softer rocks worn away and the harder rocks remaining to form the peculiar shape.

symbiotic combinations of algae and fungi called lichens, are established on the surface of the rocks (Fig. 5-5). Thus wind not only erodes the rocks physically but transports biotic agents of erosion, for the lichens or algae in their growth will produce more carbonic acid. As they cling tenaciously to the rocks, they will tend to hold water on the surface and bits of stone that are chipped loose or blown there from another place. In this manner, with the coming of the plants, soil starts building up slowly but surely. Moisture can now be retained for a longer time, allowing greater periods for the processes of solution to work. This plant growth represents the first stage of a primary succession. From this point on, because of the plant cover, the rocks are more fully protected from the abrasive action of wind and sand and direct action of rain. One means of soil formation is

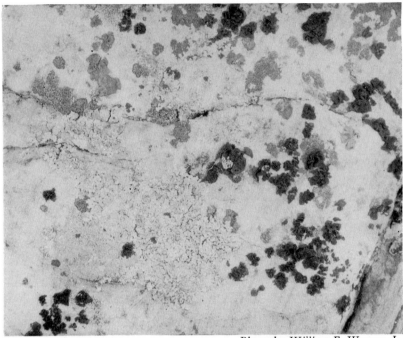

Photo by William E. Werner, Jr.

Fig. 5-5. Pioneer plants (lichens) on a boulder in the coniferous forest biome.

thus limited. However, the action of the plants themselves in corroding the rocks, in splitting them with roots, and in the enrichment of this soil with organic matter from their dead bodies more than compensates for the protection they give. Hence organisms contribute a great deal toward the building of soil and therefore to the process of succession. There is, however, more to soil building than the work of wind, rain, and decaying plant matter, as we have described it here.

Pioneer Organisms and the First Stage of Succession. A sere on a bare area begins, as we have seen, with primitive plants. A bare area may be a sand dune, a clay bank, a gravel pile, or rock. For our purposes, however, we shall continue our consideration of the principles of plant succession as it would occur on rocks, realizing that the details might be different if the habitat was different at the beginning. It is evident that only certain kinds of organisms could invade bare areas. Conditions on the bare rock are particularly stringent. Water on its surface is overabundant while it is raining but scarce or absent between storms. The sun heats a rock to high temperatures during the summer, but during the winter it may be covered with ice. There is no place for roots to grow for anchorage, so that an ordinary plant would soon be blown away by the wind, even if it could find a spot suitable for germination. Without plants, most animals find such an area inhospitable for invasion, for plants provide food and cover for them. Large animals like foxes or birds may make their homes in rocky areas, but even they must go elsewhere for food.

Plants such as lichens that may first invade an area ready for succession are called *pioneer plants*. They must be tolerant of severe climatic conditions and largely self-sustaining. They must be able to undergo long periods of adverse conditions to be able to take advantage of favorable moments for growth and reproduction. It is possible that some pioneers may not only tolerate these severe conditions but may require them for their existence. Thus certain mosses are found to be pioneers in situations where there is abundant moisture. Such moisture is necessary for their life cycle in order that fertilization may occur, for the sperm must swim to the egg in those plants.

Strangely enough, plants that are so tolerant of physical conditions of the environment are quite frequently intolerant of other organisms. In the case of the bare rock sere, we may assume that the pioneers were lichens. They have helped to corrode the rock and have perhaps collected some wind-blown soil. They, and any accumulated soil, maintain better moisture conditions, so that different kinds of plants may become established. One of the major mechanisms of succession is at once demonstrated as the next stage begins to develop; namely, that each community produces new environmental conditions which allow organisms less tolerant of severe climatic and environmental conditions to take over and destroy the existing community. The new invaders, profiting, in this case, by the gains made by the lichens toward soil formation, may crowd out the pioneer plants. We assume for the purposes of discussion that these invaders are mosses which were unable to invade bare rock (Fig. 5-6).

The Moss Stage. In the early period of succession, there is still another obvious difference between stages, and that is complexity. As each succeeding stage develops, larger numbers of species are involved. The mosses which succeed the lichens may develop a dense cover,

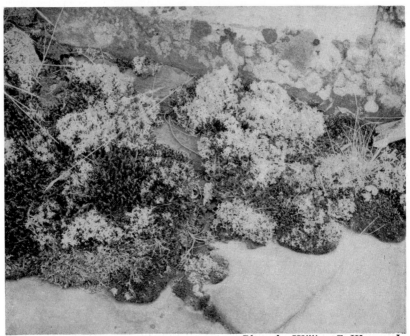

Photo by William E. Werner, Jr.

Fig. 5-6. The lichens are being crowded out by mosses, which benefit from the soil prepared by the lichens.

which will attract insects and other small invertebrates. These animals, like the mosses themselves, require more moisture than could be secured while the lichens were dominant, as well as food and cover, which the lichens did not offer them. The smaller animals may attract some vertebrates as predators, such as the tiny insectivores, shrews.

The mosses continue to build up deposits of organic matter and soil as more rock is etched and broken away and as the old mosses and lichens die. The most significant change that these organisms can produce in an environment is that wrought by their own dead bodies.

Throughout life they have taken in and accumulated in their systems salts, water, gases, minerals, and other compounds. Many of these substances have been synthesized into complex organic compounds such as fats, carbohydrates, and proteins. When the organisms die, they deposit these concentrated materials in the soil, and the products of their bacterial decay are instrumental in enriching the soil.

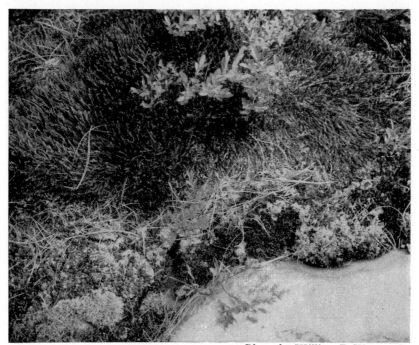

Photo by William E. Werner, Jr.

Fig. 5-7. Invading grasses, weeds, and small shrubs are beginning to overrun the mosses.

As the humus (decayed organic matter) accumulates, erosion of the rocks may slow down, although minerals are still leached from the soil and find their way eventually to the sea. Geologists believe that the saltiness of the oceans is due to this continual leaching process. At present, the saltiness of the oceans has reached a content of approximately 3.5 per cent, indicating the vast amounts of materials that have been taken from the soil. This may indirectly indicate the magnitude of the soil-building process from rock erosion and plant decay.

Probably the factor which is of most importance in succession is
that of competition. Because of the changes wrought by the old community, new species are able to compete with the old species for space.
In the new environment, the new species are more successful than
the ones whose places they have usurped. Thus the lichens pave the

Photo by William E. Werner, Jr.

Fig. 5-8. The herb stage. Milkweed, evening primrose, white snakeroot, and
goldenrods are among the prominent plants.

way for the mosses, and the mosses may eliminate them. The mosses
further contribute their products to the environment, and improve it
to the point that other plants may then successfully compete with
them (Fig. 5-7).

The Herb Stage. Assuming that the rocks now covered with mosses
are in an area where the climax vegetation will be a forest, the next
invaders or competitors with the mosses may be large annual herbs
such as goldenrods, asters, evening primroses, and milkweed, as well as
a variety of grasses and other weeds (Fig. 5-8). In wetter areas, sedges

of various species may predominate, along with water hemlock, blue-eyed grass, and rushes. In dry situations, where succession may proceed more slowly, plants such as poverty grass may be the only serious competitor of moss in this stage. Insects, usually quite abundant in the herbaceous stage, are the principal types of animals in the community. Especially numerous are grasshoppers, beetles, bugs, bees, and ants. During the summer many species of flies and butterflies are also to be found. Perhaps attracted by this source of food are the shrews and moles, while meadow mice find ample food in the grass, and jumping mice also make their homes here. Snakes of various kinds, including the garter snake, ribbon snake, green snakes, and DeKay's snake may be found preying on the insects, earthworms, and other invertebrates, while such others as the milk snake, king snake, and blue racer survive in this habitat as predators of the small mammals. Larger mammals that also may be found in this community include rabbits, woodchucks, gophers, and ground squirrels. It should be understood that this prolific assortment is not always present in every herbaceous community. Especially in dryer situations, mammals and reptiles may be few or lacking, and certain of the burrowing mammals require particular types of soils for their tunneling. However, there are other animals which may be temporary visitors. Many species of birds come here to seek out the insects, and some, such as the killdeer and several species of sparrows, nest here. Certain amphibians, particularly the meadow frog, are found where sufficient moisture is present; and larger mammals, such as deer, foxes, skunks, weasels, and opossums seek food in the meadow.

The Shrub Stage. Among the various herbaceous plants, the saplings of trees and shrubs will begin to grow (Fig. 5-9). Just as mosses and lichens provided conditions under which the herbaceous plants could grow, so the grasses now do the same for the woody plants. The soil has been further enriched, the taller plants furnish shade and act as a windbreak, and the moisture conditions of the soil and the air just above the surface are improved. In general, as succession proceeds, the tendency is for the environment to become more *mesic*, that is, moderately moist. Thus wet areas will become drier and dry places wetter.

As the shrubs grow taller, they will become the dominant plants. This means that some of the plants of the herbaceous stage will not be able to survive. Sumac, aspen, poplar, blackberries, hawthorn, black locust, red cedar, white cedar, juniper, and mulberry are all examples of shrubs or small trees that may be prominent at this stage (Fig. 5-10). Usually only a few of these species will be present in any one location, the species being dependent upon several conditions including drainage, rainfall, original rock type, and the vagaries of distribution. Sometimes one species may predominate, even to the exclusion of all the

Photo by William E. Werner, Jr.

Fig. 5-9. Beginning of the shrub stage. Here, alders and viburnums have started to invade the herb community.

others. Saplings of trees may also be found in this stage, including maples, elms, pines, and oaks. Some trees are able to establish themselves along with the shrubs, while others are not able to gain a good foothold except in the shade of previously established plants. The shrubs may drastically reduce the number of herbaceous plants, and since the latter furnish the food for many of the insects and their predators, such animal forms are reduced in numbers. But while some animals may be fewer, others become more abundant. Especially numerous in this seral stage are birds, which use the shrubs for cover and often for nesting sites. Blackberries, mulberries, spirea, dogwoods, and viburnums may provide food as well as cover, and the birds, feeding on their fruits or seeds, may further distribute these shrubs by voiding undigested and viable seeds in their feces.

Frequently the herbs during this stage are so reduced in number that insects and herbivorous mammals become quite scarce. Shrews,

Photo by William E. Werner, Jr.

Fig. 5-10. Shrubs and saplings of trees are now dominant, the grasses and herbs having been reduced in numbers and importance.

moles, and a few mice may be the only small mammals of the herbaceous stage still to be found. However, new species may now enter, perhaps because of reduced competition, or the food and cover available in the altered surroundings. The white-footed mice and chipmunks may be among the newcomers in many parts of the country. The predators noted in the herbaceous stage are less likely to be encountered among the shrubs, for the supply of food in this community is not so abundant. Certain birds prefer this habitat to others, and nesting species may include towhees, song sparrows, gold-finches, catbirds, brown thrashers and yellowthroats.

The kinds of soil in any area may affect the course of succession. Not all herbaceous plant stages are alike, and not all shrub stages are identical, even under similar climatic conditions. This is due to the different conditions under which a sere may start. One of the major physical differences which may affect the type of soil produced at first, and thus the types of plants which will occur there, is drainage. In moist, poorly drained areas, organic material as it decays tends to produce weak acids. Even if the original rocks were alkaline, the condition may be neutralized and an eventual acid condition will prevail. This may be unfavorable to bacteria, insects, and other organisms that normally decompose the organic remains. Therefore, organic materials remain on top of the soil and are not incorporated into it. In well-drained areas, the organic material may be washed away before it has a chance to become a part of the soil, while in more mesic conditions, organic matter has an opportunity to be converted into chemicals which may be mixed with the soil by earthworms, burrowing animals, and water. Many of these chemical end products may then be leached away, along with some of the mineral particles which the plants have dissolved from the rock, but the soil in the meantime has changed considerably.

The tendency is that, under given climatic conditions, the soil will eventually be made uniform, since the climax community—which to a large extent manufactures the soil—is also uniform. But until the climax is reached, the soil may be different and may affect the course of succession. Thus in the shrub stage wet areas may be populated with alder, hornbeam, and elm, while dry areas may support growths of arrowwood, dogwood, and black locust. If the original rocks were limestone, the shrub stage may be dominated by cedars (Fig. 5-11). With time, however, the well-drained areas wear down, accumulate more organic matter, and become mesic, while the poorly drained soil fills in with dead remains, and eventually mesic conditions exist here too. The original rock, covered by more and more soil, has less influence on the type of plants growing on it. The result is a development in the direction of uniform soil conditions.

The Tree Stage. As the shrub stage matures and the sapling trees within it mature, the differences of soil and drainage have not yet been overcome. In poorly drained areas, red maple, willows, and cottonwood may become the dominants in the first tree stage. In more mesic situations, this stage may include paper birch and white pine, while in well-drained and dry locations, aspens, gray birch, and cottonwood— or oaks, hickories, and locusts—may be found (Fig. 5-12). Shrubs from the earlier shrub stage may continue to exist as before, but now in a secondary role. Plants that cannot tolerate great amounts of sun

Photo by William E. Werner, Jr.

Fig. 5-11. Red cedars, *Juniperus virginiana*, dominate this shrub community over original limestone rocks.

begin to establish themselves under the trees, which soon form a complete canopy over them. Mosses, lacking the competition of the grasses, again become common, and ferns make their appearance, especially in the mesic and moist situations. As trees die and fall to the ground and leaf litter accumulates, fungi become abundant, and certain insects, including ground beetles, carpenter ants, wasps, bees, and flies may be found. Earthworms, millipedes, centipedes, sowbugs, and insect larvae are also present, especially in and under the rotting logs. Except in dry areas, salamanders may occasionally be found, taking refuge under stones and logs. The most common mammals of this stage are often white-footed mice and shrews, although the larger predators—foxes, raccoons, skunks, and weasels—play a part in such communities. Snakes, turtles, and lizards may also be quite common.

The Climax Stage. In those parts of the country where the oak-hickory community is the climax (p. 75), there may be only one tree

Photo by R. C. Axtell

Fig. 5-12. Aspens (*Populus*) and gray birch (*Betula populifolia*) are dominant in this dry location.

stage in succession, the oaks and hickories growing up during the shrub stage. In such an event, the species of herbaceous plants which invade the developing climax community are those characteristic of the oak-hickory forest. For the most part these plants are the spring-flowering species, though mosses and ferns also become more common (Fig. 5-13).

If the climax type is to be composed of beech, hemlock, and maple, there may be several tree stages in which different tree species serve as

Photo by Allen H. Benton

Fig. 5-13. The ground in deciduous forests is often well covered with herbaceous plants such as the maidenhair fern, *Adiantum pedatum*.

dominants. Thus the aspens, gray birch, and cottonwood of dry areas may be superseded by red maple, white pine, and oaks, then by oaks and hickories, before the climax dominants make their appearance (Fig. 5-14). In mesic areas, paper birch and white pine may be followed by the climax forest, while in less perfectly drained areas red maple, willow, and cottonwood may be overtaken by such dominants as sycamore and sugar maple before the climax forest is established. There may be varied combinations of these dominants in intermediate stages, but as the climax type is finally approached, the communities become more and more similar; this is a process known as *convergence*.

The beech-hemlock-maple climax forest is mesic. It, too, has many herbs of the spring-flowering type, mosses and ferns, often in more profusion than in the drier oak-hickory forest. Animals are similar to those in the earlier tree stages, but the vertebrates in particular are more abundant. This is partly because the climax tree stage shows stratification of habitats, the treetops being suitable to some species, lower branches to others, the shrubbery providing habitat for still others; some vertebrates live on and under the ground. The soil has now matured, and the species will not be replaced by others unless climatic or topographic change, or some catastrophe alters the situation drastically. Shrubs that can tolerate shade, or cannot tolerate sun—such as witch hazel, maple-leaved viburnum, and flowering dogwood—may form an understory beneath the canopy of the dominants. But

Photo by William E. Werner, Jr.

Fig. 5-14. In this intermediate stage before the climax forest is achieved, white pines (*Pinus strobus*) and red maple (*Acer rubrum*) are dominant.

competition with invading species is for the most part over; now it is a matter of competition among existing species of the community.

The description of succession from bare rock to forest climax is only one example of succession. The beginning might equally well have been a sand dune, flood plain, or sand bar; the climax perhaps prairie, coniferous forest, or tropical rain forest. The speed with which succession occurs may vary from a few years in the tropics to hundreds or even thousands of years in an arid area, although most successions are comparatively short. The manner in which the dominants of the climax community reassert themselves, however, is essentially the same everywhere. Even with widely differing origins, convergence is still the rule and the climax community the end point. Succession may start from ponds, bogs, or swamps, and still the final community will be the climax type. Thus even the aquatic succession (see Chap. 6) ends up the same, although it is frequently a much more lengthy process.

Aberrant community types. Sometimes, factors that cause setbacks in succession recur frequently at more or less regular intervals. Fire and flood are common catastrophes which may intervene before the climax community can be reestablished. The highest community which can develop under such conditions may have many of the earmarks of a climax, appearing as a stable community. However, since it is not the highest type of community possible under the prevailing climatic conditions, but is maintained for a long time, it is called a *subclimax*. If the factors creating the conditions are man-made, it may be called a *disclimax*. These biotic communities may be one stage removed from the climax type, or may develop only to an earlier stage, or in some cases they may possess their own peculiar features.

An example of this kind of community may be found in the area between Albany and Schenectady, in eastern New York. Here an area of sandy soil covers a wide belt some twenty miles long and five or six miles in width. Much of this land was once covered with a climax forest of white pine. With increased population of the region, the trees were cut, and parts of the sandy soil were farmed for a time. Fires occurred frequently, burning what little humus was present, and the whole area became a sandy plain. White pine could not tolerate the fires, but another pine which occurs in this region, the pitch pine, could withstand both fires and the poor soil. Today the pitch pines grow scattered about as in a savanna, and the main vegetation beneath them is a dense growth of shrubs, including bear oak, shrub oak, dwarf cherries, and staghorn and smooth sumac (Fig. 5-15). Most of these shrubs occur in small numbers elsewhere in this region. Here the bushes and dwarfed trees are dominant, or at least codominant with the pitch pine, and they form a community distinct from any in the nearby region. Indeed, no seral stage of normal succession in this region resembles this vegetational type. Yet if the fires and other results of human activity were ended, the area's normal climax would eventually be reestablished.

Other efforts of man also create subclimax conditions. Agricultural practices, lumbering, and grazing may remove the climax community, allowing a stage of development lower than the climax type to persist. Sometimes the effect is deceiving, as is the case when certain species

Photo by Allen H. Benton

Fig. 5-15. A pitch pine–shrub oak community, maintained in a subclimax stage by human activities.

of dominant trees are heavily lumbered to the exclusion of others. Heavy browsing or grazing may be sufficient to change the climax; in the West, the natural grass climax community may be changed to a desert cactus type by overgrazing. Areas periodically flooded may be held a stage short of the climax. For example, the regions of river bottoms and flood plains within a climax forest possess a subclimax vegetation.

Many of the features of the terrain which affect vegetation take an exceptionally long time to be so modified that the climax com-

munity can be established. For example, a high, steep hill or escarp-
ment may take thousands of years to wear down to the level of the
surrounding area. In the meantime, due to excessive drainage, shading,
and other environmental conditions produced by differences in altitude,
slope, and exposure, the highest community type which can be reached
may not be the climax but a stage or so in succession from it. Such
a community is called by some ecologists an *edaphic climax*, since
local conditions other than climate have caused this difference from
the expected climatic climax. In an
area where the normal climax is a
beech-maple-hemlock forest, the
edaphic climax on a steep slope
may be an oak-hickory community.
Only after a relatively long time
would the final stage in succession
be completed.

Microsuccession. It was mentioned earlier in this chapter that
within communities there are small
variations, and that a miniature
succession occurs here. This kind
of microcommunity succession may
be found, for example, in dead
trees, animal droppings, carcasses,
and plant galls. These habitats serve
as little niches where communities
of plants and animals live, succeed

Photo by William E. Werner, Jr.

Fig. 5-16. A goldenrod ball gall,
caused by the gallfly, *Eurosta solidaginis.*

each other, and finally come to an end by the destruction of the niche
as it becomes a part of the larger community.

Galls offer an example of a simplified animal succession in a microhabitat which may help in understanding this phenomenon. In studying the ecology of the goldenrod ball gallfly. *Eurosta solidaginis,*
Uhler (1951) discovered that the gall formed by this fly served as a
home for several insects, some of them preparing the way for others,
and in so doing, making the habitat unsuitable for further tenancy by
their own species.

The goldenrod ball gall (Fig. 5-16) is an abnormal growth of plant
tissue found in the stems of goldenrod (*Solidago* sp.). It is formed

after the fly inserts an egg into the growing tip of the young golden-rod, and the young larva hatching from the egg eats its way to the meristematic tissue. This tissue, probably due to some stimulation from a substance in the saliva or feces of the larva, forms a growth around the larva which may reach dimensions of about 20 by 25 millimeters. Thus the animal has caused a change in its environment, in this case the interior of the plant. The larva eventually eats out the center of the gall, to form a chamber in which it will overwinter. In the following spring, it will pupate and emerge as an adult, but during the adverse conditions of winter the plant gall has served as food and protection and has probably produced a stabilizing effect on humidity and temperature. After pupation of about two months, the adults emerge to start the life cycle over again, but the old gall is no longer suitable and is not used again by the fly. It has been made undesirable for further use by this species, at least in part by its own activities.

Sometimes, to the confusion of students of galls, the fly which caused the gall does not emerge from it, but some other insect does. The emerging insect is a parasite or predator on the larval fly and so is part of the first community in this succession. Two species of gall wasps, both of the genus *Eurytoma*, parasitize and finally eat their host, the larval gallfly. In the spring of the host's intended pupation and emergence, these parasites begin their new life cycle. In spring also, while the gallfly pupa is still within the gall, another insect—a beetle larva of the genus *Isohydnocerca*—may enter the gall and devour the fly. There may also be gall gnats of the family Cecidomyidae living in the gall, feeding on the plant tissue. These little gnats contribute still more to the community with their own parasites. In the meantime another beetle, of the genus *Mordellisterna*, finds this developing community attractive and eats it way into the gall, feeding on its tissues and occasionally upon the host.

The next major stage of this succession begins as these inhabitants leave the hollow gall, no longer suitable for them. Now a wasp, *Ancistrocercus tigris*, uses the empty sphere to lay eggs and store paralyzed caterpillars on which its larvae will feed. These wasp larvae are parasitized by several other insects, which may therefore be found in the gall during its second summer. Beetles, thrips, and ants may use the empty galls as a home, some perhaps only temporarily. Finally this second major stage ends after the second winter, as the dead goldenrod falls to the ground.

While the gall lies on the earth, it may be used briefly by invertebrates before invertebrates and bacteria bring about the ultimate destruction of its tissue in this third and final stage. The organic remains of the plant, the fecal material from the many animals which have lived in it, and perhaps the remains of parasitized insects will now be added to the soil. Thus the successional pattern in this microhabitat has ended. Each succeeding community has utilized the gall after preparation of suitable conditions by the members of the former community. The end point, as is true of most microsuccessions, is the community type in which the microhabitat existed, in this case probably a meadow.

The processes of change which bring about succession are fundamentally the same, whether they occur in microhabitats such as the one just described, or in the larger habitats in which these smaller ones exist. Biotic forces are of great importance in producing the changes, especially in terrestrial succession. In the next chapter it will be shown that, in aquatic succession, physical agencies assume a more important role.

REFERENCES CITED

UHLER, LOWELL D. 1951. "Biology and Ecology of the Goldenrod Gall Fly, *Eurosta solidaginis* Fitch." Cornell University Agricultural Experiment Station, Memoir 300, Ithaca, N.Y.

SUGGESTED READING

BECKWITH, STEPHEN L. 1954. Ecological succession on abandoned farm lands and its relationship to wildlife management. *Ecol. Monographs*, 24(4): 349–376.

CLEMENTS, FREDERIC E. 1928. "Plant Succession and Indicators." The H. W. Wilson Company, New York.

COSTELLO, DAVID F. 1944. Natural revegetation of abandoned plowed land in the mixed prairie association of northeastern Colorado. *Ecol.*, 25(3): 312–326.

DAUBENMIRE, R. F. 1947. "Plants and Environment." John Wiley & Sons, Inc., New York.

ELTON, CHARLES. 1947. "Animal Ecology." 3d ed. The Macmillan Company, New York.

GRIGGS, ROBERT F. 1956. Competition and succession on a Rocky Mountain fellfield. *Ecol.,* 37:8–20.

HAYWARD, C. LYNN. 1952. Alpine biotic communities of the Uinta Mountains, Utah. *Ecol. Monographs,* 22:93–120.

KITTREDGE, JOSEPH. 1948. "Forest Influences." McGraw-Hill Book Company, Inc., New York.

LEMON, PAUL C. 1949. Successional responses of herbs in the long leaf-slash pine forest after fire. *Ecol.,* 30:135–145.

MENTZER, LOREN W. 1951. Studies on plant succession in the true prairie. *Ecol. Monographs,* 21:255–267.

ODUM, EUGENE P. 1953. "Fundamentals of Ecology." W. B. Saunders Company, Philadelphia.

POTZGER, J. E., AND ESTHER POTZGER. 1950. Secondary succession in an Illinoian tillplain habitat. *Proc. Ind. Acad. Sci.,* 59:95–101.

SMITH, CHARLES C. 1940. Biotic and physiographic succession on eroded farm land. *Ecol. Monographs,* 10:421–484.

WEAVER, JOHN E. 1954. A seventeen-year study of plant succession in prairie. *Amer. J. Botany.,* 41(1):31–38.

———— and F. E. CLEMENTS. 1938. "Plant Ecology." McGraw-Hill Book Company, Inc., New York.

CHAPTER 6

AQUATIC PLANT SUCCESSION

One cannot step into the same river twice.

Heraclitus

In the discussion of terrestrial succession, it was mentioned that aquatic areas also undergo succession, and that both processes were basically similar. Lakes, ponds, bogs, swamps, and streams all possess a variety of communities of plants and animals which are unlike any found on land. These communities are similar to the terrestrial ones, however, in that they are also dynamic and change in an orderly fashion toward the climax community. The factors bringing about the changes are somewhat different from those in terrestrial situations, and in many instances the physical elements are more important in accomplishing the succession. Perhaps because of this fact, aquatic developments are sometimes described as "evolution" of aquatic situations, even though a true succession does occur.

Aquatic Environments. There are two major kinds of aquatic successions. One involves still bodies of water (*lentic* environments) such as lakes, ponds, bogs, and swamps. The other type includes brooks, creeks, rivers, or other moving waters (*lotic* environments). Lentic environments evolve by means of a combination of physical and biotic forces. These forces operate to fill in the basin of the body of water, or drain it, or both. Thus lakes become ponds, ponds become bogs, and these finally evolve into solid ground. As such changes occur, the communities in them undergo succession and help to bring about the changes.

Lotic environments, on the other hand, evolve for the most part as a result of physical forces alone, the direction of evolution being from brook to stream, stream to river, or more exactly from fast to slow stream. The succession goes from swift- to slow-water communities, the latter in some respects similar to pond or lake communities. The climax of the lotic sere is therefore different from that of the lentic, which culminates in a terrestrial climax community.

As in terrestrial situations, one is confronted with the problem of origin and rate of change of the aquatic environments undergoing succession. Are lakes and ponds being created continually, or does lentic succession proceed slowly? The abundant examples of bodies of water themselves do not give us the answer, but a study of geology and succession does. Lentic environments evolve slowly, and only occasionally are new lakes or ponds formed.

THE FORMATION OF LAKES AND PONDS

Tectonic Lakes. There are several ways in which depressions may be created and thereby form basins for standing water. Occasionally, as the earth's crust shifts, a fissure may form or a narrow strip of the land may sink—a process known as faulting. Such fissures or sinks may then fill with water and form lakes known as tectonic or rift lakes. As one might expect, these lakes are long and narrow. They may also be deep; the deepest lakes known are of this type, e.g., Lake Baikal, Russia, 4,992 feet; Lake Tanganyika, Africa, 4,707 feet.

Crater Lakes. Another type of lake is produced by volcanic activity, and such bodies of water are known as crater lakes (Fig 6-1). Once a volcano has become extinct, its hollow interior may be filled with water. Frequently these lakes, like rift lakes, may be very deep, although they are circular in outline. Crater Lake in Oregon—in part formed by volcanic activity, in part by shifting of the earth's surface—is 2,000 feet deep.

Land-elevation Lakes. Lakes may also be produced by elevation of land, cutting off arms of the sea. Lake Ontario, as stated on page 103, is an example of this type of lake. Other lakes may be formed at sites where rivers empty into the sea. Wave action or siltation may dam the river's exit and form either a fresh-water or brackish lake.

Glacial Lakes. Glacial action has provided the earth with many of its lakes (Fig. 6-2). As glaciers move over land, there is a tendency

Photo by William E. Werner, Jr.

Fig. 6-1. Mono Lake, California, formed in the crater of an extinct volcano.

Photo by William E. Werner, Jr.

Fig. 6-2. Lake Tahoe, on the California-Nevada border. This is a lake caused by glacial activity.

for them to gouge out previously existing valleys, for the ice is plastic and fills up the valleys, forming a higher and consequently heavier cover here than on the higher areas. The result is that in these valleys deep lakes with steep sides may form when the glacier melts. Many of the lakes of northeastern North America owe their formation to such glacial action. A striking example of lake basins deepened by glaciers is that of the Finger Lakes of central New York. If a glacier stops advancing at the end of a valley, the rocks and soil incorporated in it (glacial drift) may be dropped at the point where it stopped, forming a terminal moraine. This moraine may act as a dam across the end of the valley, forming a lake or increasing the depth of a preexisting lake.

Photo by William E. Werner, Jr.

Fig. 6-3. A beaver dam, which changes the communities in a stream from fast-water (lotic) to slow-water (lentic) types.

When glaciers start melting, large pieces of ice may be left behind, and their weight may form a depression which will eventually become a small lake or pond. Ponds and small lakes of such an origin are generally distributed over recently glaciated regions.

Lakes Formed by Other Processes. Lakes may also form under a variety of other conditions. Occasionally, they have their origins in the dissolution of rocks under the surface. An example of this process is Reelfoot Lake in Tennessee, which formed as a result of the dissolution of limestone under the ground. Landslides may block off valleys, forming dams, behind which ponds or lakes may develop. More frequently encountered are ox-bow lakes, created by meandering streams cutting S-shaped beds in a valley floor. The curves may become so extreme that the stream comes together at its bends, and a whole arm of the stream may be cut off, eventually to form a crescent-shaped lake alongside the stream.

The activity of animals is another cause of pond formation. Beaver dams across small streams may produce a large though shallow pond, while wallows of animals like the buffalo may form small temporary ponds (Fig. 6-3). Man's activity accounts for many bodies of water, not only by intent (the large irrigation and power dams, reservoirs, and farm ponds), but also by chance (bodies such as those which result from quarrying and mining).

PHYSICAL CONDITIONS IN LAKES

In order to understand the biological succession that occurs in lakes, it is necessary to have some insight into the physical conditions existing in them and to understand how changes in the conditions affect the lives of the lakes. Biologists who study inland waters are known as limnologists, and the science of limnology may be considered a part of the broader field of ecology. Limnologists have classified lakes into three categories, according to the amount of plant and animal life which the waters sustain.

Oligotrophic Lakes. Lakes which do not produce abundant organisms in relation to their volume and which always possess abundant oxygen in their lower regions are called *oligotrophic* (little-producing) lakes (Fig. 6-4). They are usually deep lakes that, like other deep lakes, during the summer often have on their bottoms a region of cold water (the *hypolimnion*) which is larger than the surface region of warm water (the *epilimnion*). The hypolimnion in oligotrophic lakes contains considerable oxygen at all times. Separating the epilimnion and hypolimnion is the thermocline (Fig. 6-7), a layer in which the temperature of the water falls very rapidly with increasing depth; by definition, the decrease in temperature must be at least one degree

Photo by Allen H. Benton

Fig. 6-4. An oligotrophic (little-producing) lake; deep, with cold water near the bottom and little plant life.

Photo by William E. Werner, Jr.

Fig. 6-5. A eutrophic (good-producing) lake, with rich plant and animal life. Algae and duckweed float on the surface.

centigrade per meter of increase in depth, or 0.548 degrees Fahrenheit per foot. A relatively shallow (though still "deep") lake may be oligotrophic because there are so few organisms produced that little oxygen is expended in their decay on the bottom; while a deeper lake may be more productive of organisms but remain oligotrophic because the hypolimnion is so large that there is ample oxygen to decay the

Photo by William E. Werner, Jr.

Fig. 6-6. A dystrophic (bad-producing) lake, with water stained brown by undecayed organic matter.

organic matter without undue depletion of the oxygen (Macan and Worthington, 1951).

Eutrophic Lakes. Good-producing, or *eutrophic*, lakes (Fig. 6-5) sustain a rich plant and animal life. Such lakes are usually shallow and have a hypolimnion smaller than the epilimnion. During the summer all the oxygen in the hypolimnion is used up by oxidation of dead organic matter on the bottom. Organic materials are abundant both in the water and on the bottom.

Dystrophic Lakes. The third class of lakes is given the name *dystrophic* (bad-producing) (Fig. 6-6). Such lakes may have plants and animals of certain types growing in them, but owing to the lack of calcium, decomposition of organic matter cannot occur very rapidly. As a result, undecayed organic matter accumulates on the bottom in the form of peat, and often stains the water brown.

SUCCESSION IN LAKES

The line of evolution or succession of lakes begins with oligotrophic lakes. These are the deepest type of lake, so that ordinarily more time is required to change them to dry land. All lentic environments may become dry in one of two major ways. They may fill up with materials washed into the basin and with the remains of dead organisms which once lived in the lake; or the outlet may cut its stream bed down so that it is eventually level with the bottom of the lake. Some oligotrophic lakes are so deep that they do not appear to be changing, yet surely some sediment must wash in through the tributary streams, and some organic matter must be deposited on the lake bottoms. From data secured by means of cores on the bottom of one lake in England, Macan and Worthington (1951) indicate that only 30 feet of sediment have accumulated in the last 11,000 years. There may be considerable variation in the rate of filling, even in one lake, but filling is inevitable.

Aquatic Communities. There are several communities of plants and animals living in deep lakes. Those along the shore occupy a relatively small area or volume in proportion to the total area or volume of the lake, and their composition will be discussed later. In the deeper waters, one may find at least two distinct communities, known as the limnetic and the profundal. The limnetic community exists in the region of open water of the epilimnion, down to a level known as the *compensation depth*—the depth at which plants manufacture as much oxygen in photosynthesis as they utilize in respiration. For the most part, the occupants of the limnetic community are *plankton*—microscopic or near-microscopic plants and animals, so small that they are not able to move about rapidly and determine the direction of their own travels. Their movements are thus subject to the physical movements of their environment. There may also be some swimming forms (*nekton*), such as fishes, and some surface dwellers (*neuston*), including algae and certain insects. The plant species of plankton (phytoplankton) are really the fundamental units of this community, for these minute plants—including diatoms, blue-green algae, and bacteria —provide the food for the animal part of the plankton (zooplankton) and ultimately, if indirectly, for all higher forms of animal life. Important groups of animals in the zooplankton include numerous protozoa, rotifers, and various minute crustaceans such as cladocerans, copepods, and ostracods.

The profundal community is found in the deeper waters of a lake, so deep that not enough light penetrates to enable the phytoplankton to manufacture more food than they consume. Inhabitants of this community include zooplankton, nekton, and certain forms which live on the bottom and are known as *benthos*. Compared to the life found in other types of lakes, the profundal community in oligotrophic lakes is relatively large in numbers of species and individuals. The cool oxygenated water allows the existence of animals such as lake trout, cisco, and a variety of invertebrates such as the amphipod (*Pontoporeia affinis*), the opossum shrimp (*Mysis oculata*), fingernail clams of the family Sphaeridae, and bloodworms of such genera as *Calospectra* and *Spaniotoma*. Each species has a maximum depth at which it may live, and there is great variation in the composition of profundal fauna from one lake to another as well as from one region of a lake to another (Welch, 1952).

Seasonal Changes in Oligotrophic Lakes. Certain fundamental seasonal changes have pronounced effects on the population of deep lakes, especially on the plankton whose members have short life cycles (Fig. 6-7). Winds blowing on a lake's surface are able to set the water in motion. In the spring, though not in the summer, the water of the lake is cool from top to bottom; there is therefore little temperature variation and hence little density, or viscosity, difference. The strong spring winds are able to stir the water from top to bottom, a phenomenon known as the spring overturn. This circulation supplies oxygen from the surface to the deeper levels of the water and distributes organic materials and other nutrients from the bottom throughout the lake. Accumulated toxic waste products may also be released and generally distributed.

The nutrients brought to the surface from the bottom, especially nitrogen and phosphorus, in coaction with the abundant oxygen and carbon dioxide and the warmer spring weather, are involved in the great increase of plankton which occurs in the spring. Since sufficient

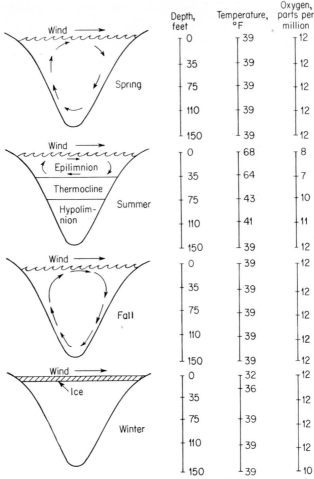

Fig. 6-7. Seasonal changes in an oligotrophic lake.

light for photosynthesis usually does not penetrate water beyond 20 to 30 feet, it is important that bottom materials be brought to the area where they may be utilized.

The minute phytoplankton, especially diatoms, are the first organisms to show this spring increase, and soon the animal populations which feed upon phytoplankton, notably the copepods and cladocerans, also begin to become more abundant. Although the plankton as a whole increases at this time, not all species experience a population increase simultaneously. The blooms (high populations) of individual

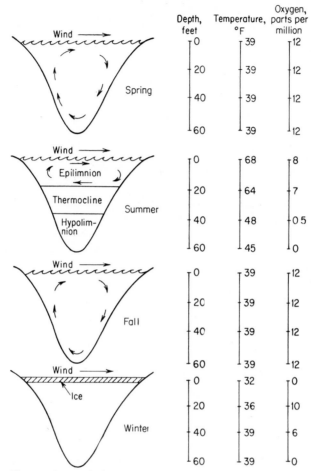

Fig. 6-8. Seasonal changes in a eutrophic lake.

species at different times indicate a complexity in the factors which govern the population dynamics of each species. That is, different species find the most suitable conditions for reproduction under varying circumstances. Thus some species of phytoplankton bloom relatively early in the season, when certain nutrients are available but when the temperature is low and herbivorous zooplankton are scarce. Others bloom later in the season when nutrients are scarcer, but temperatures are then warmer and other factors more advantageous.

After some time (one to two months), the plankton populations decline, sometimes rather suddenly. Water at the surface has warmed rapidly, and there has been built up a large temperature gradient from the top to the bottom of the lake. The consequence of this is that the cooler, denser water of the bottom does not mix readily with the warm, light surface water. Thus a thermocline may develop, which then eliminates any further mixing of the surface and bottom water. The water of the epilimnion continues to circulate, and the hypolimnion, although isolated, does not become depleted of oxygen. However, the epilimnion is now isolated from the bottom nutrients, and this may be one of the factors involved in the plankton decline in late summer.

As fall approaches, the water on the surface and in the whole epilimnion cools. The cold water, being denser, moves toward the bottom, destroying the thermocline. There is no longer a great temperature difference from top to bottom of the lake, and strong fall winds are able to circulate the water completely, in the same manner as was done by the spring winds. This fall overturn once again redistributes bottom materials, and frequently there are fall plankton blooms which decline as winter approaches.

With the coming of winter, the temperature of the whole lake becomes lower. Large lakes may not freeze from shore to shore, but when freezing does occur, the water directly under the ice is the coldest, with the temperature increasing to 4° Centigrade at the bottom, the temperature at which water is heaviest. Since oligotrophic lakes are fairly deep, the cold water holds sufficient oxygen for the life that might become imprisoned under the ice, and winter stagnation does not occur. If the lake does not freeze, the water may circulate throughout the winter. If it has frozen, the ice melts with the approach of spring, and circulation resumes. In either case, overturn in the spring will again induce the plankton to increase.

Development from Oligotrophic to Eutrophic. As time passes, oligotrophic lakes will fill in by the two processes previously mentioned. Their sides may also be eroded away to some extent and thereby help to fill in the deeper parts of the basin. Exactly when a lake passes from the oligotrophic to the eutrophic stage is difficult to determine, for there is great variation of physical and biological conditions in lakes. One criterion that has been used to designate eutrophic lakes is that they possess a hypolimnion smaller than the epilimnion. It is not always easy to use this criterion, however, since thermoclines may not develop every summer, especially in shallower lakes. When a thermocline forms, the hypolimnion may be so small, and organic materials so abundant, that stagnation occurs in the hypolimnion.

Life and Seasonal Changes in Eutrophic Lakes. Life is abundant in eutrophic lakes, and plankton populations become especially high in the spring and fall. (Fig. 6-8). However, organisms in the profundal zone are not so numerous as they are in the oligotrophic lakes, especially in the oxygen-low hypolimnion. Certain fish species, such as pike, large-mouth bass, and perch, and invertebrates including bloodworms of the genus *Tendipes*, mosquito larvae, and phantom midges (*Chaoborus*), are typical of the benthos and profundal regions. *Chaoborus*, however, exists as a member of the benthos in the profundal zone only during the day and rises to the surface to become a part of the neuston in the limnetic zone by night.

The fall overturn will bring an upsurge in the plankton bloom, which will decline with the approach of winter. If eutrophic lakes freeze over, the situation of aquatic organisms becomes grim. With a smaller total volume of water than the oligotrophic lake and a much higher total population of organisms, oxygen may become extremely scarce. If the ice cover remains for a long time, especially if a cover of snow prevents light penetration and photosynthesis is thus reduced, great destruction of life may occur. Decomposition of the abundant organic matter in the water and on the bottom adds to the difficulties by further depleting the oxygen supply, although some oxygen is being continually added by phytoplankton and rooted plants of the shore zone. When spring arrives, the overturn again allows the entire lake to benefit from the nutrients on the bottom and the oxygen from the atmosphere.

Development of Eutrophic Lake to Dry Land. As eutrophic lakes continue to become shallower, they reach a point at which thermoclines never form, and circulation occurs throughout the summer. The entire volume of water may become quite warm at this time. Rooted aquatics usually become established, even in the deepest parts of the lake (Fig. 6-9). This stage of vegetation-choked water, sometimes called the senescent stage, is highly productive. Small fishes, frogs, water snakes, and turtles may abound, as well as a host of insects and other invertebrates.

When the senescent lake becomes shallower, it may become a pond; that is, merely a smaller area of open water. Or it may develop directly into a swamp or marsh. A swamp is usually considered to contain trees, while a marsh, by definition, does not. Ponds may become so shallow that they dry up in the summer months, thus becoming tem-

Photo by William E. Werner, Jr.

Fig. 6-9. Vegetation-choked stage of a eutrophic lake. The large plant shown here is the lotus, *Nelumbo lutea*. The water is covered by duckweed, *Lemna minor*.

porary ponds (Fig. 6-10), unsuitable for occupation by permanently aquatic animals. Because of this major change in environment, forms of life are more limited, although many insects and other animals may be common. Plants growing here are predominantly emergents (plants which live with their roots submerged in water but whose vegetative and flowering parts are mostly above the water). Cattails, arrowheads, pickerel weeds, and various kinds of sedges and rushes are among the most abundant of them. Certain invertebrates are of interest because they are found in temporary ponds. Among the widely distributed members of this group are the fairy shrimps of the genus *Eubranchipus*. Some relatives of this genus are able to live in temporary alkaline or saline pools in the West. Because of the temporary nature of these ponds, many of the larger predatory species are absent.

Photo by William E. Werner, Jr.

Fig. 6-10. A temporary pond, which will dry up completely during the summer. In spring it serves as a home for the fairy shrimp (*Eubranchipus*) and as a breeding place for amphibians.

Eventually the pond, marsh, or swamp will dry up completely as terrestrial plants and animals invade the site of the former lake. Bushes, trees, and herbaceous plants which are tolerant of soggy ground will add their remains to the soil, until conditions will become sufficiently mesic to tolerate a purely terrestrial community. Finally, the end of the eutrophic-lake succession is the terrestrial climax community (Fig. 6-11*a*, *b*).

Conditions in Dystrophic Lakes. Dystrophic lakes proceed along a different line of succession. They are frequently formed as the result

Photos by William E. Werner, Jr.

Fig. 6-11. Terrestrial succession on the site of former lakes. (*a*) Early stages of succession in a moist area which has not long been dry; (*b*) a coniferous forest on the site of a former glacial lake, Yosemite Valley, Calif.

Photo (a) by William E. Werner Jr., photo (b) by Ralph S. Palmer
Fig. 6-12. Development of dystrophic lakes. (a) A dystrophic lake in Ontario, Canada, in early stages of succession. A vegetation mat is just beginning to grow out over the water at left. (b) A dystrophic lake in Maine in the pond stage, with quaking mats well out over the water.

of glacial action similar to that which forms some oligotrophic lakes. Due to physical and chemical states which prevent the decay of organic materials, biotic conditions in such lakes are different, and succession takes a different course. Calcium and oxygen are usually deficient, and the pH of the water is generally low. The abundant organic matter of the water is in the form of undecayed organisms which create deposits of peat on the bottom and frequently impart to the water a brown stain.

Photo by Ralph S. Palmer

Fig. 6-13. The pitcher plant, *Sarracenia purpurea*, a typical bog plant.

Dystrophic lakes are usually poor in numbers and types of organisms. Larger plants, e.g., *Chara*, which remove calcium from the water, may be present, but in general the phytoplankton and rooted aquatics are scarce. Zooplankton may be numerous, but larger invertebrates are frequently low in abundance, as are such vertebrates as the fishes. Sphagnum moss is the typical plant found growing in the beach or shore (psammolittoral) zone of these lakes, along with sedges and other plants which form a mat.

Development of Dystrophic Lakes to Dry Land. As the dystrophic lake accumulates peat on the bottom, it hastens its own end. The sphagnum and rooted vegetation of the shores may grow out into the water, advancing over the surface of the lake. It is thereby developing into a peat bog, with a shore of vegetation forming a quaking mat, and a bog lake in the center (Fig. 6-12*a*, *b*).

The surface mat eventually closes over the bog lake, and sphagnum and other vegetation fill up the basin. The outstanding physical condition of such a community is the low pH of the saturated "soil" of the mat, which is sometimes less than 4.0. A variety of plants are especially adapted to these conditions of moisture and low pH, and these make up the bog community. Here we find the insectivorous pitcher plants (*Sarracenia*) (Fig. 6-13) and sundews (*Drosera*); cranberry (*Vaccinium oxycoccus*) and cotton grass (*Eriophorum*). Shrubs which invade the bog usually include leatherleaf (*Chamaedaphne*), Labrador tea (*Ledum*), and bog rosemary (*Andromeda*). Several species of orchids are restricted to this habitat. Diatoms and certain species of algae may be found among the saturated sphagnum.

Eventually the basin will be further filled by encroaching bushes and by the dead bodies of plants and animals, until finally the terrestrial climax community will cover it. The length of time required for this to occur varies widely, depending on such variables as the original depth of the basin, its drainage, and other physical conditions which affect the growth of organisms and the rate of sedimentation. As in the succession of oligotrophic lakes, a series of communities has been established and changed, each one replacing the preceding one, until eventually the climax is reached.

ZONATION OF AQUATIC COMMUNITIES

Along the edges of eutrophic, oligotrophic, and senescent lakes, there may be shores which descend gradually to the depths of the lake, with bottoms of sand, mud, gravel, or clay. Frequently aquatic vegetation will be found growing here, and a whole series of communities may be formed. Floating aquatics will occupy the deep water, and various kinds of rooted vegetation will follow in regular sequence up to the beach. These communities show a zonation similar to that of vegetation on a mountain, except that it occurs for a much shorter distance and is therefore more easily observed. In effect, this zonation illustrates the process of succession in lakes. It is possible to observe from it how lakes become more shallow by the action of such communities and how the changing depth of the water affects the composition of the communities.

Small Floating Aquatics. The areas of lakes involved in zonation include the littoral zone (the region in which there is light penetration to the bottom) and the psammolittoral zone (the region along the edge of the water). The deepest water of the littoral zone may have a surface cover of small floating plants such as the duckweeds—*Lemna*, *Wolffia*, and *Spirodela*. Sometimes these plants will cover a small lake or pond (Fig. 6-14). Of course, in this region as in most of the succeeding ones there is a plankton and nekton population. Where the water is shallower, perhaps twenty feet or less, some rooted aquatics may be found, including *Vallisneria, Anacharis, Myriophyllum,* and *Ceratophyllum.* These are all totally submerged plants. One of the largest and most abundant groups of submerged aquatic plants found in the littoral zone belongs to the genus *Potamogeton,* which includes more than fifty species in North America.

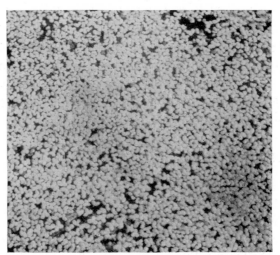

Photo by William E. Werner, Jr.

Fig. 6-14. Duckweed, *Lemna minor,* covering the surface of a pond.

Rooted Floating Aquatics. As the depth of the water decreases toward the shore, a zone containing a community dominated by rooted floating aquatics will be found (Fig. 6-15). Typical of such plants are white water lilies (*Nymphaea*), the cow lily (*Nuphar*), and *Potamogeton natans.* Many animals are associated with these plants, using them as places for support as well as for food. Many herbivores feeding on the phytoplankton are present, while carnivores are there to feed on the herbivores. For example, the small fresh-water coelenterate *Hydra* may often be found hanging downward from the undersurfaces of pond lily pads. This little animal extends its tentacles into the water to catch small water animals such as insects, copepods, and cladocerans. These in turn feed on protozoa, bacteria, and minute algae (Pennak, 1953).

Emergents. In shallower water, a zone may occur possessing a community dominated by emergent plants. These species have their roots and lower stems in water, but most of the plant projects into the air. Some of the more common species of this community are cattails (*Typha*), bulrushes (*Scirpus*), reed grass (*Phragmites*), and wild rice (*Zizania*) (Fig. 6-16). In this zone the bottom is usually abundantly

Photo by William E. Werner, Jr.

Fig. 6-15. The zone of floating rooted aquatics, in this case water lilies *Nymphaea odorata*.

covered with the rotting organic debris of the old emergent plants, and this forms a situation favorable to small animals. Insect larvae such as dragonflies, damsel flies, and adult and larval beetles and bugs may abound in the mud and water, along with a rich zooplankton. Larger forms such as frogs, salamanders, turtles, and water snakes may inhabit this community. Certain fishes like the bullhead (*Amieurus*) and the mud minnow (*Umbra*) are often present.

Saturated-soil Regions. Next to the shoreline, there is frequently a region in which the soil is saturated. Here a community exists in which the dominant plants are various sedges (*Carex*), rushes (*Juncus*), smartweeds (*Polygonum*), and many others (Fig. 6-17). This community may have a large number of microscopic plants and animals, so that the water edge, or psammolittoral zone, may possess the most densely populated community of all the zones.

Photos by William E. Werner, Jr.

Fig. 6-16. Floating rooted aquatics and emergents, here mostly cattails (*Typha*).

Shore Communities. On drier land, farther from the shoreline, is a community dominated by rank herbs. Water is still abundant in the soil. Wild hemp (*Cannabis*), sunflowers (*Helianthus*), jewelweed (*Impatiens*), joe-pye weed (*Eupatorium purpureum*), and boneset (*Eupatorium perfoliatum*) may be among the common plants (Fig. 6-18). Animals are those of the terrestrial communities which can forage into the wetter locations. Common species include field mice, shrews, raccoons, and weasels among the mammals, various nesting birds (Fig. 6-19), and frogs and snakes among the lower vertebrates. Hordes of insects also constitute an important part of the community. Still farther back on land will be found the shrub community, with elderberry, red maple, box elder, cottonwood, willows, alder, and viburnum among the forms represented. A few shrubs such as the buttonbush may grow in more aquatic situations, but these are scanty. From the shrub stage, the development to the climax community will be a sere similar to the

Photo by William E. Werner, Jr.

Fig. 6-17. The region of saturated soil around the shore line of a pond, with sedges as the dominant plants.

one described for terrestrial succession, with perhaps different dominants appearing in the various communities.

Evidences of Succession. The communities from the open water of the lake or pond through the littoral region to the climax on the shore may all be seen at one time; but they represent dynamic changes occurring, which will eventually result in the filling in of the lake and the elimination of the communities themselves. As time passes, each community will invade its neighbor toward the center of the lake. In

Photo by William E. Werner, Jr.

Fig. 6-18. Rank vegetation in the damp soil near the edge of a pond. Jewelweed and smartweed are dominant.

Photo by E. G. Tabor

Fig. 6-19. Marshes are nesting sites for many birds. Grassy marshes are the preferred habitat for the marsh hawk, *Circus cyaneus*, whose young are shown here in the nest.

all the communities, organic matter and silt are constantly accumulating, decreasing the depth of the water. With this change of environment each community invades the one next to it in deeper water and is in turn invaded by the one behind it in shallower water. Thus, as the filling process occurs, the submerged aquatic plants will be displaced by the floating rooted aquatics, and these by the emergent

Photo by William E. Werner, Jr.

Fig. 6-20. A sandy beach on a wave-swept shore. Notice that large aquatic vegetation is absent.

aquatics. As succession continues, the emergents will be replaced by sedges and rushes, and these in turn by rank herbs and shrubs. Gradually the terrestrial communities will move in where once there was open water, until finally the terrestrial community climax will occupy the area.

The communities of plants and animals in the sere are similar in various kinds of lentic environments, although the species may vary. For example, muddy bottoms may support different plants and animals than gravel bottoms, and on shore the species found on sandy beaches may be different from those on rocky beaches (Fig. 6-20).

pecies composition of similar communities will vary with
ivironmental conditions, but the general pattern of the
ill be about the same.

STREAM SUCCESSION

The development of streams is quite different from that of lakes and
other lentic environments. Whereas in the succession we have reviewed above, organisms help to bring about the successional changes
to a great degree, in lotic environmental evolution, physical forces
play the dominant and almost exclusive role. Since physical forces,
therefore, shape the development of biological communities in streams,
the physical evolution of streams will be considered first.

Elevation Gradients, Currents, and Stream Loads. If we lived in a
flat world there would be no streams, for the water in streams is flowing from an area of higher elevation to an area of lower elevation, and
ultimately to the sea. The difference in elevation from the origin of a
stream to its terminus, divided by the distance it travels between these
two points, gives the average elevation gradient of the stream. The
greater the gradient, the greater should be the rate of flow, all other
factors being equal.

When a land mass is newly elevated, the water will run off the surface into the natural depressions which are present and eventually find
its way to the ocean. At first, many of these depressions may hold
water as ponds or lakes, but with their filling and the erosion of their
outlets, they tend to be obliterated. At the same time, the streams may
be small and, if the elevation gradient is large, proportionately swift.
Such a swift stream is able to carry or move large rocks as well as
gravel and silt from the hills to the plains. This load, combined with
the washing action of the water, will wear down the stream bed as its
smaller tributaries are wearing down their stream beds and the surrounding hills. In effect, the hills are being slowly carried to the sea.
As this occurs, the stream at any given point becomes larger, the
stream bed lower, and the stream as a whole longer. Another result is
that the elevation gradient is decreased and the flow slackened at any
given point along the stream.

As long as the rate of flow remains fairly high, the stream will carry
a load of soil eroded from the more elevated regions. As the rate of

flow decreases, the size of the particles it carries will decrease, until finally only silt will be held in suspension when the flow becomes sluggish. When the stream, which by now has perhaps developed into a river, empties into the ocean, the final precipitation of the finely divided particles of earth will occur, forming deltas which may be of vast extent.

If it were possible to watch long enough, a single location along a stream could be observed and the process of change from a swift stream to a sluggish one could be recorded. But this would require many generations. Fortunately for the ecologist, however, this succession may be observed in a short period of time just as we can observe the various communities involved in the succession of lakes. In the latter case, we look at different lakes in varying stages of development, or we study the zonation of littoral communities. With streams one merely needs to travel the length of any one to see the various seral stages in its succession. Thus the headwaters of the stream possess the aspects of a young stream, the larger and slower regions an intermediate stage; and finally, where the stream becomes a deep river, the characteristics of a mature stream are present.

Physical Factors in Stream Succession. In the headwaters, various physical factors which are interrelated with the swiftness of the current are important to the life of the stream. There is a tendency toward large fluctuations in volume and flow of water from season to season. During the spring especially, small streams are unusually swollen and frequently overflow their banks. During the summer, these same streams may become almost completely dry. Such extreme variations require special means for organisms to remain in place and to survive under widely different conditions. The swift current can carry away small particles of rock so that, in general, the swifter the stream, the larger are the rocks remaining in its bed (Fig. 6-21*a*, *b*). The large rocks form places of shelter and attachment for organisms, although even these big boulders may be moved during high water.

Although the current flows swiftly in headwaters, it is usually relatively shallow here, with only occasional deep pools. These conditions, too, affect the biota. The shallowness of the water permits excellent aeration (Fig. 6-22), but it also means that the temperature here may vary more or less with the temperature of the atmosphere. The only exception to this will be when the stream is covered with ice, at which

Photo (a) by Ralph S. Palmer, photo (b) by Allen H. Benton
Fig. 6-21. The effect of swiftness of current on size of rocks in the stream bed.
(*a*) Huge boulders in a swift mountain stream; (*b*) large rocks in a relatively
fast stream.

time the temperature of the water is stabilized near the freezing point. Since the amount of carbon dioxide and oxygen that may be dissolved in water is directly affected by the temperature, it follows that there is a continual variation in the amounts of these gases in the water, except during the period when the stream is covered with ice. However, oxygen content of swift streams, because of constant aeration, is usually high. Some stability of the water temperature is afforded by trees and shrubs that usually line the banks of small, swift streams. Their shade prevents excessive warming by the sun, which would otherwise quickly heat the shallow water.

Photo by Ralph S. Palmer

Fig. 6-22. A shallow swift stream permits excellent aeration of the water.

Adaptation for Swift-water Life. Because life in the swift streams is precarious or impossible for many organisms, the inhabitants of this environment are like the pioneers in other successions: they are able to endure severe environmental conditions. Various attributes of swift-water organisms enable them to survive the rigors of their habitat. They may have special hold-fast mechanisms, or a streamlined shape, special respiratory apparatus, or unique food-getting devices. In addition, many of the smaller forms must be able to reproduce rapidly, for the loss of life during the high-water period is great.

Permanent rooted aquatic plants are practically nonexistent in swift streams. The swiftness of the current makes attachment difficult, and the fluctuations in water level are also prohibitive to their existence. Instead, filamentous algae such as *Cladophora* and *Ulothrix* cling to the rocks by means of hold-fasts; among their filaments are smaller algae such as diatoms and desmids. These minute plants are the basic food for all animals living in such water.

The animals of this habitat are adapted either to swim against the current for short periods as they dart from rock to rock, or to cling by some means in open water or behind or under rocks. Their body forms frequently reflect the environmental conditions of their lives, in being streamlined or otherwise adapted for the least resistance to the friction of the water. One of the more abundant insects of this community is the black fly. Its larvae are frequently so numerous as to cover large areas of the rocks, giving them a velvety black appearance. These larvae are able to maintain their positions in fast water by means of an adhesive disk at their posterior ends. If they care to move, or if they are swept loose, they spin a silken lifeline from their mouths to prevent being carried downstream. Midge larvae are also common in swift water, as is the water penny— the larva of a small beetle, which is so flattened that it is able to cling, as does a limpet, to the undersurface of rocks.

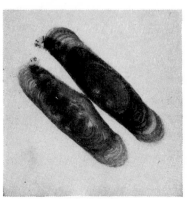

Photo by M. B. Scotland

Fig. 6-23. Two caddis flies, *Agraylea multipunctata*, in their cases. The cases are not secreted by the insects as are shells of mollusks but are manufactured from available materials. Larvae of this order are aquatic, and many are adapted for life in swift water.

Since traveling in fast water is perilous, it is not surprising that some swift-water animals have come to exist by means of devices which enable them to catch their food as it goes by. An example of such an animal is the larva of *Hydropsyche*, a net-spinning caddis fly. Its silken basket is arranged to catch plankton drifting with the current. Other caddis flies live in cases which they have fashioned from bits of stones or debris (Fig. 6-23); they also feed on plankton. Certain snails, limpets, and crayfish are among the larger invertebrates of this community, while flatworms and larvae of such insects as May flies, stone flies, dragonflies, and damsel flies also make the stony habitat of the bottom their home.

A few species of fish are able to survive the rigors of the swift-water community. Brook trout and such smaller fishes as the long-nosed dace (*Rhinicthys cataractae*), the black-nosed dace (*Rhinichthys atratulus*), the common shiner (*Notropis cornutus*), and the stone roller minnow (*Campostoma anomalum*) live in this habitat. These fishes usually spend most of their time behind rocks and dart for the shelter of other rocks when they move, not maintaining a position in the current for any length of time. Several swift-water forms like the long-nosed dace, have terete bodies, while the stone roller is rather unusual in having a lower lip specially reinforced with cartilage, which it uses for scraping algae off rocks. In some of these species the swim bladder is reduced or nonfunctional, enabling the organisms to stay on the bottom of the stream.

Higher vertebrates are not numerous in swift streams. Worthy of mention are a few salamanders which may be found under the rocks in swift water. These include the dusky salamander (*Desmognathus fuscus*), purple salamander (*Gyrinophilus porphyriticus*), and two-lined salamander (*Eurycea bislineata*). The beautifully adapted water shrew (*Sorex palustris*) is an excellent swimmer and has fringes of hair along its feet which permit it to walk upon the surface of the water. It is found along small swift streams in wooded areas. Mink, raccoons, and other predators may feed along the edge of the stream but are not properly part of the stream community itself, in spite of their undoubtedly important effect upon it.

Although a relatively small number of species of organisms are able to live in the swift-stream community, the number of individuals may be very great. Thousands of invertebrates, of several phyla, can exist on a single rock, not to mention the bacteria and protozoa and other phytoplankton and zooplankton which exist around it. A single sweep of a seine may bring up a hundred small fishes. What is lacking in variation is made up for in numbers.

Physical Conditions of Slow Streams. Where the elevation gradient is less, the stream will be slower. Usually such a slow stream will be deep and muddy-bottomed, located in a wide valley carved out by the stream itself (Fig. 6-24). The rate of flow and depth may still vary, and be exceptionally great in rainy seasons. The lack of a strong current has its effect on other physical factors and ultimately on the type of community living in this habitat. Since it takes a strong current to move large rocks, few will be found, and silt or sand may form the bottom sediment. Near the shore, in shallow water where rooted vegetation grows, there may be accumulations of organic matter, which combines with the silt to form deep muck. Water temperature in slow streams is usually higher than that of swift streams, although deep bottom waters may be cool. There is less chance for aeration of

Photo by Ralph S. Palmer

Fig. 6-24. A slow, meandering stream in a wide valley.

the water here than in a fast stream, so that oxygen content will be lower and carbon dioxide content higher.

The Life of Slow Streams. Since in still water there is no problem of maintaining position, plants are nearly always to be found along the shores of slow streams, and sometimes rooted aquatic plants such as *Potamogeton* may extend out to the center of a shallow stream. In backwaters, and sometimes along the shores, there may be the same zonation of communities found in lakes (Fig. 6-25). Plankton is also different in the slow stream. In addition to the desmids, diatoms, and other small forms of algae found in swift streams, protozoans and rotifers abound. In some rivers, plankton increases in numbers as the stream progresses from its headwaters, reaches a maximum, and then declines near the mouth of the river (Welch, 1952). Part of the decline may be due to the effects of the rooted aquatic vegetation, which acts as a strainer to prevent the further movement of the plankton downstream.

Animals of the slow stream are more varied than is the case in swift water, and include greater numbers of large species. Yet the bottom

Photo by W. E. Werner, Jr.

Fig. 6-25. Aquatic vegetation zones in a backwater of a river show marked similarities to the same communities in lakes. The Mississippi River at Hannibal, Mo.

fauna may not be more numerous; for without stones, suitable dwelling places, except for burrowing animals, are lacking. Snails, clams, bryozoans, amphipods, leeches, crayfish, and earthworms may be included in the fauna. Many insect larvae and adults, similar to those of littoral communities of lakes and ponds, will be present. Vertebrates are more plentiful as well as more varied. Usually fish species which occur in fast waters are not found in slow streams, perhaps because of their oxygen or temperature requirements. Some require particular conditions for parts of their life cycle, such as a certain type of bottom for spawning. Silt covering the bottom rubble may prevent successful breeding by certain fast-water forms. In the larger rivers, gill-breathing salamanders like the mud puppy, *Necturus*, and large turtles like the snapper, *Chelydra*, are frequently present.

The Upstream Movement of Succession. As the headwaters of a stream wear the hills down, more and more of the stream will have a slow current, and so succession moves upstream. The slow-water community invades and replaces the swift-water community. If we travel the length of a stream, we may observe a gradual change in biota as the shift from slow to swift water takes place. There will be irregularities in the transition, for rapids will be interrupted by pools, and these pools may possess some species belonging to the slow-water community. Furthermore, the current is not uniform across a stream, nor from the surface to the bottom, and these variations will produce deviations in the community. In general, however, the sere is clearly recognizable and demonstrates a kind of succession.

REFERENCES CITED

MACAN, T. T., AND E. B. WORTHINGTON. 1951. "Life in Lakes and Rivers." William Collins Sons & Co., Ltd., London.

PENNAK, R. W. 1953. "Fresh-water Invertebrates of the United States." The Ronald Press Company, New York.

WELCH, P. S. 1952. "Limnology." 2d ed. McGraw-Hill Book Company, Inc., New York.

SUGGESTED READING

CATENHUSEN, JOHN. 1950. Secondary successions on the peat lands of glacial Lake Wisconsin. *Trans. Wis. Acad. Sci., Arts & Letters*, 40(pt. 1): 29–48.

COKER, ROBERT E. 1954. "Streams, Lakes, Ponds." University of North Carolina Press, Chapel Hill, N.C.

DANSEREAU, PIERRE, AND FERNANDO SEGADASVIANNA. 1952. Ecological study of the peat bogs of eastern North America. I. Structure and evolution of vegetation. *Canad. J. Botany*, 30(4):490–520.

MOULTON, F. R., (ED.) 1939. "Problems of Lake Biology." Science Press, Lancaster, Pa.

NEEDHAM, JAMES G., AND J. T. LLOYD. 1937. "The Life of Inland Waters." Comstock Publishing Associates, Inc., Ithaca, N.Y.

PENNAK, R. W. 1939. The microscopic fauna of sandy beaches. American Association for the Advancement of Science, Publ. no. 10. pp. 94–106.

RUTTNER, F. 1953. "Fundamentals of Limnology." Trans. by D. G. Frey and F. E. J. Fry. University of Toronto Press, Toronto.

CHAPTER 7

ECONOMIC FIELD BIOLOGY

> Then, early in June, the adventurers broke through the
> interminable wastes of dim woodland, and stood on
> the threshold of the beautiful bluegrass regions of Ken-
> tucky; a land of running waters, of groves and glades,
> of prairies, cane brakes, and stretches of lofty forest.
> It was teeming with game. The shaggy-maned herds of
> unwieldy buffalo . . . had beaten out broad roads
> through the forest, and had furrowed the prairies with
> trails along which they had travelled for countless
> generations. The round-horned elk . . . abounded, and
> like the buffalo travelled in bands not only through
> the woods but also across the reaches of waving grass
> land. The deer were extraordinarily numerous, and so
> were bears, while wolves and panthers were plentiful.
>
> *Theodore Roosevelt,* "The Winning of the West"

As we saw in the first chapter of this book, field biology is important
from an economic point of view. Nearly all of the major groups of
plants and animals include at least some species of direct or indirect
importance to man. Some field biologists study organisms regardless
of their economic value. Frequently their findings are directly useful.
Other field biologists work in practical areas such as conservation and
management of wildlife, pest control, soil and water management,
forestry, agriculture, and medicine, where the primary concern is with
matters of immediate economic importance.

Basic and Applied Research. Perhaps it is well to point out here the difference between *basic*, or pure, and *applied* research, for these terms are frequently misunderstood. When the goals of research are strictly economic, the research is said to be applied. To illustrate, certain entomologists, such as those working in agricultural experiment stations, may attempt to discover an insecticide to control an insect pest doing great damage to crops. The results of this work, if successful, will be of immediate economic use. The work might be called, therefore, applied research. An ecologist might be working on the same species of insect to determine the conditions under which the larvae develop most rapidly. His work may or may not be of economic importance *at the moment*. Such research, conducted without any specific economic viewpoint, is considered basic research, and hence the work of the ecologist and other field biologists is frequently in this category. However, it is likely that the results of basic research will be of economic value at some time in the future. It is impossible, therefore, to distinguish clearly between the two types of research. When Albert Einstein developed the mathematical formula $E = mc^2$, his work had no practical importance, and he was motivated by no desire to achieve any immediate practical end. Yet when the work on atomic energy was turned toward the development of an atomic bomb, this formula became tremendously important, and its value has perhaps not yet been fully exploited. In biology, similarly, basic research is usually important to other workers in applied science.

Much applied research is carried out by field biologists, and this economically important work will constitute the major subject matter of this chapter. Most of the biologists who do applied research are connected with state and Federal departments concerned with wildlife management, conservation services, forestry, and agriculture, or they are teachers in departments dealing with these subjects in our universities. They are interested in the control of pests and injurious plants and animals and in the conservation of our food resources, soil, water, forests, fish, and game.

CONTROL OF PEST SPECIES

One of the greatest problems confronting agriculture is that of losses due to insect pests. In the United States, the losses in one year as the result of the depredations of more than 600 injurious insect species amount to about four billion dollars (Haeussler, 1952). This staggering sum assumes special importance when we recognize that it represents the fertility of American soil, which produced the food consumed by the insects.

The control of these pests is not easy, largely because there are so many kinds of them. There are more species of insects than there are of all other kinds of animals put together. This variation is accompanied by equally great variation in life habits, so that it is impossible to deal with all insects in the same way. An insecticide effective against one species may be totally useless against another, or it may be effective at certain periods of the life cycle and not at others. Further, some insects are beneficial. We do not want to kill them along with the pests, or do damage to other valuable animals and plants. It is easily seen, then, that the problem of insect control is ecological in nature. An insect pest must be studied to discover what kinds of foods it may eat; when it breeds; when the low points in its population occur, and why; its natural enemies; its susceptibility to various kinds of poisons; its activities at all stages of its life cycle; its range and the factors limiting its range; and all the other facets of its life which the other chapters of this book discuss. It should also be noted whether the insect makes any beneficial contributions, such as the control of other pests.

Chemical Control of Insects. Unfortunately, chemicals have in some cases been applied to insect control without prior thorough field study of their effects. One serious consequence of such activity is often the increase of another pest as serious as the first. Attempts to control the larva of the codling moth (the apple worm) with DDT resulted, in some areas, in an increase of a pest called the two-spotted mite. The codling moth larva ruins the fruit, while the two-spotted mite destroys the foilage. Before the advent of DDT, codling moths were becoming more and more resistant to other insecticides, although there was no serious problem with the mites. Soon after the DDT was introduced, codling moths were well under control, but the two-spotted mite had increased to the point where it was an important pest. Apparently the DDT was not only effective in destroying the codling moth, but it was also killing the natural enemies of the mite. A thorough study of the moth and its associates in the apple tree microcommunity might have prevented the occurrence of such an unhappy event.

Biological Control. The use of natural predators, parasites, or disease to control pest organisms is known as biological control (see p. 8). Insects have been used to control plants in some instances, as in the case of the Klamath weed, *Hypericum perforatum.* They are also of value in the control of other insects. Conversely, plants (fungi) have been used in the control of insects. A familiar pest to many people, particularly in the eastern United States, is the Japanese beetle, *Popillia japonica.* This insect does extensive damage to various kinds of plants (Fig. 7-1), and its larvae may do extremely serious damage in

Photo by William E. Werner, Jr.

Fig. 7-1. The Japanese beetle, *Popillia japonica,* and its damage to a grape leaf.

turf on lawns and golf courses. Various methods of control were tried soon after its arrival in this country around 1916, in hope of suppressing it before it could spread. Its life history was studied in great detail in order to find ways in which it could be controlled effectively. The beetle was not a major pest in Japan, where it had several natural enemies. Some 49 of its insect parasites and predators were studied in the hope that they would provide a biological control in this country (Hadley and Fleming, 1952).

Of all the natural enemies that the beetle had in the Orient, only a few proved to be effective or desirable in this country. One of the imports was the red-eyed fly, *Centeter cinerea,* a parasite. It failed to be fully effective here because in the United States it emerged two to three weeks before the maximum emergence of the Japanese beetle.

Other parasites such as *Dexia ventralis* also proved unsatisfactory because they require more than one host species to complete their life cycle. The most important parasites of this beetle in its native land are two species of parasitic wasps, *Tiphia popilliavora* and *Tiphia vernalis*. They have proved to be effective in reducing the beetle population wherever the wasps have been established.

In searching for all the possible enemies of the Japanese beetle, another type of biological control was then developed. Among the organisms producing diseases in this Oriental pest are two species of bacteria, now called *Bacillus popilliae* and *Bacillus lentimorbus*. They cause maladies known as Type *A* and Type *B* milky disease. These bacteria, particularly Type *A*, were found to be effective in killing the larvae of the beetle. In order to obtain spores of the bacteria for use in control of the beetle, it was found necessary to use live Japanese beetle larvae as the culture medium, since usable artificial media could not be found (Hawley, 1952). The spores produced in this manner may be broadcast over areas of beetle infestation, where the milky disease will in time be disseminated throughout the beetle population. Although this type of control may take several years to be fully effective, it is apparently safe in that it is not harmful to other organisms except for a few species of American beetles. Furthermore, one application is good for an indefinite number of years, although the necessary manner of culture makes it a costly control.

Other Control Methods. In addition to biological controls, quarantine of infected areas, chemical controls, and traps have been used in an attempt to restrain the Japanese beetle. Quarantine, as in many other cases, did not prove effective in preventing its dispersal. Several chemicals, including DDT, have been used successfully against it, but of course they will kill beneficial forms as well. Traps are not so useful in decimating the beetle population as they are in surveying areas for possible new infestations. All of these methods, directed against one of the many insect pests in this country, serve to indicate how full biological knowledge is needed for the control of noxious insects.

The Sea Lamprey Problem. Unfortunately, biologists are sometimes called in too late to prevent economic disaster. Such is the case with the marine lamprey problem in the Great Lakes. The lamprey is a parasite which often kills fishes which are its hosts. It attaches itself to the abdominal region of the fish by its mouth disk, rasping its way through the tissue and living on the flesh and fluid of its host. This particular species, *Petromyzon marinus*, is typically a salt-water form but is anadromous; that is, the adults enter fresh-water streams to spawn. They require a gravelly bottom to make their nests and lay their eggs. Sea lampreys were able to gain access to Lake Ontario without the aid of man but were stopped from further extension of range by Niagara Falls. With the completion of the Welland Canal in 1824, they were able to pass into Lake Erie (Hubbs and Lagler, 1947), and no effort was made to stop this emigration. The spread of the lamprey across Lake Erie was relatively slow, perhaps due to lack of suitable streams for spawning. When it finally reached Lake Huron, it spread very rapidly throughout the remaining Great Lakes and quickly reduced the fish populations, especially that of the lake trout. So great was this reduction that the fishing industry suffered severely. In Lake Huron, the annual catch of lake trout decreased from 5,000,-000 pounds to 340,000 pounds by 1953 (Applegate and Moffett, 1955).

Biologists have now been commissioned to find a way to control the lamprey. Various weirs and other devices are used to trap the spawning adults as they attempt to enter tributary streams. It is evident that in such large lakes as the Great Lakes, this is a stupendous task, yet there is no doubt that the spawning season is the most vulnerable portion of their life cycle. Here again an introduction of a species into a new environment through man's activities has upset the balance and is depriving man of food and livelihood. Biologists can only partially undo the damage, but the more we learn about every facet of the life of the species, the better are chances for its eventual suppression.

Rodent Control. One of the major groups of pests which man must contend with is the rodents. This group of mammals includes numerous species which eat cultivated plants, including their seeds and fruits (Fig. 7-2*a*, *b*), cause erosion problems by extensive burrowing, or dig unwanted and dangerous holes. Among the outstanding pest species of this group are the gophers, woodchucks, mice, rats, ground squirrels, and porcupines. Mice may cause severe damage by producing populations which bring about large losses to crops in a short time (see p. 199). Other species, such as the Norway rat, are more or less perennial and are a continual threat to the farmer's income, as well as being potential carriers of a variety of diseases. In some instances, however, it is difficult to evaluate a rodent, or some other species, as beneficial or detrimental. As Hamilton (1939) pointed out, animals such as pocket gophers, which undoubtedly do great harm to certain crops, may really be of great benefit through their part in the soil-building processes in watershed where they are abundant. Knowledge of the

Fig. 7-2. (*a*) The pine mouse, *Pitymys pinetorum*, is a major pest in orchards, where it kills trees by eating the bark from the roots and trunk. (*b*) The apple tree (below) was killed by the action of the pine mouse, which feeds on the bark of the roots and trunk.

(*a*)

Photos by Allen H. Benton

(*b*)

full life history of any species is required before control measures should be applied.

Predator Control. Frequently certain animals are thought to present a threat to crops or to other wildlife, and there may be efforts to limit or lower the population of these unwanted species. Food analysis of the suspected species' diet over long periods of time may indicate that persecution of some of these animals is unjustified. By means of stomach-content analysis, scat examination, and careful observation of the species in the field, an accurate picture of the assets and liabilities of any animal species may be secured. Foxes are often thought of as raiders of chicken houses, but biologists recognize them as useful predators of field mice. They also eat fruits and insects, as well as rabbits and birds. Foxes, like so many other wildlife species, may be injurious at certain seasons or in certain localities but a benefit to man on other occasions and in other places. This fact must not be forgotten in estimating the economic importance of any species.

Control of Disease-carrying Animals. Although most field biologists are not directly concerned with medicine, they may frequently contribute to the solution of medical problems when organisms which they have studied are involved in diseases. Frequently insects and their near relatives figure prominently in the health problems of the human race. Especially important in this connection are lice, fleas, flies, mosquitoes, and ticks. Entomologists and other biologists are able to help in the control of disease by passing on the results of their research to physicians and others who are more directly concerned with the diseases. Detailed knowledge of the habits and occurrence of a species may be used to control an organism which is found to be connected with disease.

Rats, together with their fleas, have played an important part in the medical history of the human race, especially in their relation to bubonic plague and murine typhus. Mammalogists are still studying the population characteristics and ecology of rats in an effort to develop better control over them. Mammals other than rats may also be reservoirs of disease. Recent cases of bubonic plague in this country, for example, have been traced to ground squirrels and rabbits which were acting as hosts to the disease organism. Rocky Mountain spotted fever, carried by ticks, is another disease of man which may exist in wild mammal populations such as rabbits and mice, and tularemia is frequently transmitted to man from rabbits.

Mammalogists have also been called upon in the control of rabies, for many wild animals, including foxes, raccoons, skunks, and certain bats, are known carriers of this dreaded disease. In New York, for example, red foxes have been trapped extensively in an effort to stop a rabies outbreak. At first a strip 5 to 10 miles wide was trapped around an area of infection to prevent spread of the disease—but without success. Further research revealed that red foxes frequently range at least 50 miles. Consequently, the trapping strip was increased to 50 miles in width, which is apparently effective in preventing further spread of the disease in the red fox population (Colson, 1955). It is apparent that suppression and possible eradication of many diseases must depend, at least in part, on knowledge gained by biologists working in the field.

CONSERVATION

Conservationists have studied the human population in various countries around the world in relation to water, soil, and wildlife use. Writers such as Vogt (1948) paint a gloomy picture of the present and future for the human race. Although there are solutions to the conservation problem, largely based upon knowledge gained within the last half-century, starvation on a world-wide scale is a real possibility. Severe overpopulation (the population of the world is estimated to be increasing at the rate of 110,000 per day), destructive land practices, cultural problems, and ignorance or disregard of conservation practices may be a more pressing problem than disarmament.

The Soil. Study of past agricultural practices has revealed what happens to produce the unhappy state in which man now finds his natural resources. Rainfall varies widely from one region of the world to the other, as does steepness of terrain. Where rainfall is relatively high, forests are the climax type of vegetation. Trees protect the soil, although such soil is usually thin. If the forests are removed, especially on steep slopes, erosion may quickly occur (Fig. 7-3). Then the topsoil will wash down the streams, ruining the fertility of the soil. All too frequently, forests have been destroyed to make agricultural lands on hilly terrain where the soil was not suited for crops at the outset. As erosion proceeds, the soil becomes too poor to support crops. Frequently the land is used for grazing after it will no longer grow satisfactory crops, and if it is overgrazed, the last remaining topsoil will disappear along with most of the surviving vegetation. In some regions of the world, the final indignity to the land is performed by goats, which destroy any shrubs, trees, or grass which may remain.

The end result is a wasteland. This tragic situation may be seen today in Spain, Italy, Greece, and many other countries. In our own West, where rainfall is scanty but the terrain level, wind has been the damaging element, once man has allowed intensive farming, overgrazing, and other poor land practices to permit wind action. The

Photo by William E. Werner, Jr.

Fig. 7-3. Steep slopes are subject to serious erosion problems. Here water erosion is shown in its early stages.

result is the same as in the hilly forested regions—severe erosion and consequent loss of soil fertility.

Studies of succession (see Chaps. 5 and 6) indicate the length of time required to rebuild soil once accelerated erosion has occurred, and how such soil is made. From such studies, we discover that the natural climax community is a reliable indication of what type of farming a given region may support. The signs of overgrazing and some other poor land practices are also evidenced by the community type (Fig. 7-4).

Population Problems. The problem of the human population and its food supply comes within the concern of conservationists, for they are interested in the best possible use of all our resources. The studies of biologists involving wildlife may give some valuable clues to the causes and possible solutions of the human population problem. An animal such as the white-tailed deer serves as an example. Within recent years the population in various parts of the country has in-

Photo by William E. Werner, Jr.

Fig. 7-4. This overgrazed land has become desert because of poor agricultural practices.

creased amazingly. In the eastern states the deer population was probably more or less stabilized before the coming of the white man. There were predators to prevent unduly high populations, and Indians hunted deer for food. With the invasion of the European, forests were cleared, and although predators were soon reduced or exterminated, hunting was intensive. As a result, the deer population declined. Unfortunately for man, many of the forest lands which were cleared for farms were soon eroded and then abandoned. The fields began to be restored to forest by means of succession, providing excellent food and cover for the deer. With this favorable condition, and without their natural predators, deer populations were able to grow even under considerable hunting pressure. Such pressure, of course, was stabilized by legislation, including buck laws and closed seasons. In recent years the deer have become a problem. In the agricultural regions of the Northeast, they have become so numerous as to become pests to the farmers. Their forest range is in many cases overgrazed. Now the problem has become one of reducing the overpopulation and over-grazing and the consequent mass starvation of deer in some areas. Hunters, disease, and lack of food are the population controls, since predators such as the wolves and cougars are gone from the area. If we compare this situation to the human one, we find that the natural controls over the human population are the same—disease, lack of food, and wars, which are another form of hunting. Increase in food through technical advances cannot continue indefinitely. As diseases are conquered, other means must become more important in limiting our population unless some new factor is introduced.

Is food the ultimate limiting factor in determining the maximum population of any species? As Elton (1947) indicated, although food supply must eventually establish the population limit, such a limit is seldom reached among herbivorous animals. Carnivores, however, are apparently frequently checked by lack of food. Under normal condi-tions, predators will act as a population check on herbivores, and when some disturbance, climatological or otherwise, allows a prey population to get ahead of its predators, parasites are usually the effective controls. If both of these fail, then starvation of a whole population may ensue. On the other hand, some biologists believe that natural populations may be limited chiefly by other means (see p. 217). From knowledge gained in the study of many animal populations, we may arrive at the inescapable fact that something will eventually act to check the rise in human population. Vogt (1948) believes that the population is already being limited, mainly by starvation or poor nutrition, in many parts of the world. Undoubtedly other factors will also be important in limiting the numbers of humans which the earth can support.

Without a doubt, the human-population problem is one of the most serious and pressing which faces man's economy. In order that we may live at the highest standards of living possible under the circumstances, it is necessary to obtain the utmost use of all natural resources, in-cluding our forests, soil, water, minerals, and wildlife. Since there is only a certain amount of some of these resources such as oil, coal, iron, and other minerals, they must be conserved as much as possible. Unlike forests and game, they are not self-replenishing. Furthermore, as far as man's usage is concerned, soil is also in this category of nonreplenishable resources. Although new soil may be built by natural forces in a few thousand years, at the present rate of growth of the human population, man cannot wait that long. Poor soil, however, may be made into good soil in a few years under proper conservation practices. Our aim must be to reach a point at which the constructive processes of soil building are faster than the destructive forces of soil erosion.

Water. It is almost impossible to consider soil conservation without simultaneously considering water. The amount of rainfall in an area or, even more, the ratio between the amount of rainfall and the evaporation rate, largely determines the soil type by helping to determine the climax community and the amount of leaching possible. Where rain is abundant, as in the forest biome, and drainage is good, leaching is rapid, and thin soils result. In areas where there is moderate rainfall and less leaching, as in the prairie biome, the soils become deep and fertile.

By cutting forests or plowing grasslands and then planting crops, man often leaves the soil uncovered by vegetation for months at a time. Under such circumstances, erosion may occur at an incredible rate. Gustafson et al. (1949) tell of instances in colonial times in which land was made useless in 20 years because of poor care and subsequent erosion. Some of our richest prairie lands are also being eroded, although not so seriously as the grasslands of the Great Plains. These once-rich areas have become known as the Dust Bowl in recent years because of the severe wind erosion which has occurred there (Fig. 7-5a, b). Yet it is estimated that the muddy Mississippi, which drains the prairie region, deposits as much as 400 million tons of rich prairie soil in the Gulf of Mexico each year (Bennett, 1936).

One effect of plowing is to make a region drier, through the increased evaporation rate (Gustafson et al., 1949). In the prairie region of Illinois, the first farmers settled along the streams in the wooded region to make their farms. There are probably several reasons for this: the availability of water, the idea that soil which supports a forest must be more fertile than soil which grows only prairie grasses, the need for timber for buildings. Furthermore, frequent grass fires made the prairies dangerous. In addition, at that time the prairie soils were

Photos by Soil Conservation Service, U.S.D.A.

Fig. 7-5. Wind erosion in the Dust Bowl. (*a*) An approaching dust storm. Dust of this type may be carried for hundreds of miles. (*b*) Abandoned land, where severe wind erosion has removed the entire layer of topsoil and rendered the land worthless.

frequently so wet that they could not be turned with the plows then available. Aged residents of this region still recall the marshy areas where grass grew as high as the shoulder of a man on horseback. These lands, now largely planted to corn, soybeans, and wheat, are far from being wet today.

Erosion-control Methods. Soil conservationists are attempting to do something about the alarming situation resulting from soil erosion.

Photo by Soil Conservation Service, U.S.D.A.

Fig. 7-6. Stream-bank improvement; stones slow down erosion of stream banks.

They study the cause of soil erosion and then look for practical ways to prevent it. The fundamental clue to much of the problem of soil conservation is in proper use of the land. Certain lands should never be put to agricultural use, for either crops or grazing. They are too hilly and the soil is to thin. Other lands should be used only with the utmost care, including all the preventive measures known against soil erosion. Crop rotation may reduce the drain of fertility from the soil. Stream-bank improvement (Fig. 7-6) prevents the erosion of land along waterways. Contour-strip cropping permits the use of relatively hilly land without undue erosion (Fig. 7-7). Even the best croplands on level soil must be used with caution, according to wise conservation practices, if the soil is to be maintained.

Flood Control. Another major factor in control of erosion is the subject of heated controversy. In most parts of the country, water is the main erosive force. Erosion control, then, must involve water-

Photo by Soil Conservation Service, U.S.D.A.

Fig. 7-7. Contour-strip cropping is one of the most widely used means of preventing water erosion of agricultural land. Water is held on the land and soaks into the ground rather than running off and carrying with it the precious topsoil.

shed protection and stream control. If water flows from the hills and valleys too rapidly, soil is eroded and the subsurface soils do not benefit from the rain. In addition, as a result of this rapid excursion of water from the watersheds, floods occur in the rainy season and droughts at other times.

The United States Army Engineers and the Bureau of Reclamation have been trying to remedy the major flood threats by building dams on the larger waterways where floods have occurred. The water impounded by these huge dams is used for hydroelectric power, irrigation, and recreation, in addition to controlling the floodwaters rushing down the rivers (Fig. 7-8). Many conservationists object to this method of flood control and challenge its soundness as an erosion-control device. They believe that the wisest and most economically sound answer to the problem is to protect the watershed, thus preventing soil erosion as well as floods. They point out that if the soil does not erode, the organic matter of the soil will remain and will help the soil to absorb and hold the precipitation. Without this kind of control, big dams are not economically sound, they feel, because

Photo by William E. Werner, Jr.

Fig. 7-8. Large dams such as the Hoover Dam, shown here, are used for hydro-electric power, irrigation, and recreation, as well as for flood control.

the eroded soil will be carried into the reservoirs behind the dams, which will quickly fill with silt and be rendered useless. There has also been objection to some large dams because they have obstructed the passage of fishes to their spawning grounds. In some cases, notably in the Northwest, this situation has been alleviated by specially constructed fish ladders which bypass the dams.

Many conservationists favor dams on the smaller streams in addition to watershed control. However, such dams might be of little value for hydrolectric power. Again, conservationists point out that it is difficult or impossible to have one dam effectively serve as many purposes as the proponents of large dams claim. For example, in the springtime dams should be empty for effective flood control when the high water sweeps down the stream; but they must be full if they are to be used for irrigation. If, during the summer, the water is used for irrigation, the level will be lowered and decrease the value of the structure for recreation and power. However, on some streams dams may be usable for several purposes because the flood season is predictable and of relatively short duration. On other streams, dams may be used only for flood control because floods may occur at any time of the year. A further objection to large dams is that much land, often fertile and valuable, is inundated by their creation. Actually, both dams and soil-conservation practices are needed to solve our soil- and water-conservation problems. If soil-conservation practices are not followed, dams silt up rapidly. On the other hand, soil-conservation practices alone cannot prevent all types of floods or provide large amounts of water for hydroelectric power and other uses.

Drainage of Wetlands. Another conflict of interests comes between conservationists and the Bureau of Reclamation in the efforts to drain swampy or marshy areas. The purpose of such drainage, carried on by the Reclamation Bureau, is to increase the amount of land available for agriculture. Conservationists object to further draining of wetlands for several reasons. Proponents of watershed control point out that swamps and marshes are natural reservoirs which are helpful in preventing excessive runoff of precipitation. Biologists insist that marshy areas are of great value because they are the refuge of waterfowl and many other important kinds of wildlife. In fact, most conservationists would like to see much of the formerly reclaimed land returned to marsh habitat and further draining stopped.

If marshes continue to be destroyed, waterfowl must decline, for only in the wetlands will they live and reproduce (Fig. 7-9). At present, the area of habitats suitable for wildfowl is being reduced steadily. In some areas, such as on the Pacific Coast, so much marshland has been drained for agricultural purposes that migrant waterfowl have become pests, destroying the crops in the regions that were once their natural feeding grounds. Farmers attempting to protect their crops add to the heavy hunting pressure from sportsmen, and this may prove to be disastrous to the bird populations if suitable habitat is not provided.

Another argument against drainage of wetlands is that such action often proves to be fruitless or more costly than the results justify. Frequently land that is drained is found to be useless for agricultural purposes due to the chemical nature of the soil. Furthermore, it has been discovered that drainage of such areas may result in lowering the water table of surrounding land, making it less productive. In view of these serious disadvantages of wetland drainage, it would seem

Photo by E. G. Tabor

Fig. 7-9. Wetlands are valuable as a home for wildlife, as well as for their water-holding capacity. Here a Virginia rail, *Rallus limicola*, is incubating its eggs in a marsh.

logical to make a study to assay the value of the wetland in terms of wildlife and water resources, and then compare this to the probable value of the land for agriculture and the costs involved in producing and sustaining the drainage.

Pollution Control. A final major phase of water conservation is the problem of pollution. Many cities and industrial plants continue to dump wastes into streams. Not only does this practice make the use of such water for human consumption impossible without costly processing, but it also creates health hazards and damages aquatic organisms. The putrefaction of sewage by bacteria consumes oxygen and consequently affects organisms such as fish, which require large amounts of oxygen. Toxic wastes in the rivers may also kill fish and other food animals, such as mollusks.

On the eastern seaboard, the shad industry offers a good example
of the damages which pollution may cause. The population of shad,
a highly desirable food fish, has shown wide fluctuations recently. In
good years, the catch might reach 4 million pounds, while in poor
years it might fall to 40 thousand pounds (Talbot, 1954). This species
is anadromous, spawning in certain large rivers along the coast from
Florida to Canada. A number of studies by the U.S. Fish and Wildlife

Photo by Soil Conservation Service, U.S.D.A.

Fig. 7-10. Ten years of protection from grazing has allowed the wood lot on the
left to recover from damage. On the right, the saplings and leaf litter have been
destroyed.

Service and the conservation departments of New York and New
Jersey showed that pollution was one of the major factors involved in
the decline of this species. Sewage and other wastes from New York
City and other cities along the Hudson River have caused the last 150
miles of the river to be seriously polluted. It is believed that pollution
control in this area would result in a great increase in the shad
population of the river. Pollution creates similar problems in most of
our major rivers and in many smaller streams, often because money
will not be expended to process wastes properly. In some instances,
however, there is no known way to process wastes so that they will
not be harmful.

Forest Conservation. Our forest lands are not in an exemplary condition either, although they may be restored; so the chances for their improvement are greater than with soil. Of 1,072 million acres originally in forest, only 624 million remain forested, and of this only 45 million acres are in a condition similar to the virgin state (Buell, 1949). Not only are our forests economically important in themselves and hence deserving of the studies of biologists, but the welfare of our forests is intimately connected with that of the soil, water, and wildlife. Forestry management is practiced mainly on government-owned lands and on larger privately owned forests. It is of course aimed at the best and fullest possible use of our forests and at sustained yield over an indefinite period of time. In addition to proper cutting, foresters are concerned with control of pests and fire, protection of watersheds, proper use of land by large game and cattle, and successional problems (Fig. 7-10).

Forest Fire. Protection from fires is one of the major problems of foresters. Forest fires annually consume appalling amounts of our forests (Fig. 7-11). In 1947, for example, fires burned more than 23,226,000 acres of forest, doing 55 million dollars worth of damage (Brown, 1949). The loss of timber in itself is serious enough, but fires also mean destruction of the litter on the soil and consequent loss of protection of the topsoil from erosion. The loss of wildlife in large fires may also be great. After a fire, growth of a forest back to the condition where it will produce timber useful to man may take at least a century (Fig. 7-12).

The most effective way to reduce fire losses is, obviously, prevention of forest fires. Nine out of ten wildfires are caused by man, seven out of ten through carelessness. Education of the public in the matters of how to safeguard against careless use of fires in forests and effective enforcement of regulations are, therefore, first steps in fire prevention. Foresters maintain lookouts and use aerial reconnaissance to spot blazes. Mechanization of forest-fire-fighting equipment has greatly increased man's ability to cope with the problem. Bulldozers are able to clear fire lanes, flame throwers are used to start backfires, and roads and trucks aid greatly in gaining rapid access to burning areas. Development of aerial fire-fighting techniques has proved a great success, especially in wilder parts of our country. Aerial photographs of fires give a better idea of the situation in a shorter time than was previously possible. Formerly, a blaze which started in a mountainous

Photo by N.Y. State Conservation Dept.

Fig. 7-11. Forest fire! Such fires consume millions of dollars' worth of timber yearly and also ruin the soil- and water-conserving properties of forests.

Photo by N.Y. State Conservation Dept.

Fig. 7-12. The fire is out, but it may take centuries before the forest has recovered fully.

region was difficult to reach, so that by the time fire-fighters arrived, the blaze might already be large. Now highly trained men and fire-fighting equipment are parachuted in to control flames quickly.

Forest Insects. Another cause of loss to our forests is insect damage. It is estimated that insects cause as much damage to forests as fire (Haeussler, 1952). Some of these insects, being introduced species, are like the Japanese beetle living in new territory without their normal predators and parasites. Included in this category are the European elm bark beetle, and the gypsy moth. Others, like the Engelmann spruce beetle, the spruce budworm, and the tussock moth, are native. Native species may reach epidemic proportions as a result of natural catastrophes in the forest. For example the Engelmann spruce beetle, which destroyed a large proportion of the spruce in national parks in Colorado from 1942 to 1947, probably was able to build up its population on weakened trees blown over by a severe windstorm in 1939 (Wygant and Nelson, 1949).

Whether they are introduced or native, the forest insect pests present a difficult problem of control to the forester. Especially in the western United States, it is frequently difficult to detect pest outbreaks until they have already done great damage. This is in part because of the difficulty that rough terrain imposes in making forest insect surveys. Rough terrain also hampers effective treatment and survey of the results of the treatment.

Again, each insect may possess special characteristics that make its control different from that of other species. An insect may harm trees in a variety of ways—from defoliation, which weakens the tree, to destruction of fruit or seeds, which prevents reproduction. Chemical treatments have been developed for the control of out-breaks of defoliating types of forest insects, by means of aerial spraying (Craighead and Miller, 1949). In the Northeast the gypsy moth, which defoliates deciduous trees, is now largely controlled by aerial spraying of DDT. Although quarantine and intensive control measures have been used against this imported pest, the moth has spread further into the Middle Atlantic States from New England, especially since 1953. The spread of the population is easily noted with gypsy moth traps which attract males within a radius of one-half mile by means of bait manufactured from the female sex glands (Masterson and Mitchell, 1956).

For many of the other insects which damage forests, biological controls may prove to be the answer, but this requires a detailed study of the ecology of each species under consideration. Unfortunately, there is as yet no known method of control for many of our most serious forest insect pests.

Watersheds. The importance of forest fires and insect pests is frequently felt in watershed control, for destruction of the forests by fires and pests may cause serious erosion. Forests on the lands that catch the water which eventually supplies crops and cities have several protective actions. They prevent rain from hitting the soil directly and thus eroding it. The roots of the trees help to hold the soil and make it porous, so that the water will soak into the ground and travel to streams via the water table, instead of running off along the surface to cause floods. The litter from the trees covers the ground and prevents it from drying rapidly. Eventually, this litter becomes part of the soil, maintaining its fertility and increasing its water-holding capacity. If the forests are destroyed by fire or insects, periods of high precipitation will cause washing away of the leaf litter, along with some of the soil. The colloidal soil suspended in this water clogs up the pores of the soil in the ground so that less water can soak in, compounding the difficulty. Since water cannot soak into the ground, runoff is increased and erosion proceeds at a still faster rate. The results are floods during times of high precipitation or melting of snow, and lowering of the water table so that streams dry up in summer.

In the West, however, water is scarce because of the low rainfall. People in this area argue that trees lose a great deal of water to the atmosphere from their leaves (transpiration) above and beyond the amount that would be evaporated from the soil without the shade of trees. Farmers therefore asked for the cutting of the watershed forests so that more water would be available to them for agriculture in the valleys. Wilm (1949) described several long-term experiments that were conducted to determine the results that cutting of timber on watersheds would have on the production of water and on erosion. These experiments showed that under certain watershed conditions selective cutting of the mature trees did increase the flow of water in streams substantially, and that consequent erosion was only slight. Cutting could not be carried out on all watersheds with this beneficial effect, however, and in any case care had to be taken to avoid erosion.

Of course, some parts of watersheds are planted in crops, and here the usual practices of soil conservation must be used in addition to small dams and basins to collect debris that is washed down during floods. Various stream-improvement devices are also used to prevent erosion of stream banks. As Phillips and Frank (1949) pointed out, watershed control alone will not prevent floods. Reservoirs and dams are also required in an integrated program with watershed treatments.

Forest Management. The way in which forests are used is the concern of forest managers. They are interested in forest production, including maximum sustained yield of timber, reforestation, grazing, and forest succession. From long-continued studies, methods of cutting have been developed so that forests may be cut for best advantage of the present and future yields. The method of colonial times was to cut off a forest completely, which frequently led to erosion and loss of productivity.

Several methods of cutting now employed are based on ecological principles, especially on the concept of succession. Thus, in forests composed of dominants whose seedlings are tolerant of shade, such as beech and sugar maple, only the mature, diseased, or overcrowded trees are removed. This selective cutting system allows a continual natural reforestation and an almost continual yield. Such a forest would have trees of nearly all ages. Some types of trees do not flourish under these conditions, and so other methods of cutting must be used. Harvest of such species may be accomplished by cutting all of the mature trees at once without detrimental effects. One such method, known as the *shelterwood* system, employs two or more cuttings during the growth of a stand of trees and a cutting of all the mature trees in the final harvest. The earlier cuttings allow seedlings to become established so that when the mature trees are finally harvested, reforestation is already under way. Another method of cutting is a modified clear-cutting system. Small irregular strips or sections are cut off entirely, but they are small enough so that seeds from the surrounding mature trees will reforest the clearings. As long as the clearings are far enough apart, erosion is not a serious problem. Such a cutting system is particularly good for those species of trees whose seedlings require or tolerate large amounts of sunlight.

Succession figures prominently in cutting systems and reforestation. Thus sugar maple seedlings require only 2 per cent sunlight, while seedlings of loblolly pine need the full benefits of sunlight (Barrett, 1949). In other words, seedlings of loblolly pine will not grow in the shade of older trees. They are not part of the climax community but are found at an earlier stage of succession before deep shade has developed. Sugar maple, on the other hand, forms a large part of the climax forest, and seedlings of this species normally grow under the deep shade of the mature trees. If trees which occur in early successional stages are not desired as timber trees, the forests should

Photo by N.Y. State Conservation Dept.

Fig. 7-13. Artificial reforestation is one method of replenishing our forests.

therefore not be clear-cut. This is true in the Northeast, where clear-cutting results in a second growth of inferior species such as gray birch, poplar and red maple under most conditions. If species of the early stages of succession are desirable trees and are preferred to species of the climax, one of the clear-cutting methods should be used.

Reforestation. A knowledge of succession can also be used to hasten reforestation by indicating what kinds of trees can be planted successfully under given circumstances. It would be useless to plant hard maple seedlings, for example, in an open field. Artificial reforestation is accomplished either by growing seedlings in the nursery or by direct seeding (Fig. 7-13). The former method is more costly, but avoids some difficulties which are caused by direct seeding, namely, losses of seeds due to action of rodents, birds, insects, and the weather. The fact that small mammals can affect reforestation and the direction of succession is demonstrated in the studies of Tevis (1956). He described a situation in a Douglas fir forest of California in which several rodents, including white-footed mice, chickarees (red squirrels), and Townsend chipmunks destroy a large percentage of the seeds of the Douglas fir in clear-cut areas. The result is that Douglas fir is at a disadvantage in succession, and instead of a climax community with this desirable

Photo by Soil Conservation Service, U.S.D.A.

Fig. 7-14. Forest grazing is holding back pine reproduction and forcing out the grass.

species as dominant, we find that the undesirable tan oak becomes established. In the absence of Douglas fir, the mice are able to thrive on the cut-over areas by eating the numerous insects which feed on the saplings of the oaks and other vegetation associated with the various successional stages. Whenever Douglas fir seeds are available, however, they will eat them avidly.

Grazing in Forests. Grazing is often practiced on forest lands, especially in the more open forests of the West. Grassy areas in the forested regions provide food for livestock and are important in the local economy, but overgrazing and browsing can be detrimental to the forests. Young seedlings may be eaten, and the conditions for erosion may be established. Cattle will trample down the soil when it is wet, making it hard when it dries. The litter may be destroyed, allowing abnormal drying during the warm months. Both of these conditions foster rapid runoff of precipitation by preventing the soil from soaking up rain water, and this leads to accelerated erosion (Fig. 7-14).

Wildlife Conservation. The value of wildlife is rather difficult to appraise, for it must include other factors besides the actual monetary value of the animals as food. The aesthetic value of wildlife, in terms of human enjoyment, cannot readily be measured in dollars and cents. The recreational value of hunting and fishing, as well as bird watching and related pursuits, is likewise unmeasurable. Easier to determine, and very important to the locality where the game lives, is the expenditure of money in the locality for food, ammunition, guns, camping equipment, and other supplies to the tune of millions of dollars per year. In any case, wildlife is of great economic worth and is sufficiently important to warrant the time and money spent by biologists in their efforts to learn about its natural history, conservation, and management.

Wildlife management is that phase of biology which is concerned with the best possible development, use, and conservation of wildlife. Most of the species involved are not considered commercially important, although such economically important species as the oyster, the lake trout, and the various fur bearers are studied. The significance of most of the species, however, is due to their aesthetic and recreational value. The object of management for all species is to make sure that a species does not become extinct because of overexploitation, disease, or the various natural causes which may threaten. On the other hand, wildlife management is also aimed at full utilization of all our wildlife for the benefit of the greatest possible number of people.

Although the idea of management of wildlife sounds like a simple one, it is frequently difficult to carry out. Conflicts arise over the use of land by wildlife, as opposed to agriculture, and jurisdictional problems due to land ownership or control often occur. Most pressing is the need for information on the life history of the many species concerned. In the report "The Nation Looks at Its Resources" (1953), enlightening discussions by the men most interested in wildlife management point out several areas in which controversy over land use creates still unsolved problems. The major ones concern the competition of deer and cattle for grazing lands in the western forests; the use of wetlands for waterfowl or their drainage for crops; and the problem of managing forests for the multiple uses of their timber, grazing, wildlife, and water conservation.

Jurisdictional problems over wildlife management may occur, as in forest management, between different government agencies, since intelligent management may require large areas, regardless of artificial political boundaries. In areas where most of the land is broken up into small, privately owned plots, uncooperative landowners can make proper management impossible. Deer herds, for example, may utilize lands of several owners. If one or more of these owners prevent hunting on their land, they may thus form a refuge for the herd during the hunting season. Without the necessary harvesting of the surplus, the herd may grow to a level which endangers crops on the lands of surrounding owners. Thus wildlife management is not entirely a matter of biology, although in the final analysis it must depend on fundamental biological knowledge of the species.

Data Needed for Wildlife Management. Information that especially aids management may be grouped into six main categories: habitat requirements, food habits, reproduction, population size and fluctuations, range, and interrelationships with other species. If this seems to cover almost the total ecology of the species, it is probably a correct impression. However, certain facets of the natural history of a species may be of more importance than others in its management.

When a species is to be managed, one of the first things that must be known is the size of the population (see p. 201). Population censuses are taken to discover the local or over-all abundance of a species, whether or not the population fluctuates widely, and if so, what the causes may be for the fluctuations. The accumulation of this knowledge may elude the investigator, even after a full ecological investigation; yet it must be attempted. The problems of population study are considered in detail in Chap. 8.

One of the major factors to consider in searching for methods of management of a population is its interrelationships with other species. Such interrelationships may be helpful or harmful. Predators, parasites, and disease organisms tend to diminish the population. Frequently the activities of man may be the cause of the decline of a species and of the resultant necessity for management. The Alaska fur seal is a good example. Commercial hunting pressure by American, Russian, and Japanese sealers had reduced this species drastically prior to 1910, threatening to exterminate it. There was no question that man was the factor which created these population difficulties. By treaty among the nations most concerned with this industry, strict protection was accorded to the seal population, and the species began to recuperate. As the seals become more abundant, some harvesting was again possible. But this time it was carefully controlled and based on complete studies of reproduction, natural mortality, and the other factors which affect the welfare of the species. If the same danger of extermination were to be prevented from occurring again, much had to be known about the ecology of the species. First the population as a whole had to be censused each year to determine the rate of population increase. Details of reproduction, such as time and age of breeding, gestation period, number of young per litter, conditions suitable for breeding, and sex ratios most suitable for maximum production had to be determined. Now that such studies have been at least begun (e.g., Bartholomew and Hoel, 1953), a hunting season and maximum number of animals that may be harvested annually could be established without jeopardizing the existence of the species.

The Food and Cover Problems. Sometimes man is not the direct cause of the decrease of a species, but may affect its natural survival, causing a management problem. In agricultural lands there has been a tendency to clear land up to the fence (Fig. 7-15). Such a practice leaves very little natural food and cover for rabbits and important game species. The young or adults then become the easy prey of various predators. By leaving brush along the fence, cover is available within easy reach of their feeding area (Fig. 7-16). Predators thereby have a more difficult time catching the rabbits and the population is allowed to maintain itself at a higher level (Fig. 7-17).

With many of our game species, food may limit their numbers at certain times. The problem of game management is then to find ways of supplementing the food supply, especially in unfavorable seasons. Grouse, for example, may be aided by the introduction of certain kinds of apple trees in parts of their range where winter food may be scarce. Waterfowl are substantially aided by water-control measures, for example, by small dams or dikes. Such measures provide a more stable environment, including the food and water supply during the

Photo by William E. Werner, Jr.

Fig. 7-15. Many farmers like to clear land up to the fences. Though this provides a maximum use of the land, it is bad for wildlife.

Photo by William E. Werner, Jr.

Fig. 7-16. A multiflora rose hedge. This type of hedge is planted to provide food and cover for game.

dry summer months. The planting of natural foods such as wild rice near their feeding areas is also used to aid waterfowl. In some cases, as in the regions of California previously mentioned, suitable waterfowl habitat has been so reduced that these birds are being specially fed by hand and on grain and grass crops grown in refuges, in order to reduce their damage to agricultural crops (Biehn, 1951).

Competition for food between wildlife species often assumes importance in management. This is especially true in the management of fish populations. Some of the pan fish, such as sunfish and perch, are

Fig. 7-17. A rabbit nest (opened to show the young inside) in a brush pile along a hedgerow.

Photo by Allen H. Benton

competitors for the same food as the larger and more desired game fish, such as pickerel and bass. If the pan fish increase in numbers, they eat up not only the supply of food for the game fish but also that needed by other members of their own species. One consequence is that the pan fish are stunted and hence become even less desirable. More fishing pressure may then be placed upon the game fish. This in turn reduces the population of the larger species. The end result is a large amount of small pan fish and very few game fish. Control of such a situation is not easy, but reduction of the pan fish may be accomplished by induced fishing pressure on them or by selective netting. In some lakes and ponds the drastic step of killing all the fish and restocking may be necessary (Petty, 1953).

The predator problem. The opposite situation, overabundance of undesirable predators, produces a different and exceedingly complex problem for wildlife managers. As is so often the case in biology, there is no one solution that will apply to all situations. In fact, it seems that biologists cannot agree on whether predator control is always suitable, let alone how to accomplish it. Latham (1951) summarized the various present views on this controversial issue. He pointed out that people who think of the losses of individual victims of predators favor predator control, while those who are concerned with the survival of all species are opposed to it. Certainly predators help to maintain the natural population of prey species at the proper level in nature. When predators attack our livestock, we must weigh this damage against the damage to crops that could result from an increase in the predators' *natural* prey—mice, rats, and gophers, for example—if the predators were reduced. This, of course, is seldom considered. Any predator which even approaches the vicinity of livestock is likely to be destroyed, whether or not it has any evil intentions upon the livestock. The mouse-eating hawks of the genus *Buteo* are as severely persecuted as any predator, although it is well known that they rarely harm either livestock or game.

If, as a result of study of the ecology of the predator, it is decided to attempt to reduce its numbers, the problem remains—how? One method is the bounty system, which requires payment of a specified sum for each animal of a certain species that is killed. This system has seldom proved successful in predator control and it is costly; it also leads to widespread dishonesty and is very difficult to administer properly. Poisoning has been used, but is dangerous to other species and even to humans in areas of heavy population. Fencing may protect livestock from certain predators, but this is often prohibitively costly, and of course has no value for wild prey species. The use of biological controls, such as disease organisms and parasites, has not been established in the control of predators in this country, although it might be workable in some cases. The problem remains an enigma, but some solutions may be forthcoming with the increased study of this difficult question.

Habitat improvement. Occasionally the availability of suitable habitat will limit the population of a game species. Attempts are then made to increase such habitats. In recent years, habitat improvement has proved to be one of the most effective tools in wildlife management. Many of our streams, for example, are not favorable for trout, which require a constant flow of cool water. By the placing of log dams or other devices to produce pools at intervals along shaded streams, trout habitat may be created. Research may indicate whether or not the environment is suitable for a particular species and thereby save a great deal of effort and money in management or stocking operations. In New York, the bobwhite quail is established in considerable numbers to make it available to sportsmen. Despite pressure for stocking upstate coverts, the conservation department has found that the winters of the northern part of the state will prevent the development of a population there. No restocking is attempted in that region (Smith, 1956).

Many more examples could be cited of the ways in which field biology is involved in the economics of our society. We must avoid, however, attempts to overstress the economic value of our natural resources and remember that in many ways the value of the organisms about us, with which the biologist works, is above any price that might be mentioned.

REFERENCES CITED

APPLEGATE, VERNON C., AND JAMES W. MOFFETT. 1955. Sea lamprey and lake trout. In "Twentieth Century Bestiary." Simon and Schuster, Inc., New York. pp. 9–16.

BARRETT, LEONARD I. 1949. Forest renewal. In "Trees, Yearbook of Agriculture." U.S. Department of Agriculture. pp. 120–126.

BARTHOLOMEW, GEORGE A., AND PAUL G. HOEL. 1953. Reproductive behavior of the Alaska fur seal, *Callorhinus ursinus*. *J. Mammal.*, 34:417–436.

BENNETT, H. H. 1936. Soil erosion and its prevention. In "Our Natural Resources and Their Conservation." A. E. Parkins and J. R. Whitaker (eds.) John Wiley & Sons, Inc., New York. pp. 65–100.

BIEHN, EARL R. 1951. "Crop Damage by Wildlife in California, with Special Emphasis on Deer and Waterfowl." California Department of Fish and Game, Game Bulletin no. 5. 71 pp.

BROWN, A. A. 1949. Progress, but still a problem. In "Trees, Yearbook of Agriculture." U.S. Department of Agriculture. pp. 477–479.

BUELL, JESSE. 1949. The community of trees. In "Trees, Yearbook of Agriculture." U.S. Department of Agriculture. pp. 103–108.

COLSON, RALPH. 1955. Rabies. *N.Y.S. Conservationist*, 9(5):8–9.

CRAIGHEAD, F. C., and JOHN M. MILLER. 1949. Insects in the forest: a survey. In "Trees, Yearbook of Agriculture." U.S. Department of Agriculture. pp. 407–413.

ELTON, CHARLES. 1947. "Animal Ecology." 3d ed. The Macmillan Company, New York.

GUSTAFSON, A. F., H. RIES, C. H. GUISE AND W. J. HAMILTON, JR. 1949. "Conservation in the United States." Comstock Publishing Associates, Inc., Ithaca, N.Y. xi and 445 pp.

HADLEY, CHARLES, AND WALTER E. FLEMING. 1952. The Japanese beetle. In "Insects, Yearbook of Agriculture." U.S. Department of Agriculture. pp. 567–573.

HAEUSSLER, G. J. 1952. Losses caused by insects. In "Insects, Yearbook of Agriculture." U.S. Department of Agriculture. pp. 141–146.

HAMILTON, WILLIAM J., JR. 1939. "American Mammals: Their Lives, Habits, and Economic Relations." McGraw-Hill Book Company, Inc., New York. xii and 434 pp.

HAWLEY, IRA M. 1952. Milky disease of beetles. In "Insects, Yearbook of Agriculture." U.S. Department of Agriculture. pp. 394–401.

HUBBS, CARL, L., AND KARL F. LAGLER. 1947. "Fishes of the Great Lakes Region." Cranbrook Institute of Science, Bulletin 26. xi and 186 pp.

LATHAM, ROGER, M. 1951. "The Ecology and Economics of Predator Management." Final Report, P.-R. Project 36-R. Pennsylvania Game Commission, Harrisburg. 96 pp.

MASTERSON, WILLIAM E., AND DAVID MITCHELL. 1956. The gypsy moth. *N.Y.S. Conservationist*, 10(6):18–19.

PETTY, A. C. 1953. Warm water fish populations. *N.Y.S. Conservationist*, 8(1):24–25.

PHILLIPS, GEORGE R., AND BERNARD FRANK. 1949. To help control floods. In "Trees, Yearbook of Agriculture." U.S. Department of Agriculture. pp. 609–614.

THE MID-CENTURY CONFERENCE ON RESOURCES FOR THE FUTURE. 1953. The Nation Looks at Its Resources. Resources for the Future Inc., Washington. xii and 418 pp.

SMITH, RALPH H. 1956. Bobwhites—on the rise? *N.Y.S. Conservationist*, 10(5):17.

TALBOT, G. B. 1954. Shad in the Hudson. *N.Y.S. Conservationist*, 8(5):17–19.

TEVIS, LLOYD, JR. 1956. Responses of small mammal populations to logging of Douglas fir. *J. Mammal.*, 37:189–196.

VOGT, WILLIAM. 1948. "Road to Survival." William Sloane Associates, New York. xi and 335 pp.

WILM, H. G. 1949. Timber cutting and water yields. In "Trees, Yearbook of Agriculture." U.S. Department of Agriculture. pp. 593–602.

WYGANT, N. D., AND ARTHUR L. NELSON. 1949. Four billion feet of beetle-killed spruce. In "Trees, Yearbook of Agriculture." U.S. Department of Agriculture. pp. 417–422.

SUGGESTED READING

ALLEN, SHIRLEY W. 1955. "Conserving Natural Resources: Principles and Practice in a Democracy." McGraw-Hill Book Company, Inc., New York.

BLACK, JOHN D. 1954. "Biological Conservation: With Particular Emphasis on Wildlife." The Blakiston Division, McGraw-Hill Book Company, Inc., New York.

DALE, TOM, AND VERNON G. CARTER. 1955. "Topsoil and Civilization." University of Oklahoma Press, Norman, Okla.

LACK, DAVID. 1954. "The Natural Regulation of Animal Numbers." Oxford University Press, New York.

LEOPOLD, ALDO. 1949. A Sand County Almanac. Oxford University Press, New York.

LEOPOLD, LUNA B., AND THOMAS MADDOCK, JR. 1954. "The Flood Control Controversy: Big Dams, Little Dams, and Land Management." The Ronald Press Company, New York.

OSBORN, FAIRFIELD. 1948. "Our Plundered Planet." Little, Brown & Company, Boston.

SEARS, PAUL B. 1935. "Deserts on the March." University of Oklahoma Press, Norman, Okla.

SCOTT, ANTHONY. 1955. "Natural Resources: The Economics of Conservation." Canadian Studies in Economics, no. 3. University of Toronto Press, Toronto.

TRIPPENESEE, REUBEN, E. 1948. "Wildlife Management." vol. 1. McGraw-Hill Book Company, Inc., New York.

CHAPTER 8

PRINCIPLES OF
POPULATION STUDY

In all things there is a sort of law of cycles.

Tacitus

One of the most important trends in modern biology is the recognition of the necessity for studying populations as well as individuals. In this chapter, we use the term *population* as defined in the introduction, to indicate all the individuals of a particular species in a given area.

In taxonomy, a single specimen was formerly considered quite adequate for the description of a new species, and a collector was usually satisfied with a few specimens of each sex of the species in which he was interested. Now taxonomists work with series of specimens and attempt to analyze a significant sample of the population, often with complicated statistical procedures.

The student of animal behavior studies not only individuals but their behavior as part of a population. The wildlife biologist must know the properties not only of the individual of beneficial or harmful species but of the population as well. As Leopold (1933) has pointed out, "some properties are not discernible in the individual, but only in the mass." Such characteristics as intraspecific tolerance, sexual habits, maximum and optimum density, and many others are discernible only by a study of the population.

POPULATION PROBLEMS

The problems of population study may be broken down into four general groupings. The most obvious problem related to populations is numbers. How many individuals of a given species of plant or animal are there? How do their numbers vary from time to time? What percentage of a game population is taken by hunters each year? These questions are of fundamental importance from both the scientific and economic points of view, and unless we have some idea of the numbers involved in our work, we are subject to serious errors or deficiencies in our understanding of the species we study.

After we have learned the approximate number of animals or plants in the population with which we are concerned, we come to problems concerned with distribution of the population. How is a population distributed throughout the range of the species? How large an area is occupied by one individual or one family group? What are the climatic, ecological, and physical boundaries of the range of a population? How dense is the population in the most favorable areas?

Another basic property of a population is its composition with regard to age and sex. Wildlife managers are especially concerned with fairly precise knowledge of this factor. Ecologists, both those who study plants and those who are interested in animals, need to know the relative abundance of the various age classes in a given habitat. The fluctuations and changes in these factors over many years in plant communities, and from year to year in animal populations, are matters of great importance.

The fourth general aspect of the study of animal populations in particular, and to a lesser degree of plant populations, is behavior. This cuts across the other fields to some degree, in that distribution and composition of populations may be related to behavior. But behavior also includes social habits, sexual relationships, population movements, and innumerable other characteristics which are best studied at the population level.

If we are to understand anything about the dynamics of populations, we must have information from all these aspects. Unfortunately, much of the basic work remains to be done. A summary of present knowledge of these matters in regard to mammal populations was prepared by Blair (1953), indicating both the extent and shortcomings of studies in this important area.

Let us now consider these population characteristics one by one, and in more detail. Populations must first be counted in some reasonably accurate manner before we can begin to learn much about their other characteristics. This would seem at first glance to be a relatively simple operation, but any field biologist will assure you that such is not the case.

The first complication lies in the fact that animal populations do not remain constant in numbers for any appreciable period of time. Plant populations are more easily counted, for they will remain in one place until the process is completed; but even here the population does not remain constant for long periods. Populations vary with the season, fluctuate from year to year, and do not permit the student to make assumptions on the basis of a single count or estimate.

Population Sampling. A second difficulty in population studies is the acquisition of an adequate sample. Biologists and statisticians differ as to just what constitutes an adequate sample, and undoubtedly there can be no one definite answer which will cover all problems. Generally it is considered wise to secure as large a sample as possible, and the reliability of the data will be directly related to the size of the sample. Further, the size of the sample may vary according to the availability of the species. The student of fishes, who can collect a hundred in one sweep of a seine, is likely to secure larger samples for study than is the mammalogist, who will have much more difficulty in securing his specimens.

An adequate sample must not only be adequate in size but it must be drawn at random from the population. The attempt to secure a random sample is, for the most part, an attempt to avoid any selectivity by the worker, and to insure that chance is the only agent in selecting the sample. In ecological studies, workers have devised complicated techniques for insuring randomness in sample selection; but it is still difficult to be certain that this goal is achieved. The distribution of any species, plant or animal, is not random. It depends upon environment, although chance is in many cases the agent which brings it into the proper environment. The wind, for example, blows seeds about in a relatively random manner, though even here it is likely to blow more or less in one direction. But random distribution of the species is not achieved because most of the seeds do not land in a spot suitable for growth. A sample drawn from a small area, however carefully selected, may be misleading if it is drawn from an area of high population or from an area where the species is relatively rare. To ensure an accurate appraisal of the population, it is necessary to sample areas with various levels of abundance of the species in question, and to sample them repeatedly.

Another difficulty in securing a random sample from an animal population springs from variation in susceptibility to counting. Some mammals, for example, enter traps readily, and can be counted with a fair degree of accuracy after sufficient trapping has been done. Other species, although equally abundant in nature, are seldom taken in traps,

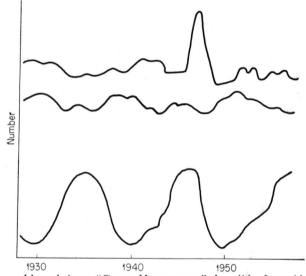

Adapted from "Game Management," by Aldo Leopold, with the permission of Charles Scribner's Sons, New York.

Fig. 8-1. Diagrammatic representation of the three major types of population variation. Top, irruptive; middle, nonfluctuating; bottom, cyclic.

and appear to the beginning collector to be very rare indeed. Professional biologists tend to feel that in many cases rarity is not a property of the animal species but a property of the human species; that is, many so-called rare species are rare only because there are few collectors or because the people who want to collect specimens do not know where to look or how to find them.

Population Fluctuations. It has been known for many years that animal populations are subject to periodic fluctuations in numbers. Leopold (1933) divided populations into three types on the basis of these fluctuations (Fig. 8-1). One type maintains a relatively constant population level, with only minor fluctuations occurring randomly over a long period. This may be called the *nonfluctuating* type, if we keep in mind that this term is relative. A second type has rather regular ups and downs in population numbers, with great variation in numbers between high and low points. This may be called the *cyclic* type. The third type is that which has periodic increases and declines in numbers, often reaching a very high density, but without any cyclic regularity; that is, with high population densities not occurring at any

Photo by Ralph S. Palmer

Fig. 8-2. The field mouse, *Microtus pennsylvanicus*, has a population cycle of about three years. At the high point of the cycle the species may reach fantastic levels of abundance.

fixed time interval. This may be called the *irruptive* type of population.

In the United States, for example, the bobwhite quail tends to maintain relatively stable populations in a given area. Unless the conditions of the habitat are changed drastically, the population of bobwhites will be relatively nonfluctuating. The ruffed grouse, the snowshoe hare, and the field mouse (Fig. 8-2), however, have regular and predictable cycles of abundance, ranging from extreme profusion to an almost complete extirpation. An example of irruptive population behavior is that of the house mouse in Kern County, California, in 1926. Hall (1927) estimated that the population in a limited area of highly favorable habitat reached more than 80,000 mice per acre. Fortunately for humans, such irruptions are relatively uncommon, and do not appear to occur in all species.

Cyclic Populations. Population fluctuations of the cyclic type have led to much discussion about causes. Early workers attempted to find a relationship between such fluctuations and environmental variables, including disease, food supply, sunspots, and habitat conditions, but no satisfactory conclusion could be reached. Later workers, such as Grange (1949), have emphasized the part played by the numerous forces which act upon both the animal and its environment. This approach has been carried to its logical extreme by Palmgren (1949) and Cole (1951). These ecologists suggest that the variations which appear to be cyclic are dependent upon so many variables that the resultant fluctuations are quite random. An exhaustive summary of the most widely held theories is contained in The Wildlife Society's "Symposium on cycles in animal populations" (1954). Other current theories, however, deserve mention.

Two Finnish biologists, Siivonen and Koskimies (1955), have put forth the suggestion that lunar cycles actually control cyclic populations. Cyclic species, they believe, have a particularly sensitive period which will govern the success of reproduction for a certain time. Interaction between the lunar cycle and this sensitive period is suggested as the basis for population cycles. This theory places reproduction, or the lack of it, as the most important element in cyclic behavior of populations.

Most of the theories which have been advanced to account for animal cycles have suggested some outside environmental factor as the cause of the sudden dying which brings about the population crash at the end of a cycle. The possibility that the cause of this population decline lies within the animals themselves has been suggested by Christian (1950), and his theory has been further advanced by the experimental work of Frank (1957) on large numbers of captive animals in Germany. Briefly, these biologists suggest that exhaustion of adrenal and pituitary function causes death of large numbers of animals in a high stage of the population cycle, thus reducing them to the low point very suddenly. The reasons for this exhaustion are thought to be associated with the stresses caused by overcrowding at high population levels. Frank has succeeded in causing population crashes in captive populations under crowded conditions by adding an additional stress factor such as food scarcity or unfavorable climatic conditions.

At present we do not understand the cause or causes of cyclic fluctuations in animal populations, but it is possible that one of the theories mentioned above may prove to be correct. In view of the increasing human population and the problems which such population growth will inevitably bring, it is important that we should learn as much as possible about the dynamics of population fluctuations. Whether the same rules which apply to animal populations can be applied to human populations is not certain, but increased understanding of the one may provide some help in solving the problems of the other.

Census Methods. It is evident that much remains to be learned about animal populations. Even the old and standard methods of counting animals have been questioned by modern biologists. It is not easy to count accurately a population which varies widely from time to time, which shifts about from place to place, and which is so secretive that its members cannot be seen. Fortunately, not all animal species are so discouragingly secretive, and the obvious method of counting by direct observation may be used. If it is not possible to count all those in the area under consideration, the number in a certain portion of the area may be counted, and this number, multiplied by an index factor, may indicate quite accurately the total population. This direct-count method is used in estimating waterfowl populations, in counting big-game animals, and in computing populations where the animals are abroad during the day and can be readily seen. Airplane counts are useful in making both waterfowl and big-game surveys. This method may not always give an absolute count of the population, but it will indicate relative numbers from year to year. Such information may be sufficient to allow those interested in management or control of these species to establish proper regulations. Adaptations of the direct-count system include song counts of breeding bird populations, brood and covey counts of game birds, and airplane counts or aerial photographs. Such methods may give sufficiently accurate results, if one can assume that all or almost all of the animals present in an area have been counted. In cases where this cannot be assumed, other means of counting have to be devised.

As an improvement on the direct count, several indirect methods have been developed. The oldest and probably the most widely used indirect counting method is the Lincoln index. (This method is used for fishes as the Peterson method, and perhaps could best be termed the Lincoln-Peterson index.) The technique in its modern form depends upon the introduction into a given population of a certain number of marked individuals, such as banded birds, tagged fishes, or toe-clipped mammals. At a later date, a sample of the population is removed and counted. Theoretically, the relationship between marked and unmarked individuals in the sample should be the same as in the population as a whole. Thus $P:M = p:m$, when P equals the total population, M equals the total number of marked individuals in the population, p equals the total sample drawn, and m equals the number of marked individuals in the sample.

As an example, suppose that a mammalogist live-traps 35 deer mice from a 20-acre wood lot, marks them by toe clipping, and releases them. A week later, when they have had time to resume their places in the population, he retraps the area and catches 12 marked mice and 24 unmarked mice, a total of 36 individuals in the sample. Using the Lincoln-Peterson index, he sets up this ratio: $P:35 = 36:12$. The total population thus equals 1260/12, or 105 mice in the 20-acre area.

This method, as Adams (1951) points out, makes several assumptions which may be unwarranted. If the marks are not permanent, or if they put the marked animal at a disadvantage and thus lead to higher mortality of marked animals, or if marked animals are either easier or more difficult to catch than unmarked ones, or if the population changes greatly between the first and second sampling, the results may be very misleading. To reduce error and increase the reliability of such counts, many biologists have turned to highly complicated statistical calculations. Statistical analysis has assumed increasing importance in many branches of biological work in recent years because of the possibility of testing for accuracy. Nowhere is this more evident than in the new techniques for determining the numbers of plants and animals (see Appendix, p. 310). Most of these methods are too complex and too specialized to be considered here, but the interested student will find a discussion of their use in the study of mammals in a paper by Dice (1941).

Under some circumstances it is not essential to have an accurate count of the actual number of animals, but game managers wish to know whether the animals are more or less common than in previous years and whether they have reached numbers too great for the food supply. Often this can be done by a survey of the habitat. An obvious browse line (Fig. 8-3) invariably indicates that the deer in that forest are too plentiful for the amount of food available. Small deer which cannot reach browse are in danger of starvation when such a stage is reached. The alert wildlife manager may be able to determine much about population levels by a study of such indirect indications.

The problems of botanists in counting populations would seem to be simpler than those of zoologists. The major difficulty in counting plants is that it is impossible to count an entire population, so that

Photo by N.Y. State Conservation Dept.

Fig. 8-3. A browse line, with no branches below a certain level, indicates an overpopulation of deer. During the coming winter younger and smaller deer will not be able to reach sufficient food, and starvation will ensue.

samples must be taken. Methods of sampling have been briefly discussed in Chap. 4, and these methods have been tested in ecological work of all kinds. Although they will give adequate results if properly used, much depends upon the user. The problems of choosing an adequate sample, assuring randomness of the sample, and checking the statistical significance of the results are as important to the plant biologist as to the animal biologist. A good review of sampling methods in plant studies has been prepared by Schumacher and Chapman (1948).

DISTRIBUTION OF POPULATION MEMBERS

The distribution of the members in a population, and of the population as a whole, is fairly well known for most of the more prominent plants and animals. Geographical distribution may change as time goes on, but the general outlines of the range of most species are well known. We are well on the way to an equally detailed knowledge of ecological distribution; that is, the preferred habitat of each species. Many distributional problems remain, however, for today's biologists. We need more knowledge of the reasons for the limited distribution of some forms and the much wider distribution of similar forms which, to us, show no evident superiority. Some species have become extinct within man's memory because their habitat changed or was destroyed, and they were not able to adapt to the new conditions. Certain species survive in limited areas, as Jeffrey's pine in California and Kirtland's warbler in Michigan. Many of our native orchids (Fig. 8-4) occur in a limited range of ecological situations, and only a

Photo by Allen H. Benton

Fig. 8-4. Most of our native orchids have a very narrow range of ecological tolerance. This is the pink lady's slipper, *Cypripedium acaule*, one of the more common species.

few species are really common and widespread. Some of these species have evidently traveled up an evolutionary blind alley to the point of no return. It is important to find out what the limits of tolerance are for each species in regard to habitat. This information is of special value for species which are of economic importance and may be subject to management.

Territorialism. In the case of animals, their distribution in relation to other members of the same species is of great importance. Howard (1920) presented the theory of *territorialism* in birds, and we now know that this concept can be extended to include many other kinds of animal life. Territory, as Howard uses it, may be defined as that part of the *home range* (larger area traveled by an individual while carrying on its activities [Fig. 8-5]) which is defended by its occupant against members of the same species. In a breeding colony of grackles, for example, the territory might include only a portion of the tree in which the nest is built, while the home range would include feeding

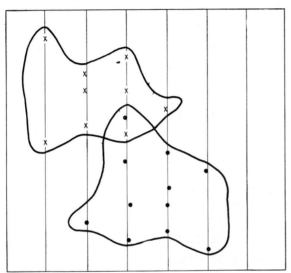

Fig. 8-5. Hypothetical diagram of the home ranges of two small mammals, as recorded by repeated captures in traps set on a grid system.

grounds several hundred yards away, a watering place elsewhere, and all the area between. Some animals have a territory which is defended because of its importance in the breeding cycle, such as the nesting territory of birds, and another distinct territory which is associated with feeding, and which is likewise defended against other members of the same species.

It is relatively easy to study territorialism in birds, and we know with a high degree of accuracy the extent of both territory and home range for many species, at least for the breeding season. In other animals, this phenomenon is less easily observed. Nocturnal or subterranean species present special problems, as do species too small to be readily studied as individuals. Home range and territory are, in most species, highly variable in different individuals, and may depend to some degree upon type of habitat; availability of food, water, and cover; season, sex, age, and condition of the individual; and other variables. It follows that the determination of these areas must be a complicated and extended procedure. The study of home range in mammals will serve to illustrate some of the possible approaches.

One of the most profitable techniques for determining home range has been grid trapping. In this technique, live traps are set in a regular pattern or grid, perhaps six feet apart in each direction. When an animal is captured, it is marked and released. If captured again, it can be recognized and its movements can gradually be plotted to form a clear and accurate picture of the home range (Fig. 8-5). This technique, of course, requires repeated captures and continued study over long periods. As with the techniques for population study, these methods have been submitted to searching statistical analysis. Recent summaries of the statistical approach to home range include those of Hayne (1949) and Stickel (1954). These workers point out that home-range figures are of varying degrees of accuracy, and that unless the same method is used consistently, different studies will not produce comparable results. Stickel (1954) suggests that the most fruitful method is to delineate the area in which captures of one individual were made, and then to add a boundary strip of one-half the distance between traps. This allows for the fact that the animals presumably range, on the average, halfway to the nearest trap beyond the one in which they are captured.

The most recent technique in this field—a very promising technique —is the use of radioactive minerals which can be recognized at some distance with a Geiger counter. Godfrey (1954), during her studies of the European vole, *Microtus agrestis*, found it possible to record a single individual up to 50 times. She used cobalt-60 attached to the vole by a specially constructed leg band which protected the animal from radioactivity. Data from this study indicated that home range of animals recorded less than 20 times was not sufficiently well demarcated to give accurate results. Since most grid-trapping studies are based on animals captured less than a dozen times, it seems likely that some of our conclusions about the home range of animals are untrustworthy.

It has already been indicated that territorialism appears to be a widely distributed phenomenon in the animal kingdom. Much more work must be done, however, before we can understand its importance as a general characteristic of vertebrate populations, and even less is known about its occurrence in invertebrates. Since territorialism involves intraspecific strife—that is, combat between individuals of the same species—it can be observed easily in large or diurnal forms. Even in such favorable circumstances, however, the student may find it difficult to distinguish between territorial strife and quarrels which take place for other reasons. Fighting may occur over food, mates, in defense of young, or between male and female as part of the courtship procedure.

AGE AND SEX COMPOSITION OF POPULATIONS

Enough has been said to indicate that it is not always easy to discover even the basic facts about a population. It is no wonder that our attempts at management of wildlife are often bungling and unsuccessful in their early stages. The factors affecting density, distribution, and fluctuations in populations are too varied to be readily determinable. And the wildlife manager must know more than just the numbers and distribution of a population. Of primary concern is the age and sex composition of a population. In those species which are hunted or trapped, it is necessary to establish seasons, bag limits, and other regulations which will assure a sustained yield of the species for the future. The total take by human agencies, added to natural mortality, must not exceed the annual increase, or the whole population is in danger. Ecologists sometimes express this fact in a formula: Total population is equal to reproductive capacity minus environmental resistance. That is to say, if the species is to maintain its numbers, mortality must not exceed reproduction. In order to add to the total population of a species, which is often one of the goals of wildlife management, we must either increase the reproductive capacity or reduce the environmental resistance. The reproductive capacity may be increased by nutritional improvement in some cases, e.g., in white-tailed deer, but it is usually easier to tamper with the environmental resistance by reducing predators, increasing the available food, or in some other manner. This formula, of course, holds good for any species, whether plant or animal. But in order to apply it in terms of management we must know a great deal about the species and its ecology.

In some cases, a population of generally desirable organisms will develop to such a level as to be too abundant. Overpopulation may result

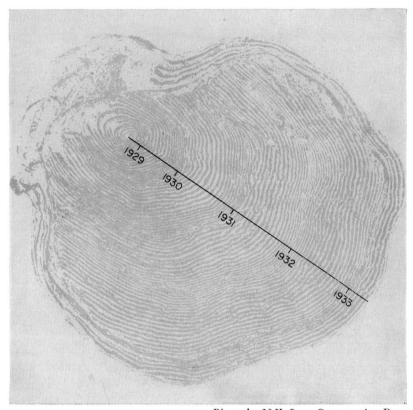

Photo by N.Y. State Conservation Dept.

Fig. 8-6. Age of a fish can be determined with a high degree of accuracy by the microscopic study of the scales. The width of the bands varies with the seasons.

in large-scale starvation, widespread disease, damage to human interests, destruction of habitat, and weakening of the whole population. When this occurs, it is obvious that environmental resistance in the form of increased hunting pressure would actually be beneficial to the population as a whole. Successful management of wildlife resources requires that the population be kept well away from either extreme scarcity or extreme abundance.

Age Composition. The importance of age composition in wildlife management may not be immediately obvious. It is significant because it can furnish clues to the condition of the population and the effectiveness of management procedures. Not enough is known about the normal ratio of adult to immature individuals in wild populations, but it is obvious that the population should include some old individuals, a number of adults in the prime of life, and a larger number of younger individuals. If the population includes a preponderance of older individuals, and the younger age classes are small or lacking, it

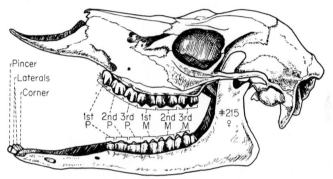

Drawing by N.Y. State Conservation Dept.

Fig. 8-7. Skull of a white-tailed deer. P = premolar; M = molar. The age at which the various teeth appear is quite consistent, as is the rate of wear.

may indicate that reproduction is not satisfactory, or that mortality of the young is too great, or that natural mortality is not sufficient to remove the older individuals—and the population is therefore top-heavy with these animals. If there are many young individuals but relatively few in the older age classes, it may indicate that mortality is so heavy that a small number survive to old age, and that reduction of the kill is necessary. It will be readily apparent that these facts are of importance to those charged with the responsibility of establishing seasons and bag limits.

To determine the age composition of a population, one must first learn to recognize the various age classes. In many groups, techniques are available by which biologists can do this. The scales of fishes show rings (Fig. 8-6) which permit determination of age in much the same manner as do the rings of trees. In mammals, tooth eruption and tooth wear are most often used (Fig. 8-7). In birds, the color and condition of plumage may help, and in some groups the bursa of Fabricius, a blind sac within the cloaca, may be measured as a criterion of age. By checking the large numbers of specimens which are taken each year by hunters and fishermen, large samples of the population may be examined, and a statistically valid picture of the population may be

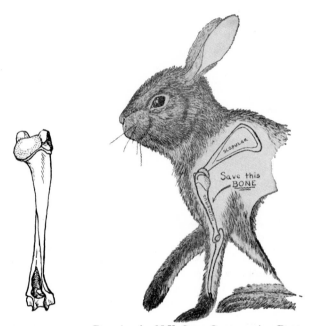

Drawing by N.Y. State Conservation Dept.

Fig. 8-8. To aid in the management of the cottontail rabbit in New York, hunters collected the humerus from thousands of rabbits killed during the hunting season, thus helping determine age composition of the population.

obtained. Such knowledge leads to the possibility of intelligent management procedures (Fig. 8-8).

Sex Composition. Sex composition of a population is important because of the varying sexual habits of different species. It is believed that in most species the sex ratio at birth is about one male to one female. By adulthood, the ratio may change in favor of the females because of differential mortality caused by differences in habits, color, or some other characteristic. In polygamous species, a preponderance of females is not harmful, and, indeed, is probably quite normal. In such species, it is usual for females to be protected by law from hunting, if they can be distinguished from males in the field. This type of regulation, under conditions of heavy hunting pressure, may lead to an oversupply of females, and an occasional season during which females may be taken is often necessary. The white-tailed deer of the eastern part of the continent is an example of this situation. In general, only antlered bucks can be taken, and those with large antlers are most desired by hunters. In this way females (except for the rare individual which abnormally develops horns) and the young of the year are protected from destruction by the hunters. After many years of such regulations, field studies may show a population in which females and young are extremely abundant and older males are very few in number. In such cases it may be necessary to declare an open season on antlerless deer in order to bring the sex ratio to normal proportions.

POPULATION BEHAVIOR

Population behavior is another of the important clues to wise management of natural populations. The behavior of individual animals is considered in some detail in Chap. 9. We are concerned here, however, with the behavioral characteristics which cannot be seen in a single individual, but which are nonetheless characteristic of the species.

Plant Distribution. We do not usually consider plants as possessing behavior as such, but some aspects of plant life are perhaps best considered under this general heading. This is particularly true of the various ways in which plants affect one another and of the various conditions under which they are able to thrive and multiply. Some plant species are usually found as closely spaced colonies over large areas. The spruce bogs, the cattail marshes, the white pine forests, may include extensive areas where one species is obviously dominant. Other species may occur in small groups or singly throughout a range of thousands of square miles. In some cases this is the result of the manner in which seed is spread. The seeds of cattail, blowing across a suitable habitat, will rapidly populate the entire available area around the parent plants. Those of the sticktight and the burdock are carried about by animals, attached to their fur; the seeds are dropped at some distance from the parent plant in an entirely random manner. Seeds of the jewelweed are thrown a short distance from the parent plant in all directions by a coiled-spring arrangement within the seed pod. In this way the surrounding area is soon saturated with seeds which will germinate the following year. But the dispersion of this plant is not so rapid as that of wind-spread species.

The occurrence of individual plants in relation to each other may also be concerned with intraspecific tolerance. Some species of trees and other plants will not grow in the dense shade of their own kind, and such trees must of necessity be scattered. Others will grow only under the protective canopy of adult trees of their own species, and we find pure stands of such species. Such tolerance or intolerance is, of course, not active, as it is in animals. It may be based simply on physiological characteristics of the seedling plant. But its result is the same as that found in populations of animals. Many of the peculiarities of succession (see Chap. 5) are the result of tolerance or intolerance of certain plant species.

Animal Distribution. Animal populations differ from most plant populations in their motility. It is not necessary for the young of most animals to stay within the neighborhood of the parents throughout life, or to be blown about by the vicissitudes of a chance breeze. Animals are moved by a different, less tangible, but no less real force, which we term instinct. The way in which animal populations are distributed depends upon the same factors as those which determine plant distribution, but animals stay in a particular place or move to a new place primarily under the promptings of instinct. The problems of instinctive behavior are discussed in detail in Chap. 9, and we need not dwell upon them here. We shall discuss, however, certain aspects of instinctive behavior which have to do with population dynamics. Most of these behavioral traits are concerned with socialization.

Animal Aggregations. Most kinds of animals form temporary aggregations at some time: for migration, as in salmon, many birds (Fig. 8-9), and some mammals; for breeding, as at the mating grounds of prairie chickens; for feeding, as in the yards of deer; for nesting, as in the double-crested cormorant (Fig. 8-10). Animals may also band together as family groups, or have a variety of other reasons for temporary aggregations. These aggregations are usually based, at such times, on an instinctive desire for association with other individuals of the species. Often they are intimately concerned with the survival of the individual and of the species.

The importance of this type of behavior to the field biologist is tremendous. In the case of species which are hunted, an open season at the time of such aggregations may be dangerous to the survival of the species. The extinction of the passenger pigeon was probably brought about mainly by exploitation while they were in breeding

Photo by N.Y. State Conservation Dept.

Fig. 8-9. Migratory aggregation: Canada geese flock together for the northward flight, though they nest in pairs.

colonies and migratory flocks. Spring shooting at the mating grounds of the prairie chickens and migratory associations of shore birds once threatened these species with extinction. Biologists who must determine seasons, bag limits, and other hunting regulations must carefully consider these aspects of population behavior.

Some animal aggregations may result in better protection from predation because of increased alertness or the strength of numbers. The marauding bands of crows, with at least one member always on watch for enemies, are less vulnerable to attack than any one individual. On the other hand, concentrations of prey species usually attract predators, which may leave to return again and again, or may remain nearby. Wolves hang about the fringes of caribou herds, alert to secure the weak or foolish. Lions follow the great herds of African grazing ani-

Photo by Ralph S. Palmer

Fig. 8-10. A breeding aggregation: Double-crested cormorants nest in colonies like this, often in great numbers.

mals, cutting off and devouring an occasional individual. Hawks and owls haunt the roosting areas of birds and bats, snatching such prey as they can catch unaware. Predation of this kind usually succeeds only in reducing the population to the normal carrying capacity of the environment and is rarely a significant factor in the survival of a species. To the sportsman, however, predation simply means that these animals are taking game which he himself would like to have, and for this reason sportsmen in general are unable to take a detached attitude. In game populations, of course, sportsmen themselves are often the most important predators.

Although temporary aggregations are best known from their appearance in large species, or species important to man in one way or another, they occur in many other groups. To the student of natural history, it is important to know when and where such aggregations occur, not only as a part of his understanding of the life of the animal, but for other reasons as well. The collector will be able to secure specimens more easily and in greater numbers if he can find such gatherings. The student of population movements and dynamics will be able to take, mark, and study large numbers of individuals, thus improving the chance of future recoveries which will add to his knowledge of the species. The student of behavior will find many interesting facets of behavior which involve more than one animal and which can thus be observed only when the group is together. When the animals are dispersed in pairs, singly, or in family units, the work of the field biologist is in some ways much more difficult, and many important facts cannot be ascertained at all.

Animal Societies. Many animals live in association with other members of their species in a more or less closely knit society. These societies are characterized by permanence, existing throughout the year and throughout the lives of all the individuals which make up the group. The societies are, in many cases, essential to the life of the individual and thus to the existence of the species. Such groups may be very complex, based on a rigid system of order and on the precise, instinctive actions of the individuals involved.

Because human society is such an important aspect of our existence, these societies of lower animals have been of great interest to biologists and nonbiologists alike for many centuries. The Biblical writer who suggested that lazy men might well consider the ways of the ant had evidently noted that insect's bustling activity. Other philosophers such as Maeterlinck have been fascinated by the seemingly intelligent operation of a hive of bees.

Animal societies show tremendous variation in rigidity and complexity. The classic examples of fixed societies are those of insects, notably the ants, bees, and termites. In these societies, there is often a rigid caste system, each individual largely restricted to certain duties such as fighting, gathering food, or reproduction. The most extreme example of this is perhaps the beehive, where division of labor is extremely complex. Only one female, the queen, is capable of reproduction. The males, or drones, are of no value to the colony except for fertilization of the queen, and they are driven away eventually by the workers of the hive, which are sterile females and which perform all the essential duties of the colony. During the summer they gather food and store it for the long winter. Certain individuals sit at the entrance to the hive and air-condition the interior with buzzing wings. In winter, the bees are active enough to keep the hive above freezing, although they are doing nothing except producing heat. The life of each individual is completely subordinated to the life of the group.

Such control of behavior is not brought about by external laws, as would be necessary if a human society of like nature were to be formed. Instinct governs all matters in the lives of these animals, and the concept of individual liberty, which has been so important in human life, has no place in their societies. For this reason the student of human populations is likely to find more rewarding the study of less stereotyped societies, especially those of such higher animals as birds and mammals.

In these societies, there are many similarities to our own, though without the basis of law, which is so important to us. Almost every animal society, in these higher groups, has a hierarchical order, with leaders and followers. Those near the top of the order are dominant over all those below them. Since this phenomenon has been studied extensively in birds, where dominance is expressed by pecking, it has been spoken of as the *peck order*, but it occurs in other groups besides birds. Unlike some human societies, these social orders permit an individual to improve his status in the social order under certain circumstances. It is, however, extremely difficult to do so, for in addition to the physical inferiority which largely controls the peck order, psychological factors apparently play an important part. An individual near the lower end of the scale may grow to be physically capable of dominating some individuals at higher levels, but long periods of deferring to these animals evidently instill a feeling of inferiority which may prevent him from assuming a higher place in the social order.

Physical ability may also have much to do with the reproductive success of the individual in colonial species, or in those individuals who gather together during the breeding season. The older and stronger males may gather around them all of the available females, successfully driving off weaker males who are quite capable of breeding. This occurs in seals and in many other polygamous animals which form breeding aggregations.

Although man has been long considered a creature apart, biologists have recently come to suspect that human societies, though based to some degree on intelligent cooperation, may be subject to some of the controlling factors which act on animal societies. Many feel that a clear understanding of the structure, functions, and limitations of animal societies will help us in understanding human social problems. As an example of this, Calhoun (1952) pointed out that in a society of Norway rats, with abundant feed but limited space, the population became stabilized at a level well below that which would have resulted in starvation, apparently due to the direct and indirect results of intraspecific strife. In view of the rapidly rising human population and the rapidly shrinking space per person, students of population dynamics may well ponder the question which this study brings out: Will the human population level off at a point well below the starvation level, or will the numbers continue to rise until population outruns subsistence?

Laboratory biologists have studied the growth, development, and decline of populations under controlled conditions in an attempt to ascribe causes to the various phenomena which have been observed in nature. Such studies should lead to more critical field studies, although it is difficult to determine causes in the field when so many factors are uncontrolled. Nonetheless, much can be learned which will aid in the interpretation of laboratory results, and, conversely, many phenomena will be noted which may be further explained by later work in the laboratory. The importance of such studies is well expressed by Calhoun (1952): "We must have the courage and foresight to depart from the laboratory in its customarily accepted sense, and take with us into the broader laboratory of field situations our extensive knowledge derived from analytical studies of the individual and small groups."

It is necessary for the field biologist to understand and utilize the modern concepts of population dynamics which have been discussed in this chapter. At the minimum, he is likely to be required to make census studies of plant and animal populations, prepare statistical analyses of his results, and draw conclusions from his data. The study of populations is one of the currently fruitful avenues of research, and promises greater results for the future, when field biologists have gathered the preliminary data on which fundamental studies can be based.

REFERENCES CITED

ADAMS, LOWELL. 1951. Confidence limits for the Peterson or Lincoln index used in animal population studies. *J. Wildl. Mgt.*, 15:13–19.

BLAIR, W. FRANK. 1953. Population dynamics of rodents and other small mammals. *Adv. Genet.*, 5:1–41.

CALHOUN, JOHN B. 1952. The social aspects of population dynamics. *J. Mammal.*, 33:139–159.

CHRISTIAN, JOHN J. 1950. The adreno-pituitary system and population cycles in mammals. *J. Mammal.*, 31:247–259.

COLE, L. C. 1951. Population cycles and random oscillations. *J. Wildl. Mgt.*, 15:233–252.

DICE, LEE R. 1941. Methods for estimating populations of mammals. *J. Wildl. Mgt.*, 5:398–407.

FRANK, FRITZ. 1957. The causality of microtine cycles in Germany. *J. Wildl. Mgt.*, 21:113–121.

GODFREY, GILLIAN K. 1954. Tracing field voles (*Microtus agrestis*) with a Geiger-Muller counter. *Ecol.*, 35:5–10.

GRANGE, WALLACE B. 1949. "The Way to Game Abundance." Charles Scribner's Sons, New York. xxiii and 365 pp.

HALL, E. RAYMOND. 1927. An outbreak of house mice in Kern County, California. *Univ. Calif. Pub. Zool.*, 30:189–203.

HAYNE, DON W. 1949. Calculation of size of home range. *J. Mammal.*, 30:1–18.

HEWITT, OLIVER (ED.). 1954. Symposium on cycles in animal populations. *J. Wildl. Mgt.*, 18:1–112.

HOWARD, H. E. 1920. "Territory in Bird Life." John Murray, London. xiii and 308 pp.

LEOPOLD, ALDO. 1933. "Game Management." Charles Scribner's Sons, New York. xxi and 481 pp.

PALMGREN, PONTUS. 1949. Some remarks on the short-term fluctuations in the numbers of northern birds and mammals. *Oikos*, 1:114–121.

SCHUMACHER, F. X., AND R. A. CHAPMAN. 1948. "Sampling Methods in Forestry and Range Management." Duke University School of Forestry, Bulletin 7, Durham, N. C.

Siivonen, Lauri, and Jukka Koskimies. 1955. Population fluctuations and the lunar cycle. *Papers on Game Research*, 14:1–22.

Stickel, Lucille F. 1954. A comparison of certain methods of measuring ranges of small mammals. *J. Mammal.*, 35:1–15.

SUGGESTED READING

Allee, W. C. 1951. "Cooperation among Animals." Abelard-Schuman, Inc., Publishers, New York.

Andrewartha, H. G., and L. C. Birch. 1954. "The Distribution and Abundance of Animals." University of Chicago Press, Chicago.

Elton, Charles. 1942. "Voles, Mice and Lemmings: Problems in Population Dynamics." Oxford University Press, London. 496 pp.

Lack, David. 1954. "The Natural Regulation of Animal Numbers." Oxford University Press, New York.

Michener, C. D., and M. H. Michener. 1951. "American Social Insects." D. Van Nostrand Company, Inc., Princeton, N.J.

CHAPTER 9

PRINCIPLES OF
BEHAVIOR STUDY

Beware instinct . . . Instinct is a great matter.
Shakespeare, "King Henry IV," Part I, Act II, Sc. 4

Have you ever wondered why your dog turns around several times before lying down? Or why a cat twitches its tail when annoyed? Or why a robin sings so loudly just before sunset on a summer day? If you have thought about such things as these, you have wondered about one of the most interesting and controversial subjects in the entire field of modern biology—animal behavior.

Man's close association with and dependence on animals made their behavior a matter of intense interest to primitive humans; and where primitive hunting cultures exist today, this subject is still an essential part of the education of every young man. The drawings found in caves occupied by early humans and the similar kind of art common to contemporary primitive cultures indicate the importance of animals in the lives of these hunters. They also indicate a sharpness of observation which suggests that primitive peoples knew, and know, a great deal about animals. Such knowledge is necessary to survival. Whether it is the Eskimo, stalking the seal and walrus in the frozen wastes of the Arctic, or the Bushman, tracking the wallaby in the bush country of Australia, the problem of understanding animals is a very important one.

In our culture, knowledge of animal behavior is rarely a matter of life and death, except to big-game hunters. But it has great interest to

220

sportsmen and nature lovers, as well as to biologists. The biologist's interest in behavior may be a purely scientific one, but the fruits of his labor are useful in many ways. To the taxonomist, behavior may be significant evidence about the evolutionary relationships of certain groups in which the morphological evidence is not clear-cut. For example, Lorenz (1941) revised the classification of the dabbling ducks largely on the basis of their courtship behavior. To the wildlife biologist, knowledge of animal behavior is a basic necessity for intelligent management. The quail, which lives in coveys in the open field, must be managed in a different manner from the ruffed grouse, which lives a more solitary life in the forests. The psychologist, the anatomist, the physiologist, all profit in their respective fields from a knowledge of behavior.

It may be well to begin our discussion of animal behavior with a few definitions, so that the terms we are to use in subsequent pages will be clear and familiar. We must first settle on a definition for behavior. Emlen (1955) defined behavior as "the means by which an animal maintains its relation with the environment," thus stressing the functional importance of behavior. This definition immediately appeals to the field biologist because of its recognition of the environment, but it can be stated more simply that behavior *includes all the acts performed by an animal.* Whether an animal is eating, sleeping, fighting, or mating, its activities are a part of its behavior. It is an animal's way of reacting to its environment.

Causes of Behavior. Behavior is caused by various things within or around the animal which stimulate it to action. These causal agents are called *stimuli.* A stimulus which comes from outside the animal, and which the animal can perceive only through the external sense organs, is an external stimulus. It is something which the animal can see, hear, smell, taste, or feel. The approach of friend or foe, the smell of prey, the falling darkness, or the approaching daybreak—all these and many more may influence behavior.

Other stimuli are *internal,* resulting from changes in the physiology of the animal. Most such stimuli are brought about by the release into the blood stream of powerful chemicals known as hormones, secreted by the various endocrine glands of the body. Fear, anger, hunger, sexual desire may cause internal activity which will result in a particular type of behavior. It can be seen, then, that the two types of stimuli are not separate phenomena, but that they work together to control the animal's behavior. An external stimulus, in the form of a potential mate, may bring about increased hormonal activity within an animal, leading to courtship behavior. Indeed, it is often difficult to determine the type of stimulus which has caused a particular kind of behavior. We know that most dogs hunt, but the cause is not always clear. A dog may hunt because he is hungry (an internal stimulus only); or because he sees a rabbit, even though he has just eaten (the rabbit being an external stimulus which no doubt causes internal changes as well); or, in the absence of either prey or hunger, because of some internal stimulus which causes predatory animals to go through the actions of hunting even when they are well fed. Furthermore, the particular manner in which the dog hunts represents part of his behavior and varies among the various breeds of dogs.

Types of Behavior. It is not easy, then, to categorize behavior according to the type of stimulus which will bring it about. Biologists for many years have divided behavior into categories on a different basis. *Instinctive behavior* (called by various authors "innate," "native," and "unlearned" behavior) is defined as *behavior which is determined by genetical factors and unmodifiable by circumstances*. On the other hand, *learned behavior* may be defined as *that part of the activity pattern which is developed as the result of experience*. Although this distinction sounds clear and decisive, there are certain difficulties which have led to confusion. The student who is studying an animal, particularly in the field, cannot always tell whether a specific act has been learned or whether it is instinctive. We all use the term "instinct" rather loosely. We say, "I disliked the man instinctively," or, "When I hear a gun, I instinctively duck," whereas both these actions are actually the result of learning. In scientific work, we cannot use the term in so inexact a manner. Biologists have drawn up a series of criteria by which a true instinct can be recognized.

Reiss (1950) gives three criteria for the recognition of what he terms "native" behavior. First, the trait must occur universally in all members of a given species.* Second, it must occur independently of the cultural or social environment of the individual. Third, it must

---

* In some cases, however, as in bees, only certain individuals possess the instinctive behavior which enables them to perform their specific tasks.

occur spontaneously in an animal which, before the trait appeared, had been separated from other members of his own species. Lack (1953) further adds that instinctive behavior must be mainly stereotyped and unmodifiable by circumstances and that it is a complex procedure involving the whole animal.

An example of the difficulty in such problems may be helpful. Juvenile red-backed mice (*Clethrionomys gapperi*) are born blind, and the eyes do not open until about nine to twelve days of age. Before this time, they gain a reasonable degree of equilibrium and make a good deal of noise. If disturbed in the nest, an active young mouse whose eyes are not yet open may sit up on his haunches and box at the disturbing influence with his front paws. Since he has never seen this done, it seems quite certain that such behavior is instinctive. After the eyes are open, or in the case of newly captured adult animals, the approach of a potential enemy will cause the mouse to poke its nose cautiously through the top of the nest to sniff and peer around. This activity may be the result of learning, perhaps even the result of captivity. Without careful experimentation, it is impossible to know.

Prenatal Learning. Another difficulty in the recognition of instinctive behavior is the fact that some learning occurs during prenatal or embryonic stages. Such behavior can only be recognized after intensive study of the development of each species, and such studies have been made for only a few animals. Kuo (1932) concluded that the pecking motion of the chick, which had been thought to be instinctive, was actually learned by a series of neck-stretching exercises which take place as the embryo develops, probably beginning as reflexes. Probably many acts now thought to be instinctive will be found to fall into this category.

Reflexes. Some behavioral acts, based on a particular arrangement of muscles and nerves, are called reflexes. A *reflex act* is always elicited by a particular stimulus, and never without such a stimulus. A simple reflex is innate in the sense of being built into the body organization of the animal, but behaviorists do not consider a reflex to be synonymous with an instinctive act (see p. 225 for further discussion of the two types of behavior). A *conditioned reflex* is learned, and results from association of a particular stimulus with a particular event. Pavlov, the Russian physiologist who discovered this type of reflex, was able to induce secretion of saliva in dogs by ringing a bell. The conditioned reflex developed after repeated occasions at which Pavlov rang the bell while food was offered to the dogs.

Since animal behavior is concerned with the animal's embryonic stages, with its anatomy, with its physiology, as well as with the more obvious external causes, it can be approached from several directions. The explanation of behavior requires the cooperation of behavior students in several different branches of biology. Most of these workers approach the problem in one of three ways. Psychologists are concerned with learning and with learned behavior; physiologists and anatomists with the structure and function of the nervous and endocrine systems in their effects on behavior; ethologists with observation and interpretation of behavioral patterns, placing particular emphasis on instinctive behavior.

Psychological Study of Behavior. Perhaps the largest group of behaviorists includes the psychologists. Their experiments are designed to show how learning occurs and how much learning ability each species of animal possesses. Such work must of necessity be done in the laboratory, with captive or domesticated animals and with elaborate experimental setups. Most of the work an animal psychology has therefore been done on a small number of species adapted to such an approach. The rat, the chimpanzee, the domestic pigeon, the dog, and the chicken have been extensively studied. The facts learned in this way are of great value in interpreting the behavior of animals under natural conditions and are thus of interest to the field biologist, though animal psychology remains for the most part a laboratory discipline. This knowledge has not been applied as fully as it might be, perhaps because psychologists are reluctant to apply their experimental data to the less disciplined field of uncontrolled nature, and many field biologists lack the background to use these data. In recent years, however, efforts have been made to introduce the study of animal psychology into the field (Schneirla, 1950) to supplement laboratory studies.

Physiological-Anatomical Study of Behavior. The real secrets of behavior are, of course, locked within the body of the animal itself. To secure fundamental information about the structures associated with behavior and the ways in which they function, anatomists and physiologists have made important experimental studies. The nervous system, which receives and transmits stimuli, and the endocrine system, which produces the hormones responsible for certain aspects of behavior, are of special interest to these workers. The study of the development of the nervous system, and experimental tampering with it (Weiss, 1941), have produced much information about the development and functioning of behavior. A thorough summary of knowledge and theory in this field is presented in the Symposium of the Society for Experimental Biology (1950).

Ethological Study of Behavior. A third group of biologists approaches the subject from the standpoint of behavior under natural conditions, and with particular stress on instinct. Uncontrolled field conditions often lead the observer to an idea which can then be experimentally checked, and study of behavior in this way has come to be known as *ethology.* The ethologist emphasizes study of the act in itself along with the patterns of acts associated with a particular aspect of the animal's life, in an attempt to discover external stimuli which bring about the behavior being explored, and to deduce something about the underlying mechanisms and the manner in which they function. Since this is the approach to behavior which is most widely used by field biologists, and since it is the center of much research and some controversy, the concepts and terms of ethology will require definition and explanation.

THE RELEASER CONCEPT. Animals, according to leading ethologists, are born with certain predetermined (innate) behavior patterns which are of genetic origin. Their appearance may depend upon the proper conjunction of the proper stimuli, or the development of the animal to a specific age, but the patterns are "genetically coded" (Thorpe, 1954) and are constant for a particular species. These innate or instinctive behavior patterns may be distinguished from reflexes, however, in that *they are not always dependent upon a specific stimulus.* Ordinarily they result from a particular kind of stimulus which is highly specific, just as a reflex does. This kind of stimulus—a property of the stimulating object which can affect the external sense organs of the receiving animal—is called a *releaser.* An example may help to clarify the meaning of this term.

Young herring gulls are fed by their parents when they peck at the tip of the parent's beak. Tinbergen (1949) has shown that the young birds respond with the begging reaction not to the beak or to the parent but to a red spot prominently situated near the end of the lower mandible (Fig. 9-1). By the use of models, Tinbergen was able to prove that a red spot, in the same position as that on the parent's beak, was the most effective releaser for this activity. Spots of other colors were less effective, and a bill without a spot brought about begging activity in only a few individuals. Changes in the color of the bill and head indicated that these characteristics were not important in eliciting the reaction, but that the red spot was the releaser of the food-seeking reaction.

Other releasers may bring about sexual behavior, e.g., the red coloration of certain male fishes during the breeding season; nesting behavior in birds, e.g., the shape and coloration of eggs; and any other aspect of an animal's inherited activity pattern. Indeed, some students of behavior believe that all social aspects of instinctive behavior, that is those concerned with another member of the species, and many nonsocial activities as well, are controlled by releasers.

Redrawn from Tinbergen, 1951

Fig. 9-1. A red spot on the lower mandible of the herring gull's beak releases the pecking activity of the chick.

Thus far, an instinctive reaction set off by a releaser does not seem to be different from the previously mentioned reflex. Some years ago, a school of behaviorists held that *all* behavior is made up of reflexes. Instinctive reactions, however, have one peculiarity which separates them from reflexes. If the releaser for a particular act does not appear for long periods, a normally inadequate stimulus may cause the act to be performed; or in some cases it may be performed with no recognizable stimulus. Lorenz (1935) coined the word *Leerlaufreaktion* for this phenomenon. Tinbergen (1951) has rendered this in English as "going off in a vacuum."

This peculiar fact has caused ethologists to suggest the existence of some specific structure controlling each instinctive reaction. These postulated structures are called *innate releasing mechanisms* (IRM's). When the proper stimulus occurs, it is believed that the IRM which is affected by it permits nervous energy to flow through the proper channels and to bring about the specific act which is elicited by this stimulus. When the act is long deferred, because of a lack of the stimulus, it is postulated that reaction-specific energy is built up in the nervous system. If this energy continues to be built up and the releaser for the IRM which blocks its discharge does not appear, the reaction-specific energy may overflow the IRM, and be discharged as a *Leerlaufreaktion*. A captive bird, for example, may perform such complex behavior as the courtship behavior, or catching, killing, and eating imaginary insects, even though the usual stimulus is absent.

DISPLACEMENT BEHAVIOR. Occasionally a bird reacts to obvious stimuli with a type of behavior which has no apparent relationship to the stimuli and which is completely unsuitable to the circumstances. This is called *displacement behavior*, and is believed to indicate a conflict between two opposing drives caused by different stimuli. Unable to decide upon a course of action, the animal may perform some quite unrelated act.

When two birds are fighting, one may suddenly abandon the fight and perform some unrelated act, such as picking at food or preening the feathers (Fig. 9-2). In such a situation, it is suggested that the bird is stimulated to fight and stimulated to flee, with the result that it does neither. Tinbergen (1951) has indicated that displacement behavior may also occur when a drive such as the sexual drive is particularly strong but the external stimuli necessary for its release are missing. When a male animal is attempting to mate with an unresponsive female, he may turn, in what seems to our minds to be frustration, to some completely unrelated activity. The slightest encouragement from the female, however, is likely to result in resumption of the courtship by the male.

IMPRINTING. Some peculiar reactions of animals defied explanation until modern ethologists recognized the process known as *imprinting*. At a certain stage in the life of an animal, a particular stimulus may fix, in that animal's behavior pattern, a certain reaction. This reaction will, for the life of that individual, or at least for long periods, result whenever the stimulus which first elicited it is present. This same stimulus will have no effect on other individuals of the same species unless they too have been subjected to it at the appropriate time. *This shows that the imprinted reaction is learned rather than innate*, although it may well depend on some innate mechanism which is acted upon during the imprinting process. The readiness of newly born or hatched animals to accept a foster parent, even of a different species, results from this phenomenon. At a certain age, which varies in different species, any object which meets certain rather specific requirements

Fig. 9-2. Displacement activity in the herring gull. The bird on the left is gathering nesting material rather than fending off the attack of the other bird.

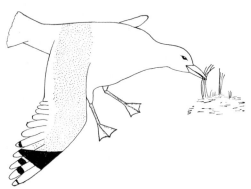

Redrawn from Tinbergen, 1951

will be accepted as a parent, and will be followed with unshakable devotion so long as the young animal has any need of parental relationships. Ramsay and Hess (1954) have shown that a newly hatched mallard duckling will accept as its parent anything which comes within its range of hearing making a ducklike quack. Obviously, under natural circumstances, this is almost certain to be its mother, and so the mechanism is more or less foolproof. But if another duck, or other object making a similar noise, is introduced to it at the proper stage, that object will be accepted and followed until the duckling reaches the age of independence. This phenomenon explains the many cases of domesticated animals which appear to regard a human as their parent.

It is common for pet owners to say, "My dog thinks he's a person," or some such statement. Actually, of course, the dog is not thinking any such thing. He is simply reacting to people as though they were members of the same species. Lorenz (1952), in an amusing and instructive book, tells of his experiences with animals of several species which he taught to regard him as a parent or species mate.

Imprinting may be accomplished by auditory stimuli, visual stimuli, or by other means. The fact that such a phenomenon exists explains the difficulty of training or taming an animal if it has reached a certain critical age before it is approached.

REACTION CHAINS. The examples we have given thus far have been concerned with relatively simple and specific reactions. Many social activities of animals, however, follow a regular and complex pattern of events. Each act of one individual leads to another act by the other. This in turn releases another activity of the first individual, and so on. Such a *reaction chain* is perhaps best typified by the courtship and mating behavior of certain animals. An example is offered by the courtship of the three-spined stickleback as described by Tinbergen (1942).

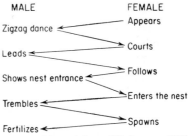

Adapted from Tinbergen, 1951

Fig. 9-3. Diagrammatic representation of the courtship activities of the three-spined stickleback.

The male stickleback builds a nest on the bottom of the pond and waits nearby for a female to appear. When a female with a swollen abdomen, indicative of breeding condition, approaches the territory of the male, he commences a zigzag movement which shows off his red underside to advantage. If the female is ready to mate, she responds by swimming directly at the male. He then turns and swims rapidly toward the previously constructed nest. The female, evidently attracted by this movement, follows him, and he puts his head into the nest entrance. This invitation encourages the female to enter the nest, and when she has done so, the male begins a quivering movement. The female then begins to spawn, whereupon the male sheds his sperms over the newly laid eggs. These reactions are shown diagrammatically in Fig. 9-3.

The complexity of such reaction chains is important in preventing the mating of individuals of closely related species which might be genetically compatible. Although hybridization does occur in nature (see p. 45), it is usually between species whose courtship pattern is similar. Otherwise the activity would be broken off before the actual mating occurred.

At the end of every reaction chain, or as a result of each instinctive act, an event occurs which satisfies the animal's immediate need. Thus the courtship behavior described above results in the laying and fertilization of eggs. Fighting behavior results in the defeat of one individual, which seems to satisfy both. These final acts of a chain, such as coition, eating, or flight, were called by Craig (1918) *consummatory acts*.

In most cases, these consummatory acts have been preceded by other activities which Craig called *appetitive behavior*—behavior which puts the animal in a position or state favorable to the satisfaction of its needs. Under the influence of stimuli, probably mostly internal, the animal begins the appetitive behavior. It must be stressed that this is done by instinct, not by reasoning. A male bird does not reason that its chances of obtaining a mate will be better if it chooses a high perch and sings loudly. Yet this is the most effective means of advertising his availability and of attracting a female. The male bird is probably unaware of his desire for a mate until her appearance releases the next reaction of courtship. His singing simply announces to others of his species that he has chosen a territory, as well as announcing his sexual vigor and readiness for mating.

THE VALUE OF INSTINCT. Instinctive responses to stimuli have a part in every aspect of the animal's life and, particularly, in every relationship with others of its own kind. The sudden onslaught of a bird defending his territory (Fig. 9-4) seems to frighten his opponent and often results in a victory without injury to either animal. The tendency to depend on protective coloration in escaping is evident in some animals, while others, equally well adapted for protection if they remained still, flee at the approach of an enemy. The woodcock (Fig. 9-5) will remain in its hiding place or on its nest until it is almost stepped on, and will then rocket away; or, if nesting, will flutter away as though it had been injured. The cottontail rabbit will crouch in its lair until it is almost literally kicked out of it. The killdeer, on the contrary, with protective coloration almost as effective in a field as is that of the woodcock in the swamp, will slip off the nest while the observer is still far distant and attempt to lead him away with a broken-wing act. Out of the breeding season, killdeers are equally skittish and often frustrate the bird watcher by taking off with loud cries and

Drawing by H. Wayne Trimm

Fig. 9-4. Defense of territory by a bird leads to many territorial battles, which are almost always won by the bird upon whose territory the battle takes place.

causing other normally approachable shore birds to depart before the observer can study them.

The survival value of behavior patterns is also shown in the behavior of groups of organisms. Almost everyone is familiar with the fact that bobwhite quail coveys sleep with their heads pointed outward in a circle, and that musk oxen, when attacked by predators, form a circle with the females and young inside and the bulls, with their heads outward, forming a strong barrier of horns. Flocks of starlings normally fly in a loose pattern (Fig. 9-6), but when they are attacked by a hawk they form a tight group, maneuvering as one bird to escape the enemy (Fig. 9-7). Since the hawk cannot attack one starling in such a group without danger of colliding with others, he cannot effectively attack the group, but must follow until one bird gets sufficiently far from the flock to permit assault.

Photo by Allen H. Benton

Fig. 9-5. A woodcock, *Philohela minor*, on the nest. Protective coloration is obvious. This bird continued to brood until touched by the hand of the photographer.

While instinctive behavior is adapted to meet the usual situations which confront an animal, it may at times lead the animal into trouble. Since instinctive responses are not reasoned and do not vary with the circumstances, they are not always suitable. Tinbergen (1951) relates how herring gull chicks instinctively seek shelter when the adult bird gives an alarm call. While he was observing a gull family from a blind, Tinbergen disturbed the adult bird, which gave the alarm call. The chicks, seeking the nearest shelter, ran directly to his blind and crouched at his feet. In this case, of course, no harm was done, but it is obvious that there was no survival value in the response of the chicks in this particular situation.

DIRECTIVE ACTIVITY. At the higher levels of animal life, as might be expected, some parts of behavior which are instinctive in lower animals are replaced by *intelligent* or *directive activity*. This is, of course, most noticeable in man and the higher primates, but it occurs in some degree among many other animals. Unless we can prove experimentally, therefore, that a particular activity is performed without reasoning or foresight, we ought not to assume that it is. We can say that in most cases an animal cannot clearly understand its needs or devise a means of satisfying them. Conversely, we must be careful not to attribute intelligent or directive behavior to animals without scientific and experimental evidence to support our contention.

"HUMANIZING" ANIMAL BEHAVIOR. The tendency to attribute human characteristics to animals seems to be a universal one, and this has led men of all times to interpret animal behavior in terms of human emotions. Today this approach results in the use of such terms as "reproachfulness" or "gratitude" with reference to some aspects of animal behavior which quite likely have no relationship to such emotions as we know them. Early settlers in the country had a charming legend about the chimney swift which illustrates the lengths to which this kind of thinking may be carried. The swifts nest in unused chimneys, building small nests of sticks glued together with saliva and plastered to the walls of the chimney. Since the nests are small and shallow, it often happens that a young swift, before it is able to fly well, falls from the nest and cannot escape back up the chimney. When such birds appeared in the fireplace of a settler's house, it was attributed to gratitude on the part of the parents for the hospitality granted them. The young bird was cast down the chimney, it was believed, as a sort of rent payment for the use of the chimney. Although this may seem absurdly simple-minded to sophisticated modern minds, many of us still apply much the same sort of thinking to our analyses of animal behavior.

This is not meant to imply that animals other than man do not have emotions. Anyone who has seen a dog terrified by a thunderstorm is not likely to doubt that animals experience fear. But we cannot determine the precise emotions of animals with which we cannot communi-

Redrawn from Tinbergen, 1951

Fig. 9-6. Normal flight pattern of the European starling.

cate, and we therefore have no logical reason to attribute to them emotions similar to our own.

CRITICISMS OF THE ETHOLOGICAL APPROACH. This brief summary of the field of ethology is sufficient to indicate the many poorly understood problems of animal behavior. Ethology is one of the youngest branches of biology, but it has been widely adopted by field biologists, and in Europe has resulted in the publication of two journals of behavior, one in German and one in English. In America, where behavior study has been carried on by psychologists, for the most part, there are fewer ethologists, and the theories on which ethological studies are based have received severe criticism. It would be unfair to leave this subject without recognizing the shortcomings of the ethological approach, since much space has been given to indicating its contribu-

Redrawn from Tinbergen, 1951
Fig. 9-7. Flight pattern of European starlings attacked by hawk.

tions to knowledge. Perhaps the most sweeping indictment of ethological theory has been written by Lehrmann (1953), whose objections may be summarized as follows:*

1. Ethologists group widely differing phenomena into the same—and hence inappropriate—categories.

For example, the pecking of the chick and the zigzag dance of the stickleback are both considered innate behavior according to the cri-

---

* These statements are the authors' paraphrase of Lehrmann, since his original wording is couched in scientific terms largely unintelligible to the nonprofessional reader.

teria of the ethologist, while actually they represent quite different kinds of phenomena if considered from the viewpoint of origin.

2. The ideas of instinct and learning in ethological theory are rigid and not in accordance with all the known facts.

Thus the clear distinction which ethologists make between innate and learned behavior simply does not exist. Furthermore, the development of behavior does not occur in the way which ethological theory postulates.

3. Information derived from the behavior of lower organisms is used to explain superficially similar behavior in higher organisms, despite obvious differences in the development of their respective nervous systems.

The way in which examples drawn from insects, fishes, and mammals are used to illustrate the same point is objectionable because the neural organization of these groups is so divergent that they cannot be compared in the same terms.

4. The theoretical structure of the nervous system and its relation to behavioral traits is not supported by present knowledge of neuroanatomy.

The idea of innate releasing mechanisms and reaction-specific energy as built-in units of the nervous system is particularly objectionable. There is no evidence that such things exist in the nervous system, and the postulation of such a complex scheme should be avoided if observed phenomena can be explained in a simpler manner.

5. Behavioral traits and their development are regarded as preformed and unchangeable.

There is evidence to indicate that certain kinds of behavior develop in a way quite different from that postulated by the ethologists. Much so-called innate behavior may vary a great deal according to the experience of the individual animal.

6. By regarding traits as preformed and unchangeable, ethologists discourage inquiry into the actual source and development of the various aspects of behavior.

Simply to say that a particular reaction or pattern of behavior is innate does not explain anything. The student who is content to stop with this conclusion is not really discovering anything significant except that a certain stimulus under a particular set of circumstances will bring about behavior of a certain type in the animal under observation.

Undoubtedly, the work of the ethologists, such as Lorenz in Austria, Tinbergen in Holland, Thorpe in England, and many others, has done much to stimulate a fresh approach to the study of behavior. As is so often the case, controversy has stimulated the proponents of both points of view to greater effort, in order to prove their own beliefs. Out of such controversies comes biological progress. Disagreement may cause some ill feelings, but in the long run it may encourage valuable research, and progress is often most rapid in the most controversial fields.

For the field biologist, there still remains much to do in the study of behavior. The bird lover with a feeding tray under the window may learn much concerning the relationships between birds and about their reactions to specific stimuli. The insect collector may emulate the great Fabre and observe the way in which insects solve the problems of life. The patterns of behavior in courtship and mating are unknown for many mammals and birds and, to an even greater degree, for the lower forms of life. Even though the beginner and the amateur may not feel competent to argue the validity of the various theories of behavior, they can contribute by observing and describing the behavior patterns of poorly known species. After enough of this information is available, we will be much nearer to a theory which explains behavior in a more satisfactory way than is now possible.

REFERENCES CITED

CRAIG, W. 1918. Appetites and aversions as constituents of instincts. *Biol. Bull.*, 34:91–107.

EMLEN, JOHN, JR. 1955. The study of behavior in birds. In "Recent Studies in Avian Biology." University of Illinois Press, Urbana, Ill. pp. 105–153.

KUO, Z. Y. 1932. Ontogeny of embryonic behavior in Aves. IV: The influence of embryonic movements upon the behavior after hatching. *J. Comp. Psych.*, 14:109–122.

LACK, DAVID. 1953. "The Life of the Robin." Penguin Books, Inc., Baltimore. 240 pp.

LEHRMANN, D. S. 1953. A critique of Konrad Lorenz's theory of instinctive behavior. *Quar. Rev. Biol.*, 28:337–363.

LORENZ, KONRAD. 1935. *Der Kumpan in der Umwelt des Vogels. J. für Ornithologie*, 83:137–213, 289–413.

———. 1941. *Vergleichende Bewegungsstudien an Anatinen. J. für Ornithologie*, 89:19–29.

———. 1952. "King Solomon's Ring." Thomas Y. Crowell Company, New York. 202 pp.

RAMSAY, A. O., AND E. H. HESS. 1954. A laboratory approach to the study of imprinting. *Wilson Bull.*, 66:196–206.

REISS, B. F. 1950. The isolation of factors of learning and native behavior in field and laboratory studies. *Annals N.Y. Acad. Sci.*, 51:1093–1102.

SCHNEIRLA, T. C. 1950. The relationship between observation and experiment in the field study of behavior. *Annals N.Y. Acad. Sci.*, 51:1022–1044.

SOCIETY FOR THE STUDY OF EXPERIMENTAL BIOLOGY. 1950. Animal behavior. Symposium no. 4.

THORPE, W. H. 1954. Some concepts of ethology. *Nature*, 174:101–105.

TINBERGEN, N. 1949. *De functie van de rode vlek up de snavel van de zilvermeeuw. Bijdragen tot de Dierkunde*, 28:454–465.

———. 1942. An objectivistic study of the innate behavior of animals. *Biblioth. biotheor.*, 1:39–98.

———. 1951. "The Study of Instinct." Oxford University Press, London. 228 pp.

WEISS, P. 1941. Self-differentiation of the basic patterns of coordination. *Comp. Psych. Monographs*, 17:1–96.

SUGGESTED READING

THORPE, W. H. 1955. "Learning and Instinct in Animals." Harvard University Press, Cambridge, Mass. viii and 493 pp.

TINBERGEN, N. 1953. "Social Behavior in Animals." John Wiley & Sons, Inc., New York. 150 pp.

CHAPTER 10

PRINCIPLES OF THE USE
OF BIOLOGICAL LITERATURE

Index learning turns no student pale,
Yet holds the eel of science by the tail.
Pope, "The Dunciad," Book I

To the professional biologist, close acquaintance with the literature of his sphere of interest is essential. To the amateur, it is often difficult to open the door to this strange never-never land of scientific writing, and many hesitate to attempt it. Admittedly, the literature of biology is complex; particularly it is difficult for the student to maintain touch with progress when he does not have access to a good library. Yet knowledge of the literature is so important that everyone interested in biology should make an effort to become familiar with the important publications in his own field. This chapter is designed to establish a few guideposts in the confusing wilderness of biological literature.

THE DEVELOPMENT OF POPULAR MANUALS

The beginner in field biology today is extremely fortunate in the wealth of material available to him. A century ago, "popular" books in biology were practically nonexistent. Gray's "Manual of Botany" and, a little later, Jordan's "Manual of the Vertebrate Animals of the Northeastern United States" were almost the only books of their kind, and they were not easy to use without specialized training. As popular interest in nature began to create a demand, however, books began to

239

appear which were designed to encourage the amateur in his studies. Because birds were among the first groups to catch the popular fancy, Coues's "Key to North American Birds" and Chapman's "Handbook of Birds of Eastern North America" were among the pioneers in this field. Several generations of budding naturalists were educated with the use of these now venerable books, some of which remain useful today.

The modern field guide, however, is a far cry from even these excellent volumes. Early in this century, pocket-size field guides of various kinds began to appear, some inaccurate and poorly illustrated, others at a higher level of quality. Their success was sufficient to indicate a need for better field guides, and the first of these was not long in coming. The pioneer publishing company in this new realm was G. P. Putnam's Sons, New York. Securing the services of outstanding authorities, including several members of the staff of the American Museum of Natural History, Putnam produced a series of books covering the most popular branches of natural history: ferns, wildflowers, insects, birds, and so on. These small volumes were of a size to fit into the coat pocket for field use, durable enough to stand the rough handling which a field book must inevitably receive, and, for the most part, accurate and authentic.

The Putnam field books were successful to a degree, but not sufficiently so to attract large numbers of publishing companies into the field. A publishing phenomenon was required to bring about a high level of competition in field guides, and this was provided in 1937 by an amateur ornithologist named Roger Tory Peterson. Mr. Peterson was well known among the bird-watching fraternity for his amazing ability to recognize birds in the field, often when only a glimpse of the bird was offered. His secret, when revealed to his friends, resulted in improvement of their own field ability, and they urged Peterson to write a book which would make his system available to all bird students. After some encouragement, he produced such a book and called it "A Field Guide to the Birds." Since he was an accomplished artist, Peterson provided the illustrations as well as the text, and the book appeared, in a small edition, in 1937. This was rapidly exhausted, and subsequent printings, including two revisions, have established this little volume as the bird watcher's Bible. The Peterson system of bird recognition is the basis of most field work in ornithology today and is being extended into other branches of biology as well.

The success of Peterson's book encouraged his publishers, Houghton Mifflin Company, Boston, to begin a series of nature books, with Peterson as the editor. Another series of nature guides was soon started by Doubleday & Company, Inc., New York, and a children's series was initiated by Simon and Schuster, Inc., New York, and by several other juvenile book houses. Today the biologist with an interest in one of the more popular groups, such as birds, mammals, or wildflowers, will find several attractive, up-to-date field guides available; the biologist interested in a less popular group, such as snakes, will be likely to find at least one guide available.

These field guides have reached a high degree of excellence, and are characterized by conciseness of text and beauty and accuracy of illustrations. Some of them contain little material other than that required for identification, while others include information of a more general nature. For general reference material, however, a different type of book is available. Although this type cannot readily be used to identify organisms, it has leaped into prominence in recent years. Part of this development may be due to a British publishing company, William Collins Sons & Co., Ltd., of London. In 1946, Collins began to publish the New Naturalist series, a collection of books on general natural history, and the New Naturalist monographs, each volume of which concerns a single species. These books are written in an entertaining and popular vein, but each is done by an authority and is thus as accurate as human frailty will permit. The early volumes in this series had excellent sales in the United States, and may have encouraged American publishers to look more favorably on manuscripts of similar type. The success of such books as Rachel Carson's "The Sea around Us" emphasized the fact that a ready market existed for good books on natural history. Many of these are now available, and more appear each year. An American Naturalist series, similar in format to the British New Naturalist volumes, has been started by D. Van Nostrand Company, Inc., Princeton, New Jersey, while many other companies have published popular reviews of biological subjects (see Appendix).

A few authors have attempted to produce books which will serve as both identification manuals and general reference books. Some of the best books of this kind are the Handbooks of American Natural History, produced by the Comstock Publishing Associates, Inc., Ithaca, New York, under the editorship of the noted zoologist A. H. Wright. Such books are, of course, too large to be considered pocket guides, but they have received wide acceptance as textbooks in specialized courses and as reference books for both amateur and professional biologists.

THE TECHNICAL LITERATURE OF BIOLOGY

The major concern of the serious biologist, however, is not with the popular books on which he cut his teeth, so to speak, useful though these books may be. Because of the necessary lapse between writing and publication, and because of limitations of space, these books cannot include complete and up-to-date information about any field of biology. It is necessary to advance to more technical literature and to more contemporary sources of information if we are to use successfully the tremendous storehouse of biological literature. Although we cannot list here more than a sample of the many sources of this kind of material, a few of the necessary steps may be pointed out and the technique of a literature review explained.

We may classify sources of information into two groups—books and journals. Like most classifications, this is not a completely clear-cut division, but it will serve our purpose. Books generally present summaries of the information available at the time of writing; but these, of course, are always a year or two out of date when they are published. Books do not normally present previously unpublished data but rather tend to work over data presented elsewhere and to synthesize it for the benefit of the group toward whom the book is aimed. These two handicaps, characteristic of practically all scientific books, are the reasons for the biologist's concern with journal literature. For it is in the journals that we learn what research has recently been completed. We find the more technical aspects of biology presented here, sometimes difficult to comprehend, but always challenging and always broadening our concepts of the world around us. The journals are the medium of communication among the biologists scattered across the continent and around the world. As the student of history sees history being written in the newspapers and magazines, so the student of science sees its advance in the pages of scientific journals.

Biological Journals. Journals come from many sources and are of many different types. Some are published by learned societies or professional groups such as the Wildlife Society, which publishes *Journal of Wildlife Management;* or the Biological Society of Washington, which publishes the *Proceedings of the Biological Society.* Journals of societies are usually published at regular intervals, generally four times a year, and are always of uniform size and format. *The Auk,* for example, journal of the American Ornithologists Union, was started in 1884, and since the second issue its cover design, page size, and format have undergone only minor changes.

Other journals are published sporadically, whenever material and funds for publication are simultaneously available. Many of these come from university biology departments, state museums, experiment stations, or other government organizations. For example, the New York State Museum has a series of publications called Museum Handbooks, and another series known as Museum Bulletins, each of which is published irregularly as funds are available to finance their printing.

The number of scientific serial publications is enormous. One of the leading biological works which summarizes current literature (*Biological Abstracts*) listed, in 1952, some 1,900 journals which were being reviewed. Obviously, the biologist cannot possibly digest one-tenth of these journals, unless he is independently wealthy and willing to spend all of his time in a library. Yet he must make an effort to keep abreast of developments; and, in conducting research, he must be able to find out what is known about his subject. Fortunately, a number of valuable and time-saving aids have been prepared for his use.

Reviewing the Literature. The purpose of a literature survey is to find out all that is known about a particular subject. Usually this is a preliminary to further research, which cannot be done effectively until the background reading has been done. Less commonly, a literature survey is carried out by someone who is merely curious to learn about the subject but has no intention of adding to the knowledge of it himself. Whatever the reason, the mechanics of a literature survey are about the same. In discussing this subject, we shall cover most of the important sources of information, although the approach is somewhat different when one is browsing over current literature from when one is gathering references for a bibliography or literature review.

Let us consider first the manner in which a student might prepare a literature review about a particular subject in biology. The first step, and one which should be taken early in the career of the serious worker, is to secure and become familiar with a good book on the general principles of studying scientific literature. Such books as Trelease (1951), "The Scientific Paper," and Smith (1952), "Guide to the Literature of the Zoological Sciences," are invaluable to the student who wishes to learn to use the tools of his trade with proficiency. Such volumes will give a more complete and detailed discussion of the problems involved than can be given here in one chapter. In particular, they will point the way to publications with more specific information about the area of biology in which a worker is especially interested.

The next step is to secure a good up-to-date reference book which covers the general field in which the worker is interested, and which includes a good list of references. A student of mammals might use Hamilton's (1943) "The Mammals of Eastern United States" or Palmer's (1954) "The Mammal Guide." A bird student might secure the proper volume of Bent's "Life Histories of North American Birds." In a reference of this kind, he would find a general survey of our knowledge, as well as a list of references for further reading.

If the worker is unaware of any reference of this kind, he may find one listed in the "Publishers' Trade List Annual." This fat volume, sometimes called "The Green Pig," because of its size and color, contains a list of all books in print and available from American publishing houses. Since it is revised frequently, it is usually nearly up to date. If it is necessary to seek books not currently in print the "United States Book Catalog" and the "Cumulative Book Index" may be used. These publications cover the years from 1928 to the present time, and are available in most good libraries.

Bibliographies. Bibliographies are never really complete, but they are of great value, and there are hundreds of them in print. Indeed, there is at least one bibliography of bibliographies. Most branches of biology have been treated by bibliographers, though not in every case recently. Nonetheless, such classics as "A Bibliography of Birds," by Reuben Strong, and "Bibliography of Fishes," by Bashford Dean, are of tremendous value and should be familiar to every student in these fields. Often local or state bibliographies are available, such as Joseph Grinnell's "Bibliography of California Ornithology," and these are of special significance to the student of plant and animal distribution.

In many fields of biology, the worker is fortunate enough to have a colleague or a society which keeps an up-to-date bibliography of a particular field. Such is the Torrey card bibliography of botany, prepared by the Torrey Botanical Club since 1894. This card file is available in many libraries throughout the country. The few North American students of fleas are kept up to date by workers at the Rocky Mountain Laboratory at Hamilton, Montana. These Public Health Service employees maintain a continuing file of references to North American fleas and periodically publish an index which summarizes the literature up to that time. The worker who has not yet achieved familiarity with the literature of his field of interest could scarcely do better than to contact a competent authority who might direct him to an available bibliography. It is impossible to list here all of the many biological bibliographies which are available to the student, but a partial list is included in the appendix.

The Reference File. When the student begins to use a bibliography or to seek specific references, he should begin to make notes for his future use. These notes may be kept conveniently on file cards; the 4- by 6-inch or 5- by 8-inch are preferable because more complete information can be kept on these larger cards. On each card, a full citation of the book or paper is written at the top. Often the student who is using a bibliography may wish to make out cards for a large number of publications which he has not yet seen. Unless this fact is indicated in some way, it may cause confusion at a later stage of the study, particularly if the card was filled with information about the article taken from an abstract journal. Some biologists put quotation marks or parentheses in pencil around the titles of articles which they have not yet seen, and then erase these marks when they actually read the reference concerned. This will prevent the unwitting copying of a quotation which one author has quoted from another, a practice which doubles the possibility of error. Every direct quotation should be taken directly from the original source, never cited from a copy in another article.

After the citation, which will include author, year of publication, title, and details of publication (Fig. 10-1), the biologist will write a brief summary of the article in question. This summary, or abstract, should be done with great care, to include all the information which he is likely to need later. Much valuable time may be wasted in going back to the same reference a second, third, and fourth time to copy something which was not written down the first time. Brevity and conciseness are important, but the abstract should include the meat of the paper and must be absolutely accurate. Direct quotations should be indicated as such, and it is wise to quote directly if there is any possibility of misinterpretation.

> Brockner, Winston W. 1954. Harris's sparrow in New York State.
>   Kingbird, 4(2):38.
>   Summarizes recent (since 1948) records of the species in the Northeast, and records an immature from a feeding station at Hamburg, Erie County, Nov. 8 to 11, 1951. Bird was seen by several observers, but was not collected. This is the seventh record from the Northeast since 1948.

Fig. 10-1. A citation of each pertinent paper, with a brief summary of its main points, should be kept on a file card.

From the papers cited in each article, the biologist will secure the names of several other references, some of which will require the facilities of a large library. The average library does not have any quantity of biological journals, and the individual who is not connected with a college or museum may have some difficulty in locating the items he needs. Most college libraries have a good selection of such journals, and the largest of these libraries are among the finest in the world. If the worker is fortunate enough to live near any of the larger universities, he will be able to find most of the journals he needs there. A state library, or the library connected with a large scientific institution, may also be adequate. If it is necessary to travel some distance to reach a good library, the worker would like to know in advance what journals he will be able to find there. This can be done by checking the "Union List of Serials." This large volume lists all serial publications in the libraries of the United States, and tells not only where they may be found, but the volumes available in each library (Fig. 10-2). Obviously, a list of this kind is never completely accurate, since accessions are constantly taking place; but it is a great help when one needs to locate an obscure journal or to check the holdings of a

---

Novitates zoologicae (British Museum, Natural History)
  London. v 1–42, No. 3, 1894–Mr 1948 ‖
  1–41 published by Tring, Eng. Zoological Museum.
  Suspended between O 25 1940 and Mr 1948.
  Superseded by the Museum's Bulletin. Zoology, 1950.

CCC 1–40	KyU
CLSU	LU
CLU	MB
CSt	MnU
CU	NBuB
CU-A	NIC
CaT	NN 1–15
DA	NNM
DLC [9,13,41–42]	NRU
DSI–M	OCL
ICF	OU
ICJ	PPAP 7–[42]
IU 1–[9]–42	PPi 7–[42]
IaAs	TxHR
KU	WaU

Fig. 10-2. Excerpt from the "Union List of Serials." The initials indicate the libraries which hold all or parts of this publication. For example, the University of California (CU) has the entire set, while the Carnegie Library at Pittsburgh, Pennsylvania (PPi) has only a partial holding.

library which one plans to visit. It is also valuable to the student who wants to know the dates of publication of a particular serial or the exact name of a journal.

Now begins the laborious and time-consuming task of checking journals. It is wise to start with the journal which is likely to contain the largest number of references to your field of interest, and to begin with the most recent issue and work backward. A good recent summary of the subject, if one has been published, will lighten the work considerably by listing the more important publications and by pointing out the things which are not known, so that the student need not waste time looking for such information.

The index to the journal, if one has been made, is a good starting point. If the journal is an old one, there may be several index volumes, each covering a period of 10 to 20 years. Some of the newer periodicals may not have issued an index, and these will require volume-by-volume coverage. It will be necessary, in any case, to examine each issue of the latest copies of any journal, since the index will not be up to date.

The process of examining journals has a snowballing effect, for each paper will list other references; these will list others, until eventually a fairly complete bibliography may be secured. When a biologist has checked the two or three major journals in his field, he will probably have discovered more than half of the significant references.

Abstract and Bibliographic Journals. The next step in the building of a bibliography is to check the standard bibliographical references. Some workers prefer to do this first, prior to the examination of pertinent journals; if the bibliographic aids are more readily available than the journals, this may be preferable. These references may go farther back into the past than the journals the worker has used, and they will include journals which he has not yet seen. Two of these bibliographic aids are of outstanding importance to the biologist: *Biological Abstracts* and *Zoological Record.*

Biological Abstracts is published monthly, and includes brief summaries—or, in some cases, mention by title only—of papers which have appeared in several hundred journals, including some foreign publications (Fig. 10-3). The abstracts are grouped into sections, so that it is easy for the user to find the particular field which may interest him. Since the publication is monthly, it is reasonably up to date at all times. Most abstracts appear within a year, or at most two, of publication. Of course, the coverage is not complete, but it is quite good for the major journals. This is without doubt one of the most useful abstract publications in existence. A general index for each volume, which indexes the abstracts by author, subject, geographical area, and systematic group, adds much to the ease of use of this valuable journal.

Biological Abstracts began in 1926 and is still being published. Its forerunner, *Botanical Abstracts,* covers the period from 1918 to 1925, and is of great value to botanists.

Zoological Record is published by the Zoological Society of London, and is probably the most complete list of zoological publications in the world. It is, naturally, of no use in botanical problems as such. This publication does not include a summary of the material contained in each paper, as is done in *Biological Abstracts,* but merely lists the papers once and refers to them under several headings.

11535. LAYNE, JAMES N. (Cornell U., Ithaca, N.Y.) *Behavior of captive loggerhead turtles, Caretta caretta caretta* (Linnaeus). *Copeia* 1952(2):115. 1952.—Three captive loggerhead turtles, *Caretta c. caretta,* averaging 15 in. in carapace length, were observed in the U.S. Fish and Wildlife Service Aquarium, Woods Hole, Mass., from June 20 to Sept. 3, 1951. The specimens were relatively mild-mannered and were fed a variety of dead fish and mollusks. They seemed unable to crush the exoskeleton of horseshoe crabs (*Limulus*). A wild specimen had eaten 2 fishes 4–5 in. in length, a sulfur sponge (*Cliona*) and a spider crab (*Libinia*). Daily activity of the captives was about equally divided between swimming actively and resting in corners on the bottom of the tank. Some degree of territoriality was indicated in the resting behavior. The specimens surfaced for air on an average of once every 2.1 min. (15 sec.–24 min.) when swimming actively, and every 12.7 min. when resting on the bottom. The longest observed period that one remained on the bottom was 25 min.

Fig. 10-3. A sample excerpt from *Biological Abstracts.*

In order to use the *Record* successfully, it is necessary to understand something of the way in which it is organized. A section on comprehensive or general zoology is included at the beginning of each volume, listing papers which do not deal with any particular taxonomic group. After this, the arrangement is entirely phylogenetic— that is, it starts with the Protozoa and proceeds to the Mammalia, each paper within each phylum being given a number in sequence. The numbers begin with (1) in each section, since various specialists use the sections separately. Arrangement in each section is alphabetical according to the last name of the author.

The worker who is searching for publications on a particular subject may not wish to search through the entire section for the few references which will interest him, and he may not know the names of the authors whose works he is seeking. For his benefit, a subject index lists the numbers of papers in each section, with the author's name, under such subjects as morphology, physiology, ecology, and others. A geographical index lists papers according to the region which they cover. This is followed by a systematic index, where each paper is listed according to the organism or group with which it deals (Fig. 10-4).

A special feature of the *Zoological Record*, of interest primarily to the taxonomist, is the list, at the end of each volume, of new generic

---

Under *Insecta*—p. 62.
    1122.—Fox, I. Notes on Puerto Rican mosquitoes, including a new species of Culex.—J. Parasit., Lancaster, Pa. 39:178–181, 1 pl. Dipt.
Under *Geography or Faunistic*, p. 276.
    FOX, Mosquitoes, Porto Rico and Culex sp. n., 1122.
Under *Systematic*
    Diptera, Culicidae, p. 438.
        Mosquitoes of Porto Rico, FOX, J. Parasit. 39:178–179.
    Culex, p. 439.
        C. (Melanocorion) sardinerae sp. n., Porto Rico, p. 179, figs., FOX, J. Parasit. 39.

Fig. 10–4. Extracts from the *Zoological Record*, showing the manner in which an article is listed under various headings to facilitate use.

and subgeneric names proposed during the year. In addition, new species and genera are listed under the section for each phylum, thus making it relatively easy for the taxonomist to find original descriptions of animals, as well as keeping him informed on the discovery of new species.

Although it is impossible for any such ambitious undertaking to be complete, each volume of the *Record* contains upwards of 15,000 references, making it one of the most comprehensive bibliographies available to the zoologist.

The *Zoological Record* has the longest unbroken series of any important biological bibliography. It was started in 1864 and has been published more or less regularly since that time. It is usually only one to two years late in appearing; that is, the issue for 1952 might have been expected to appear in late 1953 or 1954. But the Second World War caused a delay of several years in publication of the series, and the volumes since that time have been three or four years in appearing.

A more recent publication, and one which keeps more nearly up to date than most such references, is the *Bibliography of Agriculture*. This important bibliography is prepared by the U.S. Department of Agriculture, and is published monthly. Twice annually, in June and December, a summary index for the six-months volume is published. Although this bibliography is specifically concerned with agricultural publications, it contains much that is of value to every biologist. Its coverage of entomology is particularly good.

Because the *Bibliography of Agriculture* has world-wide coverage, and because it is published at monthly intervals, it is an extremely valuable item. Perhaps its greatest contribution is its complete coverage of publications of the U.S. Department of Agriculture and of the various state experiment stations.

Another relatively new publication is *Wildlife Review*, prepared by personnel of the U.S. Fish and Wildlife Service. This useful publication was started in 1935, and is published irregularly, four or five times each year. Each issue includes brief abstracts of several hundred recent publications in the field of biology, listed according to subject matter and with an author index at the end. The coverage is extensive, though spotty, with the emphasis on articles and books related to wildlife management. The editors of the *Review* have been broad-minded in their inclusion of material, however, so that this publication is indispensable to the worker in wildlife management and extremely useful to other biologists. One valuable contribution is its occasional listing of recent Russian publications, which are often unknown to American biologists. The only other source of adequate knowledge about these papers is the *Revue Zoologique Russe*, which has been published since 1920. This review, however, is in Russian.

In 1952, *Wildlife Review* items up to that year were assembled in a single volume. This book, titled "Wildlife Abstracts, 1935-1951," includes more than 10,000 items, arranged by subject matter as in the *Review*, but with a comprehensive index to facilitate its use.

The Quarterly Review of Biology is a journal devoted to reviews of recent books relating to the biological sciences. Each issue contains one or more scientific papers, but the larger part of the magazine consists of crisp, well-written reviews. No journal is more valuable to the student who does not wish to waste his time reading inferior books. Each issue reviews about a hundred recent publications, and many of the reviews are exceptionally complete. This journal has been published four times each year since 1926.

Of less value to the professional biologist but useful to the person who wants to learn about popular articles on biological subjects is *Readers' Guide to Periodical Literature*. Published monthly, the *Readers' Guide* first appeared in 1900 and is still in progress.

Some biological journals include in each issue an extensive list of recent articles in their field of specialization. Two such journals are *The Auk* and the *Journal of Mammalogy*. The student with a special interest in some limited area will find occasional helpful references in these lists, and may, if he desires, send for reprints of those which seem especially useful. Most authors (see p. 269) secure a number of copies of each publication which they have written, and are willing to send a copy to anyone who asks for it. In many cases, this is the easiest way to secure access to a particular paper, if the journal in which it appeared is not readily available.

With an extensive card file containing references to all major publications relating to his problem, a biologist is prepared to summarize existing knowledge and to recognize fruitful areas of research. Unfortunately, the literature search is so time-consuming that it is often carried on concurrently with research, rather than in advance; but at least a preliminary survey of the more recent literature is essential to an understanding of any problem. Armed with the techniques and information contained in this chapter, the worker in biology should find it possible to proceed rapidly and confidently in the survey of literature in his field of interest.

REFERENCES CITED

With the exception of the following, the publications mentioned in this chapter are listed in the Appendix, pages 281 to 301, along with other bibliographic, taxonomic, and scientific books and journals.

CARSON, RACHEL. 1951. "The Sea around Us." Oxford University Press, New York.

COUES, ELLIOTT. 1903. "Key to North American Birds." 5th ed. 2 vols. Dana Estes and Company, Boston.

GRINNELL, JOSEPH. 1909. "A Bibliography of California Ornithology (1797–1907)." Pacific Coast Avifauna no. 5.

——. 1924. "Bibliography of California Ornithology (1908–1923)." Pacific Coast Avifauna no. 16.

——. 1939. "Bibliography of California Ornithology (1924–1938)." Pacific Coast Avifauna no. 26.

JORDAN, DAVID S. 1929. "Manual of the Vertebrate Animals of the Northeastern United States." World Book Company, Yonkers, N.Y.

PROCEEDINGS OF THE BIOLOGICAL SOCIETY OF WASHINGTON. 1880 and following. Published irregularly by Biological Society of Washington, Washington, D.C.

READER'S GUIDE TO PERIODICAL LITERATURE. 1900 and following. Published monthly by The H. W. Wilson Company, New York.

REVUE ZOOLOGIQUE RUSSE (ZOOLOGICHESKII ZHURNAL). 1916 and following. Published in Moscow, U.S.S.R.

TRELEASE, SAM F. 1951. "The Scientific Paper." 2d ed. The Williams & Wilkins Company, Baltimore.

CHAPTER 11

THE CHOICE AND CONDUCT
OF A FIELD PROBLEM

Looking back, I think it was more difficult to see
what the problems were than to solve them.
Charles Darwin, Letter to Charles Lyell,
September 30, 1859

The logical culmination of an interest in field biology is to choose
and carry out a study of some aspect of the subject. Unfortunately,
many well-trained and capable field workers never utilize their knowledge in carrying out a research project. Possibly many feel that they
do not know how to set about it. Others may feel inadequate to choose
and conduct a worthwhile problem. In most cases it is probably a matter of inertia, coupled with a feeling of inadequacy. This is especially
true of those without formal training in field biology, though in many
cases these persons may be as capable as most professionals.

It is the purpose of this chapter to encourage the beginner in field
biology, or the veteran field worker without research experience, to
attempt a field problem. No one should hesitate for fear that his contributions will be insignificant or that his work will be inadequate.
We progress only by effort and experience, and though our progress
may be slow, it will be nevertheless worthwhile.

SELECTING A PROBLEM

The first difficulty involved in embarking on a study is the choice
of a problem. Some people feel that all of the best problems have long

ago been worked out. This is not true. In any area, no matter how well it has been studied, the field biologist can find many basic problems still untouched. The real difficulty lies in the selection. Of course, you cannot choose a problem unless you know what facts are missing in man's knowledge of the branch of field biology which interests you. Thus the literature survey which must precede biological research. It may be this time-consuming and sometimes tiresome task which discourages many capable students from carrying on research. Unfortunately, there is no really satisfactory substitute for the procedure.

In reading about the subject which interests you, you may note that some particular pieces of information are lacking. If so, you already have the germ of a good problem. If not, read a good reference book (see Appendix) on the subject. Take notes on unsolved problems which are mentioned or on the areas in which no information is given. With these clues in mind, examine the major journals in the subject which have been published in the last two or three years. (It must be remembered that reference books are always two or three years behind current research.) If it appears after these surveys that several of the problems which you have listed remain unsolved, you have only to make the choice and begin your study.

The literature survey serves another purpose. While you are examining the books and journals to see what information is lacking, you should accumulate a good deal of material which will aid you in the pursuit of your problem. To organize such material, a card file of 5- by 8-inch cards should be set up, with a summary of each paper or of the pertinent information from each paper on a separate card (Fig. 10-1). These can be filed alphabetically by author, and will be of value throughout the progress of your problem and often for a much longer time. Special attention should be given to techniques which you may use and to the manner in which the problems were approached and the data presented.

If the student is unable to spend much time in library work or does not have access to an adequate library, he need not abandon the idea of research. After deciding upon his general area of interest, he may be able to contact an authority on that subject, who has knowledge of the literature and of the gaps in our knowledge. Most such persons are willing to give suggestions as to what particular facts are lacking and to point out a method of approach which may be used. Such advice is always helpful, even though you may have been able to make a comprehensive survey of the literature for yourself.

Once the general area of study has been determined, it is necessary to fit the problem to your own personal requirements. This is the point where many fail. It is always intriguing to tackle the big problems, requiring broad knowledge and deep insight, but most of us must content ourselves with simpler things. Before deciding upon a problem, see that it fits you in these five ways:

1. IT MUST FIT YOUR KNOWLEDGE AND ABILITY. A beginning student in biology often suggests that he would like to experiment with such a project as the removal of the pituitary gland of a frog or rat and a study of the effects of such removal on the animal's behavior. He is usually hurt when it is pointed out that he has neither the knowledge nor the technical skill to perform the operation or to interpret the results correctly. A candidate for the doctorate in endocrinology might find such an experiment both practicable and interesting; the beginner would succeed only in slaughtering his subjects. Pick a problem which requires the skills which you possess or can master in the time you have to give to the work.

2. IT MUST FIT YOUR FACILITIES. The worker who does not have unlimited space and unlimited funds must choose his problem carefully to utilize his available supplies to the best advantage. Caged animals require space, reasonably constant temperature and humidity, and good ventilation, as well as good care. Collections of most organisms take up space and require a certain amount of materials. Even the simplest field observations may require binoculars or other instruments. It is not necessary to give up, however, because of lack of materials. If you can secure a pencil and a notebook, and if you have time to give to your problem, you can make worthwhile studies. Before embarking on a problem, however, you must consider the facilities you will need.

3. IT MUST FIT YOUR TIME SCHEDULE. If your available hours are irregular, avoid the type of study which requires regular observations. If, on the other hand, you know that you will always be free at a particular time of the day, take advantage of that fact by selecting a problem which requires daily observations. If your vacation coincides with a particular natural event such as bird migration, amphibian egg laying, or bat hibernation, some aspect of that event may be worthy of study. Whether small or large, the project must be one which can be adequately performed in the time you can give to it.

4. IT MUST FIT YOUR INTERESTS. This may seem obvious, but many persons start to work on a problem which is suggested to them, not because they have any personal interest in it, but because it looks like a good problem. Unless a worker is enthusiastic about his work and ready to submerge himself in it wholeheartedly, he is not likely to do it well.

5. IT MUST FIT YOUR TEMPERAMENT. Some people can work on a problem for many years, patiently accumulating data and making observations, as Darwin did with his theory of evolution. Most of us think on a more limited plane and like to see some results from our labors in a reasonable length of time. Usually a project should be chosen which can be completed within a year or two. In the case of a student who has only a term or a school year in which to work, this requires careful selection of the study. If at the same time he wishes to collect data on a long-term project, it would be worth his while to do so.

Temperament is important in another way. Some projects require extreme patience, as for example the study of a nesting bird. Others require extreme care and regular habits, as the taking of data on light, temperature, humidity, or other factors. You must choose a project whose requirements will not prove unduly onerous to you. You are likely to be deeply involved with it for some time, and you should find it a source of continuing satisfaction.

Seeing the problem. If you can narrow your choice of a problem in this manner, you will have a few concrete ideas which seem to fit your needs. In the final selection, be careful to choose a definite precise project. The "shotgun" type—one covering too much territory without a clearly defined aim—must be avoided; you should be able to state the problem in a single sentence, or at most in a short paragraph. The probable direction of your research should be clear to you at the start, and the results toward which you are aiming should be well defined. This is a part of what is generally termed "seeing the problem," and it is comforting to realize that every biologist, even such competent ones as Charles Darwin, has had to resolve this difficulty. If you have an adequate grasp of the background of your problem and of the literature which concerns it, you will be able to formulate some approaches which seem promising. Some of these approaches will be abandoned early in the study, as they prove unsatisfactory; the answers to your questions may seem to slip away as you come near them. But you are constantly assembling facts and accumulating knowledge and experience, and eventually, often with startling suddenness, the problem will spring into clear focus. You will be able to decide upon your best method of attack; to design the necessary experiments; to understand the relationship of your accumulated data to the total problem.

RESEARCH ON THE PROBLEM

The first step in the pursuit of research, once the problem is well defined, is the accumulation of data. In most problems in field biology, two types of data must be recorded: observational data and experimental data. The difference between the old natural history and the modern type of field biology lies largely in the use of experimental procedures by present-day workers. Nonetheless, much can be learned by careful observation and recording of data, if a few precautions are taken.

Making Observations. An observer of wild animals, especially one without professional training, is likely to make the mistake of interpreting animal behavior in terms of his own mentality (see Chap. 9). This anthropocentric approach must be avoided. If interpretation of animal activities is to be made at all, it should be based on experimental work under controlled conditions, rather than on simple observations. Although, under ideal circumstances, biological observations should be made under natural conditions, this is not always possible. Field observations should be attempted first, and careful work will often solve most of the problems without recourse to an artificial environment.

The field worker, whether studying plants or animals, must use extreme care to insure that his activities in the field do not affect the organism which he is studying. The use of an observation blind, left in place long enough to allow the animals to become accustomed to it, is often necessary for the student of birds and larger animals. Even more necessary in the study of animals is the ability to sit still; to move slowly; to ignore minor discomforts and annoyances. If the biologist lacks these attributes, it would be wise for him to confine his studies to organisms which do not need to be observed in this manner. Plants, of course, are not disturbed by the mere presence of a human observer; yet any disturbance of the habitat may affect certain plant species, and the student of plant ecology should be certain that his study areas are not affected by his activities.

Some Tools of the Field Observer. As with any science, field biology requires the student to be an inveterate note taker. No fact can be considered insignificant, though its significance may not be apparent at the time it is noticed. Key events, which may prove essential in the interpretation or understanding of a series of activities, are often missed unless one is especially careful in taking notes. This has led some field workers to depend upon the motion-picture camera for observations. Motion pictures are of undoubted accuracy, while recorded observations of the human eye are not. Pictures can be checked at a later date, at leisure and under ideal conditions; notes must be taken at once and can be checked later only against the imperfect human memory. The speed of the camera can be varied to record movements quite unnoticed by the human eye. The development of high-speed and infrared films has made it possible to record events under conditions of very poor light. Further, the moving picture is far superior to the written word in communicating to others the sequence of observed events.

Another modern device is rapidly taking its place in the battery of tools for the field biologist. This is the sound recorder, which is now available in a light, portable unit especially designed for field use. It records sounds of the animals being observed, and the observer, instead of writing field notes, may record his remarks as the activity is proceeding. Thus he does not need to take his eyes from the animals under observation, as he would have to do if he were writing. The recorder may note sounds which the observer misses, often sounds of critical importance. For an example of the use of the sound recorder in a field problem, you will find the paper by Frings et al. (1955) interesting and instructive.

The still camera, too, has been utilized extensively in field investigations, and can instantaneously record data which must otherwise be recorded laboriously in writing. The field biologist should learn to operate both still and motion-picture cameras effectively, as aids to his limited ability to translate visual images into writing. Further information on the use of these and other tools of the field biologist is given in the Appendix, pp. 301 to 316.

These instruments have disadvantages, to be sure. The noise of a camera, particularly of a motion-picture camera, may disturb some animals, especially when the instrument is used at close range. The operation of cameras requires some skill, which may involve the expenditure of a certain amount of time and money before proficiency is attained. Both camera and sound recorder are moderately expensive, and the fine instruments which are required for the most exacting field work are beyond the reach of many workers. For those with the means and skill to enjoy them, however, they may become exceedingly useful tools.

Recording Data. Whether the worker uses mechanical devices or simply a pencil and paper, it is important that all possible data should be recorded. Memory cannot be trusted, especially for those small details which are so essential to accurate field observation. The collector must have full data on every specimen, as well as notes about weather, habitat, and other details. The botanist will need to record data on soil type, drainage, exposure, pH, and other factors affecting plant distribution. The entomologist must write an account of food plants, microecological distribution, daily activity cycles, and behavior. It has been said that note taking is a faultless pursuit, for it is seldom possible to take too many notes. It is true that 100 pages of basic data may make a final report of only 5 pages, when repetitions and disconnected or incomplete observations are eliminated and the rest is reduced to the shortest possible space. But at the time when notes are being taken, the note taker is in no position to evaluate the significance of any particular item or to check his past notes to see if he has made the same observation previously. It is better to have an unused wealth of field notes than to find the notes lacking in important points.

Experiments. Under some circumstances, field observations cannot reveal what we need to know, and organisms must be brought into the laboratory. Here, by duplicating natural conditions with painstaking thoroughness, we can vary certain environmental factors such as temperature, humidity, light, and habitat type, and learn how they affect the organisms. Behavior studies of animals, in particular, may require observation of captives, since many of the most important activities of animals are carried on at night or under cover. It is often possible to maintain untamed captive animals under such conditions that they will behave normally. Studies made on animals or plants under artificial conditions, however, are not necessarily indicative of the normal behavior of the same species in nature, and such observations should, whenever possible, be checked in the field. These studies will serve to answer many questions which cannot be solved by field work, however, since the animal or plant can be kept under close observation at all times. One could learn much of the mechanics of a diving bird's swimming or a fossorial mammal's digging by observations made in captivity in a glass tank of water or soil, while similar observations would be difficult or quite impossible in nature.

Laboratory observations, too, can be used to learn certain facts about organisms which could be learned in the field only by accident. How well can a certain animal swim? In nature, it would be unusual to observe most small mammals swimming. In captivity, one has but to place the animal in a tub of water, and the question is answered. Many other observations of this type may be made readily by study under controlled conditions.

Observational data, whether accumulated under natural conditions or in the laboratory, may not be sufficient to produce the needed information. The modern scientist, furthermore, is inclined to question the validity of observational data unsupported by experimental evidence. For this reason, it is often necessary for the field biologist to devise experiments which will support or disprove the hypothesis drawn from the data previously secured. In Chap. 1 we discussed briefly the use of the scientific method and the way in which it was used to solve a specific problem. We must now attempt to apply this method to field problems in general.

Setting up the Experiment. The first requirement of an experimental setup is that it have a study population and a check population which are as closely similar as possible. The chemist may use identical test tubes and vary the contents in one component. Any difference in results may logically be considered a result of this component. The doctor of medicine gives identical pills to all his experimental group, except that one section receives pills containing the medicine to be tested and the other section receives placebos, lacking this medicine. The field biologist must introduce this method into his studies.

When the biologist is working with captive animals or with greenhouse plants, the designing of experiments is usually not difficult. The total available population may be divided into as many groups as necessary, and the factors which are to be tested may be varied one at a time. The botanist may thus discover the ecological requirements of a plant species, its optimum soil type, its ability to survive within varying conditions of light, the amount of seed or fruit produced, and the conditions conducive to highest yield. All of these facts are significant in regard to the life of the plant and its relationship to the organic and inorganic environment. In the case of plants useful to man or to wildlife, these facts may have economic significance as well. Similarly, the zoologist may learn much about intraspecific and interspecific relationships of animals maintained under controlled conditions. The results of such experiments may aid the wildlife worker, the farmer, and the sportsman, as well as add to scientific knowledge.

If it is desired to set up experiments without resorting to artificial conditions, great care must be taken to choose two populations which are as nearly identical as possible. If a particular homogeneous area can be divided, one-half to be the experimental area and the other half to be the check area, this should be done. Experiments to test the effects of various chemicals, such as insecticides and weed killers, are usually set up in this manner. If such procedure is not possible, it is necessary to find a population of the organisms under consideration which is closely similar to the population of the experimental area. When the correlation between areas is not close with respect to populations, it is necessary to consider only those species common to both areas, in order to arrive at acceptable conclusions. Such an arrangement is not ideal because the habitat itself presents another variable. The number of variables in experiments should be reduced to as few as possible, preferably to one. Thus any differences between the final status of the experimental population and the check population may be assigned a cause, with some assurance of accuracy.

Statistical Analysis. In many biological studies, it is difficult or impossible to set up experiments of the type required, yet the validity of one's conclusions must be checked in some way. Statistical analysis of data may be used in such cases to indicate whether the events recorded might have been accidental or were in all probability significant. In order to be suitable for statistical analysis, data must be such that they can be numerically expressed. Data on numbers of individuals per unit area, dimensions of organisms, and so forth, are susceptible to this kind of testing. The ramifications of this field are beyond the scope of the present book, though the worker with a sound knowledge of mathematics may learn much of value from the books and papers on this subject which are listed following Chap. 8 and in the Appendix. The biologist who is not also a mathematician may be able to secure suggestions as to statistical analysis of his data from a statistician. Statistical analysis of ecological and population data is widely practiced, and the technique has also proved useful in taxonomic studies, especially with regard to the analysis of subspecies and other infraspecific groups (see Appendix, p. 310).

Interpretation. Once the data have been gathered, experiments performed, and results analyzed, interpretation must begin. In purely observational studies, as indicated above, this may be impossible, or at best tentative. Experimental and statistical data, however, will usually lend themselves to interpretation. Of course, experimental as well as observational data may be subject to misinterpretation. Some years ago an ecologist tested several species of small mammals to determine their water intake under uniform conditions in captivity (Odum, 1944). The object of the experiment was to determine the importance of water supply in the ecological distribution of these animals. The experiment was carefully designed and the results were incontestable, so far as the conditions of the experiment went. Water intake was found to agree with what was known about the ecological preferences of the various species. It would have been possible—indeed logical—to interpret these figures for water intake to indicate the actual water requirement of the animals. This, however, would have been a serious misreading of the data. Zoologists have maintained these same species in captivity for weeks or months without supplying any water, so long as abundant supplies of succulent food were offered. It is not unlikely that many small mammals in nature rarely drink water. This example serves to indicate that an extensive knowledge of natural history may serve a useful purpose in helping the student to understand and interpret experimental data.

The Law of Parsimony. On some occasions, data do not appear to fit any hypothesis, or, worse yet, appear to fit any of a number of hypotheses. The scientist, in such cases, is obligated to utilize the law of parsimony (sometimes called William of Occam's razor, after its originator). This principle requires that phenomena must be explained in the simplest terms and with the smallest possible number of concepts unless such an explanation can be proven to be erroneous.

This generally accepted principle of logic, if adhered to, will prevent the worker from building complicated theories on insufficient data, although it may also result in an oversimplified explanation until further data are available.

PREPARING THE REPORT

If, after evaluation of the data, it appears that the study has produced results which may be of general interest, it is necessary to prepare the report for publication. Many workers are eager to publish their work—perhaps too eager; but other workers, including many capable amateurs, never publish anything. It is obviously unwise to withhold from your colleagues the results of your work, if it can be of value to them. Publication entails a certain amount of trouble, but it is not a particularly complicated procedure. The first step in this direction is to choose the journal in which you wish your material to be published. An examination of journals in the field will give you an idea of the type of material which is acceptable to each. If the observations are primarily of local or regional interest, it may be best to publish them in a journal which confines itself to the biology of your area. A journal of national or international scope would not accept such material, but most states or regions have journals which specialize in local material. If, on the other hand, your research is of broad and general interest, it would be a mistake to publish it in a local journal, where it might escape the attention of many scientists who would find it important. In questionable cases, the editor of any journal can decide whether or not a paper is suitable for inclusion in its pages.

The editorial policy of the journal is usually stated in each issue, often inside one of the covers. Some journals have detailed explanations of how the manuscript should be prepared; others are less explicit. Because of the high cost of printing, authors are expected to utilize a sort of "law of parsimony" with regard to their writings. Tables and photographs especially are expensive to reproduce, and most journals place a limit on the number of plates that can be included. If the author feels that his material requires the use of numerous illustrations, he may be asked to share in the cost of printing them. To keep the size of the paper to a minimum, care should be taken to present data as briefly and simply as possible. All extraneous material should be deleted before the manuscript leaves the author's hands.

The best method of presentation of data will require some thought. Often graphs or charts will tell the story more succinctly than words. The use of photographs or other illustrations should be restricted to those which will show something not easily expressed in words and of importance to the report. Whether or not statistical analysis is required may present a problem. This question has been carefully treated by Stearman (1955) in a paper which should be read by those who prepare scientific papers.

Some skill is required to determine the type of material which is adapted to graphic presentation and to decide what form of presentation is most effective. Often it is necessary to prepare graphs and charts of different kinds, and then to choose the one which is best adapted to your purpose. If it is still not possible for you to decide the issue, the editor of the journal in which you plan to publish your paper may be able to give you advice.

Scientific Writing. Some scientists seem to labor under the illusion that a good scientific paper should be obscure, loaded with technical terms, verbose, and not understandable to the general public. In some cases this may be necessary, but it is by no means generally desirable. The scientific writer should make every effort to write as simply, precisely, and directly as possible. A recent book on style (Gunning, 1952) gave a yardstick to determine the complexity of a particular piece of writing. To determine what is called the *fog index*, average the number of words per sentence, or between major breaks within the sentence. Then calculate the percentage of words with three or more syllables, not counting capitalized words, word combinations, and multisyllable verb forms. Total the percentage thus arrived at with the number of words per sentence, and multiply by .4. This is the fog index, which is intended to indicate the approximate grade level in school which must be reached before adequate comprehension is possible. Popular writing, obviously, must have a fog index of 10 or lower. In technical writing, an index of 13 to 15 is perhaps allowable, but this is difficult reading. In general writing, such as in popular magazines, an index of 10 is usually maintained, even though many of these magazines have a large percentage of educated readers.

Scientific writers may not be able to do so well, but the lower the fog index, the more understandable will be the writing. Of course, some technical terms must be used. This may render the paper unintelligible to those outside the author's field, but his colleagues will not be disturbed by such terms. The real test of a scientific paper is whether it is interesting and understandable to a majority of the author's colleagues. If not, it is unlikely to be a valuable contribution, unless its author is an Einstein.

Organizing the Paper. Another common fault of scientific papers is the failure to state, at the very beginning, what the paper is about. This should be done in the first paragraph. In suspense fiction, it is wise to retain some secrets from your readers until the final page, but in scientific writing this is not true. The author owes it to his readers to acquaint them at once with his intentions. It is not often that the title of a paper gives sufficient indication of its contents. It may catch the eye of the prospective reader, but if the first page or two of the paper should fail to enlighten him about its subject, he is justified in turning to the summary, or in skipping the paper entirely.

Beyond this point, it is best to follow the prescribed practice of the journal for which you are writing. There is some variation in the manner in which the various parts of the paper are presented. In general, however, the paper should include at least the following sections:

1. INTRODUCTION. The problem is clearly stated and the background sketched in.

2. ACKNOWLEDGMENTS. There is much variation in the exact placing of this paragraph, but almost every paper requires acknowledgment of the author's debts to those who have given him assistance of various kinds.

3. METHODS AND MATERIALS. Here you may outline the manner in which the problem was approached; the numbers and kinds of organisms with which you worked; the techniques you used, with reference to their source and a description of any new techniques you may have developed; and any other information which may help the reader in understanding or evaluating your work.

4. RESULTS. A brief statement of the conclusions of your research; it may include graphs and charts, or simply tell what you found out about the problem by the use of your particular approach.

5. DISCUSSION. It is often necessary to compare the results of your work with those of previous workers, or to explain and interpret your results.

This may be the bulk of your paper, or, if your results are largely self-explanatory, the discussion may be very brief. It is an extremely important part of your paper, because it is here that you show your understanding of the scope of the problem and of the meaning of your research.

6. SUMMARY OR ABSTRACT. A short summary at the end of the paper (in some journals placed at the beginning) serves two purposes. It may be of value to the person who does not have sufficient time or interest to read the entire paper, and it provides a summary of the main points for those who have read it. For journals whose contents are cited in *Biological Abstracts*, the summary of the paper may be similar to the abstract which the author prepares.

7. LITERATURE CITED. The method of making a citation varies to some degree among the different journals. The author should be sure that his usage corresponds to that of the journal for which he is writing. Unless your paper is an exhaustive monograph, literature references should include only those which are directly pertinent. This is not a bibliography, but only a list of those references which are actually mentioned in the body of the paper.

In the case of short notes such as occupy the back pages of most journals, the above divisions may not be necessary. These notes merely present the observations or experimental data in a clear, direct manner, and literature citations, unless they are numerous, are usually included in the text in abbreviated form. Again, the best guide is a study of the journal in which the paper is to be published.

From Manuscript to Printed Page. When the manuscript is completed and typed in accordance with the requirements of the journal, it must be sent to the editor. He will usually acknowledge receipt of the manuscript at once, although it may be some time before he is able to read and evaluate it. After he has done this, he may send it back to you with suggestions for improvement. Authors are occasionally upset because editors edit. This, however, is their function, and they are generally chosen because they know more about it than the average author. In the interests of economy, an author may be asked to reduce the length of the manuscript. A good editor may be able to cut a manuscript by nearly one-half without markedly reducing its value. He will, however, not usually do this so cold-bloodedly. He is more likely to ask the author to cut, and will make suggestions which will help in doing so. If the paper contains too many tables or plates, the author may be asked to eliminate some of them. The requirements with regard to tables and plates are usually stated in the journal, and the author is expected to abide by these rules or pay for the difference.

The time between the submission of a paper and its appearance in print may vary a great deal. It depends upon the number of papers which are submitted to the editor, the amount of money available, the importance of your research, and other factors. In general, six months to a year may elapse between submission and appearance of a paper. In some journals, longer and more important papers are printed more rapidly than short research notes, while in other journals the reverse is true. This time lag between completion of research and publication of results is unfortunate, but there seems to be no way to avoid it. Some journals are more prompt in publication than others; some have larger backlogs of material. But all are dedicated to the task of publishing original papers as rapidly as possible. The author should realize this fact and be tolerant of unavoidable delay.

Galley Proof. Some months after acceptance of your paper, the editor will send the galley proof for correction. This will probably be the last time you will see your paper before it appears in the journal, so you must be certain that mistakes, at this point, are kept to a minimum. This is not the time, however, for major overhauls of the manuscript or for insertion of afterthoughts. Resetting of type is expensive, and changes which will involve more than one or two lines may have to be paid for by the author. If there is an error in the way your original material was set, and this is the fault of the printer, he will correct it, but he cannot be expected to make major revisions of the material after the proof has been set. Typography, spelling, capitalization, plate descriptions, and numbers should be carefully checked. The printer or editor will supply you with a guide to printers' signs. There may be some of these marks on the proof when you receive it, since the editor may have had an opportunity to check it for obvious errors.

It is the duty of the author to check and return the proof promptly. Most editors expect that the proof will be retained in the hands of the author for no more than 24 hours. This may seem rather exacting, but editor and printer are operating on an exacting schedule. They must have cooperation from authors if they are to publish their journal on time.

Reprints. With the proof, the author may receive several other items. One is a reprint order. Most journals nowadays do not furnish free reprints, although some retain this practice. Some give a number of free copies if a certain minimum number is ordered by the author. These reprints are purchased by the author in order that he may have copies of his paper to give to his friends and colleagues and to the many interested persons who, he hopes, will want a copy. Such demands are not generally large, but they provide a means of interchange of information among scientists. A worker who does not have access to a large library, and who cannot afford all the journals he needs, may compensate to some degree by requesting reprints in his particular field of interest. A reprint file, properly indexed, may be a great timesaver for any biologist.

Another enclosure, along with the proof, may be the form for submission of a brief summary of the paper to *Biological Abstracts*. Since this abstract journal is used throughout the world, the abstract must be written with the greatest care. General directions are given on the form, but the author must take the responsibility for reducing the meat of his research to a few words. This abstract may be the only form in which his paper will be read by many interested people, and it will be used for many years. The art of abstracting is not an easy one, and the job should not be done hurriedly.

With the proof returned to the printer, the author has only to wait for the appearance of his paper in the journal. His reprints will be sent from the printer a week to a month after the paper is published, and the abstract of the paper will appear in *Biological Abstracts* from six months to a year later.

The many details involved in getting one's research published should not discourage the student of field biology. One does not need to be a professional biologist to contribute much that is worthwhile, and many amateurs have become world authorities. The late Baron N. C. Rothschild, of the British banking family, was one of the world's foremost authorities on fleas. Margaret M. Nice was an amateur observer of birds who became one of the most capable students of bird behavior and a world-recognized authority. Her early investigation was performed largely in her own dooryard. There is always room for good, sound research, whether it is done by amateur or professional. The edifice of scientific knowledge contains many small stones of information. It is to the further growth of this edifice that all scientists, amateur and professional alike, are dedicated.

REFERENCES CITED

FRINGS, HUBERT, MABLE FRINGS, BEVERLY COX, AND LORRAINE PEISSNER. 1955. Auditory and visual mechanisms in food-finding behavior of the herring gull. *Wilson Bull.*, 67:155–170.

GUNNING, ROBERT. 1952. "The Technique of Clear Writing." McGraw-Hill Book Company, Inc., New York.

ODUM, EUGENE. 1944. Water consumption of certain mice in relation to habitat selection. *J. Mammal.*, 25:404–405.

STEARMAN, R. L. 1955. Comments on the use of statistics. *Amer. Inst. Biol. Sci. Bull.*, 5(5):16–17.

SUGGESTED READING

HILLWAY, TYRUS. 1956. "Introduction to Research." Houghton Mifflin Company, Boston. 284 pp.

MAYR, ERNST, E. G. LINSLEY, AND R. L. USINGER. 1953. "Methods and Principles of Systematic Zoology." McGraw-Hill Book Company, Inc., New York. chaps. 8 and 9. pp. 155–198.

TRELEASE, SAM F. 1951. "The Scientific Paper: How to Prepare It, How to Write It." The Williams & Wilkins Company, Baltimore. xii and 163 pp.

GLOSSARY*

ACCELERATED EROSION: Removal of topsoil by erosive forces more rapidly than its formation by constructive forces.

AGGREGATION: A gathering of animals, whether temporary or permanent.

ALLOTYPE: A specimen used in the original description of a species which is of the opposite sex from the holotype (which see). The allotype may be so designated by the original describer or by a later worker.

AMPHIPOD: Any member of the order Amphipoda, class Crustacea.

ANADROMOUS: Pertaining to fishes which ascend fresh-water streams to spawn, e.g., salmon.

APPETITIVE BEHAVIOR: See Behavior, appetitive.

BAG LIMIT: The number of individuals of any given species which may legally be taken by a hunter.

BEHAVIOR: Any reaction of a whole organism.

BEHAVIOR, APPETITIVE: Any reaction which places the animal in a position or state favorable to the satisfaction of its needs.

BEHAVIOR, DISPLACEMENT: An irrelevant activity occurring (a) when an animal is under the influence of a powerful urge but is in some way prevented from expressing that urge in the appropriate way,

* Certain terms related to behavior are here defined according to "A Glossary of Scientific Terms Used in Animal Behavior," prepared by A. M. Guhl, Kansas State College, Manhattan, Kansas. Definitions of ecological terms follow, in most cases, "An Ecological Glossary," by J. Richard Carpenter, University of Oklahoma Press, Norman, Oklahoma, 1938. Where several definitions for the same term are given in these works, we have adopted the one best suited to our usage. In certain cases "Webster's New International Dictionary of the English Language," 2d ed., unabridged, has been used as a source of definitions.

or (b) when two or more incompatible drives are strongly activated.

BEHAVIOR, INSTINCTIVE: A fixed action pattern resulting from an inherited mechanism within the nervous system. Such reactions occur in response to stimuli within and without the animal.

BENTHIC: Of, or pertaining to, the bottom of a body of water.

BENTHOS: Organisms living on the bottom of a body of water.

BINOMINAL: The two-word scientific name of any species, consisting of the generic name and the trivial (specific) name, e. g., *Homo sapiens.*

BIOLOGICAL CONTROL: Control of a pest species by means of a biological agent, e. g., parasites, disease organisms, predators.

BIOME: An ecological society consisting of successional and climax communities and recognizable by the ecological similarity in appearance of its constituent climax communities.

BIOTIC: Pertaining to life or living organisms.

BIOTIC POTENTIAL: The potential power that an organism has to reproduce and survive in its environment.

BLOOM: A high population of minute aquatic organisms (plankton), especially algae.

BUFFER: (a) Chemically, a substance which, when added to a solution, prevents rapid change of pH of the solution until the buffer is exhausted. (b) Ecologically, a prey species which, because of its abundance or availability, diverts the attention of predators from other prey species.

BURSA OF FABRICIUS: A blind sac within the anus of certain birds, sometimes useful as an age criterion because its size changes with increased age.

CARNIVORE: An organism which feeds on other animals; literally, a meat eater.

CARRYING CAPACITY: The quantitative expression of the ability of a given land area to support members of a given species.

CLADOCERAN: Any member of the order Cladocera, class Crustacea; a small shrimplike creature, often abundant in fresh water.

CLIMAX: Either the relatively stable stage or the relatively stable community achieved by an available population of organisms in a given environment, often identifiable as the culminating development in a succession. Climate is the chief factor in determining the nature of the climax; there is but one climax in a given general climatic area. All other successional pauses or periods of relative stability of the population are considered interruptions or aberrations in the development of the single climax and are named to indicate such a relationship.

COMMUNITY: A general term applying to any aggregation of organisms irrespective of its successional position.

COMPENSATION DEPTH: The level at which the compensation point is located.

COMPENSATION POINT: The light intensity at which the oxygen production in photosynthesis is equal to the oxygen consumption of the plants.

CONDITIONED REFLEX: See Reflex, conditioned.

CONSUMMATORY ACT: The last act in a behavior pattern, which satisfies the urge or drive which caused initiation of the behavior.

CONVERGENCE: The tendency of organic communities in the same climatic area to become more similar as succession proceeds.

COPEPOD: Any member of the order Copepoda, class Crustacea; the tiny organism known as *Cyclops* is a common member of this group.

CUTTINGS: Pieces of herbaceous vegetation, often grass, that have been chewed into short lengths by a mammal. The length may be characteristic of the mammal which made the cuttings.

DISCLIMAX: A subclimax or long-continued community which is the result of disturbance by man or domestic animals rather than climatic factors.

DISPLACEMENT BEHAVIOR: See Behavior, displacement.

DOMINANT: An organism which controls the habitat, i.e., an organism able to control the existence of other organisms in the habitat.

DUFF: Incompletely decayed vegetative matter on the surface of forest soil.

DYSTROPHIC: Pertaining to lakes of brown color, with much organic matter in solution, poor in bottom fauna, and with a pronounced oxygen consumption.

ECOLOGY: The branch of biology which deals with organisms in relation to their environment; the study of organic communities.

EDAPHIC CLIMAX: A stable community determined by physiographic and edaphic (soil) factors rather than by climatic factors.

ELEVATION GRADIENT: The difference in elevation from the origin of a stream to its terminus, divided by the distance the stream travels between these two points.

EMERGENTS: Aquatic plants which normally have their roots submerged in the water and their upper parts projecting out of the water.

ENDEMIC: Pertaining to an organism which is native in the area concerned.

EPILIMNION: The upper layer of water in stratified lakes.

ETHOLOGY: The study of animal behavior in an observational or experimental way; primarily concerned with the causes of behavior and its biological significance.

EUTROPHIC: Pertaining to lakes low in oxygen content in the bottom waters, rich in nutrients, and productive of plant and animal life.

EXOTIC: Pertaining to an organism not native in the area concerned.

FAULTING: A process in which rocks break and one section moves along the line of fracture. The fissure may be horizontal or vertical.

GRID TRAPPING: A system of trapping animals by placing traps in a definite pattern at given distances.

HERBIVORE: An animal which feeds on vegetable matter.

HOLOTYPE: A specimen used in preparing a description of the species, which is designated by the describer to be the type of that species. It thus constitutes a permanent point of reference for taxonomists.

HOME RANGE: The area used by an individual animal in the normal activities of life, i. e., feeding, breeding, etc.

HUMUS: Decayed organic matter which makes up part of the soil.

HYDROPHYTIC: Pertaining to plants which live in wet places, or to conditions existing in such places.

HYPOLIMNION: The portion of deep lakes below the thermocline, which receives no heat from the sun and no aeration by circulation while stratification lasts.

IMPRINTING: A rapid and usually stable form of learning which takes place in the early life of the individual, by which certain characteristics come to be recognized as the species pattern and act as releasers for certain aspects of behavior.

INDICATOR: A form of vegetation or a species which indicates the presence of certain environmental conditions.

INNATE RELEASING MECHANISM (IRM): A postulated mechanism in the nervous system which causes a particular reaction when the animal is confronted with a particular stimulus (see also Releaser).

INSECTIVORE: Any member of the order Insectivora, class Mammalia, which includes the moles and shrews; in a broader sense, any animal which eats insects.

INSTINCT: See Behavior, instinctive.

INTERGRADE: An individual showing characteristics intermediate between those of two subspecies.

INTERNATIONAL CODE OF NOMENCLATURE: One of two codes (one botanical, the other zoological) set up and operated by international scientific organizations to insure uniformity of nomenclatural usage throughout the world.

INTERSPECIFIC: Referring to events or relationships which occur between individuals of different species.

INTRASPECIFIC: Referring to events or relationships which occur between individuals of the same species.

INTRASPECIFIC TOLERANCE: The degree to which members of a species permit the encroachment of other members of that species upon their home range.

IRRUPTION: A sudden rise in population which occurs irregularly and without a fixed cyclic pattern.

KRUMMHOLZ: Stunted trees forming a characteristic vegetation zone near timber line on mountains.

LEACHING: The process whereby soluble materials dissolved in water are washed from the soil.

LECTOTYPE: A specimen selected from the specimens used in the original description of a species, which selection is made *by a later worker* and designated by him as the type of the species.

LEERLAUFREAKTION: A reaction normally occurring under a particular stimulus, which is carried out without the presence of the usual releaser, or with a very weak stimulus.

LENTIC: Pertaining to still-water communities.

LIMNETIC ZONE: The open water of lakes.

LIMNOLOGY: The study of the natural history of fresh waters.

LINNAEAN SYSTEM: A nomenclature system devised by Karl von Linné (Carolus Linnaeus) which depends upon a hierarchical classification and the use of binomials for each species.

LITTORAL ZONE: The shallow zone near the shore of a body of water, out to the usual limit of influence of wave action or tides, with daylight reaching the bottom life.

LOTIC: Pertaining to swift-water communities.

MERISTEMATIC: Referring to plant tissues in which cell division and growth takes place.

MESIC: Tending toward conditions of medium water supply.

MESOPHYTIC: Pertaining to plants which require mesic conditions, not thriving in either extreme dryness or extreme wetness.

MICROCOMMUNITY: A small community within a larger community, for example, the animals and plants in a dead log within the forest. The animals and plants in the log form the microcommunity within the larger community of the forest.

MONOGAMOUS: Having one mate, whether for a season or permanently.

MORAINE: A localized deposit of stones, earth, and debris from a glacier.

NEKTON: Organisms swimming at the surface of a body of water.

NEUSTON: Organisms which are associated with the surface film of water, e. g., mosquito larvae and water striders.

NOMEN NUDUM: A published scientific name which is not valid, usually because it has been published without an accompanying description.

NOMINA CONSERVANDA: Names whose usage has been preserved by agreement or decision in spite of actual or potential conflict with established rules of nomenclature.*

OLIGOTROPHIC: Pertaining to waters which are poor in nutritive materials and which do not produce abundant organisms in relation to their volume. They contain abundant oxygen in their lower regions.

*From Ernst Mayr, E. G. Linslay, and R. L. Usinger. 1953. "Methods and Principles of Systematic Zoology." McGraw-Hill Book Company, Inc., New York.

OMNIVORE: An animal which eats a wide variety of foods.

OSTRACOD: Any member of the order Ostracoda, class Crustacea; small bivalved organisms which occur in fresh water.

PECK ORDER: A general term for the order of dominance among social animals; so named because dominance is expressed in birds by the dominant animal pecking the animals lower in the scale.

pH: A figure expressing hydrogen ion concentration, and hence acidity or alkalinity. pH 7 is neutral; lower figures indicate acidity, higher figures alkalinity.

PIONEER PLANTS: Plants which invade and exist upon bare areas.

PLANKTON: Passively floating or weakly swimming aquatic organisms.

POLYGAMOUS: Having more than one mate at a time.

POPULATION: The members of a single species occurring in a given area.

PROFUNDAL ZONE: The bottom zone of lakes where rooted aquatic vegetation does not grow.

PSAMMOLITTORAL ZONE: The region of bodies of water along the water's edge.

QUADRAT: A square area marked off for the purpose of intensive study of ecological factors.

REACTION CHAIN: A series of instinctive reactions which normally follow one another in regular sequence and lead to satisfaction of a need or drive.

REFLEX: An involuntary reaction brought about by a specific stimulus, but never elicited without the proper stimulus.

REFLEX, CONDITIONED: A reflex acquired by an animal as a result of two stimuli being repeatedly presented to the animal at the same time until one of the stimuli will elicit the reflexes suitable to both stimuli.

RELEASER: A device or property which has the special function of eliciting a reaction in a species mate.

SCATOLOGY: The study of animal droppings.

SERAL STAGE: Any stage or community prior to the climax in a developing sere.

SERE: A chain of stages comprising the development of an area from the pioneer stage to the climax.

SESTON: A collective term which includes everything that floats or swims in the water; includes both living and dead organisms.

SILTATION: Deposition of finely divided sediment, consisting of rock and clay particles.

SPECIES: Groups of organisms which do, or can, interbreed, and which are morphologically as well as genetically distinct from other similar groups.

SUBCLIMAX: A relatively stable community in which factors other than climate are the stabilizing factors.

SUBSPECIES: Groups of organisms within a single species which are morphologically different but not genetically isolated from other such groups; that is, subspecies of the same species will interbreed where they occur together. The bulk of the groups will be geographically separated, but along any area of overlap, intergrades will occur.

SUCCESSION: Any change in the vegetation which is in the direction of the climax.

SUCCESSION, PRIMARY: Succession which begins with a bare area exposed for the first time, or on newly formed soil.

SUCCESSION, SECONDARY: Succession on an area cleared or otherwise modified by man, or where the effects of previously existing organisms remain.

TAIGA: The coniferous forest biome, circumpolar in the northern hemisphere.

TAUTONYM: A scientific name in which both the generic and trivial names are the same, e. g., *Gallus gallus*.

TAXONOMY: The science of naming and classification of organisms.

TERRITORY: A limited geographical area within the home range settled upon and defended by an animal, usually the male, and used for mating and rearing of a family.

THERMOCLINE: An area in deep lakes between the epilimnion and the hypolimnion, in which the temperature drops rapidly, at least one degree centigrade per meter of increase in depth.

TOPOTYPE: A specimen collected at the type locality, i. e., the locality from which the type specimen came and which is designated as the type locality in the description.

TRINOMINAL: A three-part name, including the generic, trivial, and subspecific names, e. g., *Epitedia wenmanni testor*.

TUNDRA: A dwarfed growth of mosses, lichens, and small higher plants, characteristic of northern latitudes and high altitudes farther to the south; the northernmost biome.

TYPE: See Holotype.

VERNACULAR NAME: Any colloquial (nonscientific) name applied to any group of animals or plants.

XEROPHYTIC: Pertaining to plants which require a dry location.

APPENDIX

The biologist, like scholars of all disciplines, finds that books are among his most important tools. The book lists given here, however, are not intended to be complete. Emphasis is given to books which are useful for identification of organisms, and to books which can be read without extensive biological training. In areas where such volumes are not yet obtainable, we have recommended some relatively technical works. The brief review following each title will indicate the degree of difficulty of each book.

In most cases, we have chosen books which are still in print and thus available to the student who may wish to own a copy. Some particularly valuable works have been included in spite of their age, and such books may be available from a public library or from a dealer in secondhand books. Unfortunately a highly regarded book, when it goes out of print, often commands a price far above its original cost. Copies of the first volume of Bent's "Life Histories of North American Birds," for example, cost 50 cents when published. In recent years good copies have brought as much as 30 or 40 dollars. Obviously such publications can be purchased only by the student with unlimited funds, or by bibliophiles.

Many publications, however, are printed by an agency which sells them at cost, and the alert student may secure these books upon publication at a nominal price. For this reason we have included a brief list of some of the more important sources of biological literature of this type. The average amateur biologist may discover little of interest here; but the professional or the more serious amateur will find it essential to secure familiarity with this category of biological literature.

In addition to the lists of books, we have included a list of journals which are of particular importance to the biologist, together with the respective publishers' names. For a more complete list of such publications, the reader should refer to *Biological Abstracts*, vol. 26, May, 1952.

A list of important bibliographical tools is also included for the benefit of the serious student. The list is, again, incomplete, but will serve as a point of departure in the preparation of a bibliography.

The second part of the Appendix is concerned with tools and materials which the field biologist must use. This brief discussion is included in the hope that it will be of assistance to the beginner or amateur in choosing the instruments he will need in the pursuit of his studies. For those whose interest leads to a desire for further knowledge, a list of publications on techniques is included, along with lists of sources for many different kinds of biological materials and instruments.

BOOKS FOR THE FIELD BIOLOGIST

Lower Plants

Bodenberg, E. T. 1954. "Mosses: A New Approach to the Identification of Common Species." Burgess Publishing Company, Minneapolis. The author of this semipopular guide to common mosses has attempted to correct the faults of earlier guides and to make his book easier to use and more valuable to the nonprofessional. The illustrations are abundant and clear, the keys good.

Cobb, Boughton. 1956. "A Field Guide to the Ferns." Houghton Mifflin Company, Boston. The fern guide in the Peterson series; this is an inclusive little volume which covers ferns and fern allies of the eastern half of the United States. Specialists have added material about how to grow ferns, the history of ferns, and other such information.

Conard, H. S. 1944. "How to Know the Mosses." William C. Brown Company, Dubuque, Iowa. A moderately technical book, designed only for identification; depends upon keys with each key character illustrated; one of the Pictured-Key series.

Durand, Herbert. 1949. "Field Book of Common Ferns." G. P. Putnam's Sons, New York. One of the Putnam guides, a well-illustrated popular guide to only the more common species. Somewhat less inclusive than other guides of its type.

Grout, A. J. 1947. "Mosses with a Hand Lens." 4th ed. Published by the author, Staten Island, New York. This old stand-by among the moss books is one of the best. Each succeeding edition has been improved, and the stress on characteristics visible under low magnification makes the book useful for the worker without extensive equipment.

KRIEGER, L. C. C. 1947. "The Mushroom Handbook." The Macmillan Company, New York. A popular guide to the more common species of higher fungi. The illustrations are good, and the species included are those most generally common. More inclusive local guides may be needed for the more advanced student.

NEARING, G. G. 1947. "The Lichen Book." Published by the author, Ridgewood, New Jersey. Few scientists work on the lichens, and even fewer write popular guides. This thick book is an adequate and easily used guide with keys based on visible structural characteristics. Each species is illustrated.

PRESCOTT, G. W. 1954. "How to Know the Algae." William C. Brown Company, Dubuque, Iowa. A semipopular guide, using the Pictured-Key approach. Less inclusive and less technical than the book by Smith (see below).

RAMSBOTTOM, J. 1953. "Mushrooms and Toadstools." William Collins Sons & Co., Ltd., New York. A general discussion of fungi; one of the New Naturalist series. Like others in this series, it is easy to read and well illustrated.

SMITH, GILBERT. 1950. "The Fresh-water Algae of the United States." 2d ed. McGraw-Hill Book Company, Inc., New York. Although technical in treatment, the book contains excellent illustrations, which make it valuable to anyone who studies algae. This is the standard technical reference on American algae.

THOMAS, WILLIAM S. 1936. "Field Book of Common Mushrooms." G. P. Putnam's Sons, New York. A popular guide to mushrooms, illustrated primarily with line drawings. Color paintings and habitat photographs of selected species are a feature of this book.

WHERRY, E. T. 1942. "Guide to Eastern Ferns." 2d ed. Science Press, Lancaster, Pa. One of the best guides to ferns and fern allies of the East. A full page of text and a large line drawing opposite it for each species makes the book convenient to use. Concise but complete information on many aspects of fern life.

WILDFLOWERS

ARMSTRONG, MARGARET. 1915. "Field Book of Western Wild Flowers." G. P. Putnam's Sons, New York. One of the older Putnam field guides; covers the Pacific coast and most of the Rocky Mountain states. This is a popular guide, illustrated primarily with line drawings. Forty-eight color plates of the more colorful species are included.

CUTHBERT, MABEL. 1943. "How to Know the Spring Flowers." William C. Brown Company, Dubuque, Iowa. See entry following.

————. 1948. "How to Know the Fall Flowers." William C. Brown Company, Dubuque, Iowa. These two Pictured-Key guides cover the most common flowers of the United States east of the Rocky Mountains.

FERNALD, M. L. 1950. "Gray's Manual of Botany." 8th ed. American Book Company, New York. The classic of American technical botany manuals has been brought up to date in this large volume. It is not meant for the beginner in botany, but for the serious student it is excellent.

GLEASON, H. A. 1952. "The New Britton and Brown Illustrated Flora of the Northeastern United States and Adjacent Canada" 3 vols. Published by the New York Botanical Garden, New York. Like Gray's manual, Britton and Brown's work has long been used by American botanists. This modern edition is thoroughly revised. The illustrations make this somewhat easier to use than Gray's manual, but it is larger and more expensive.

MATTHEWS, F. S. 1955. "Field Book of American Wild Flowers." Rev. ed. Edited by Norman Taylor. G. P. Putnam's Sons, New York. For many years a leading popular guide; the new edition is a modern, well-illustrated guide, one of the best of its kind.

MOLDENKE, HAROLD. 1949. "American Wild Flowers." D. Van Nostrand Company, Inc., Princeton, N.J. One of the New Illustrated Naturalist series; not primarily an identification manual; includes discussions of every family, with brief notes on especially interesting or common species in each.

MUENSCHER, W. C. 1944. "Aquatic Plants of the United States." Comstock Publishing Associates, Inc., Ithaca, New York. One of the Handbooks of American Natural History, this book is an excellent source for information about aquatic plants, and its good illustrations and keys permit accurate identification.

WHERRY, E. T. 1948. "The Wildflower Guide." Doubleday & Company, Inc., New York. Covering the East and Midwest, this handsome little book features excellent illustrations, half of which are colored, and half are line drawings. Hints on culture of the plants in wildflower gardens are included. Introduced plants are covered separately from native plants, which often requires the user to look in two places to identify a particular plant.

TREES AND SHRUBS

BAERG, HARRY. 1955. "How to Know the Western Trees." William C. Brown Company, Dubuque, Iowa. A Pictured-Key to the trees of the Pacific and Rocky Mountain states. Format identical to other books in this series.

BLACKBURN, B. C. 1952. "Trees and Shrubs in Eastern North America." Oxford University Press, New York. Keys to the various species are semitechnical, illustrations are few. Because of the large number of species involved, use of the keys is time-consuming, but the keys are good. This is not a popular guide; it can be used readily, however, once the key characteristics are learned.

CANADA DEPARTMENT OF RESOURCES AND DEVELOPMENT, FORESTRY BRANCH. 1949. "Native Trees of Canada." 4th ed. Canada Department of Research and Development, Bulletin 61. A beautifully illustrated and inexpensive guide to Canadian trees; does not include introduced species. This book is nontechnical and easily used.

HARLOW, WILLIAM M. 1942. "Trees of the Eastern United States and Canada." McGraw-Hill Book Company, Inc., New York. One of the best pocket guides to trees. Pictures are good, discussions of each species are thorough. Designed for the person without professional knowledge of forestry.

HARRAR, ELWOOD S., and J. GEORGE HARRAR. 1946. "Guide to Southern Trees." McGraw-Hill Book Company, Inc., New York. For naturalists south of the Mason-Dixon line, this pocket-size guide will prove extremely useful. It is similar in format to Harlow's book, well illustrated and popularly written.

GRAVES, A. H. 1956. "Illustrated Guide to Trees and Shrubs." Harper & Brothers, New York. Probably the best available guide for the Northeast; beginners find this book among the easiest to use, and it is a valuable reference for the more skilled.

JAQUES, H. E. 1946. "How to Know the Trees." Rev. ed. William C. Brown Company, Dubuque, Iowa. The companion volume to the book by Baerg, above. It covers the area east of the Rockies.

LANE, FREDERICK C. 1952. "The Story of Trees." Doubleday & Company, Inc., New York. This book presents a general discussion of trees and their adaptations in popular language. Good reading, but not an identification manual.

PRESTON, R. J., JR. 1940. "Rocky Mountain Trees." Iowa State College Press, Ames, Iowa. Covers the states of Idaho, Montana, Wyoming, Nevada, Utah, Colorado, Arizona, New Mexico, and western Texas. Good keys, illustrations of each species, and range maps are useful features.

———. 1948. "North American Trees." Iowa State College Press, Ames, Iowa. The format of this book is the same as the one above. Both books are attractively presented and well written.

UNITED STATES DEPARTMENT OF AGRICULTURE. 1949. "Trees: Yearbook of Agriculture." U.S. Department of Agriculture. A compendium of information about American trees; authorities in all phases of forestry, in and out of the department, collaborated in writing this large book. One section deals with North American trees species by species, with illustrations showing the outstanding characteristics of each. Other sections include tree diseases, forest insects, forest wildlife, and many other items which make this an outstanding reference book for anyone interested in American forests.

INVERTEBRATES

General

BUCHSBAUM, RALPH. 1948. "Animals without Backbones." Rev. ed. University of Chicago Press, Chicago. This semitechnical discussion of invertebrates is a widely used text but may be read profitably by those with little biological training. Illustrations are abundant and good.

CROWDER, WILLIAM. 1931. "Between the Tides." Dodd, Mead & Company, Inc., New York. An illustrated guide to the marine invertebrates of the Atlantic coast; includes information on collecting marine specimens. The illustrations are abundant and good.

GAUL, ALBRO. 1955. "The Wonderful World of the Seashore." Appleton-Century-Crofts, Inc., New York. A good book to read during a seashore vacation; this is a popular treatment of seashore environments and the organisms which inhabit them.

MACGINITIE, G. E., AND NETTIE MACGINITIE. 1949. "Natural History of Marine Animals." McGraw-Hill Book Company, Inc., New York. A general natural history survey of marine invertebrates, with special reference to the Pacific coast of California. Persons without extensive biological training can read it with interest and understanding.

MINER, ROY W. 1950. "Field Book of Seashore Life." G. P. Putnam's Sons, New York. Covers the coastal area from New England to North Carolina. The pocket-size format makes it a good, handy book for field use.

PENNAK, ROBERT. 1953. "Freshwater Invertebrates of the United States." The Ronald Press Company, New York. A massive and concentrated volume, with keys to fresh-water invertebrates as well as detailed discussions of their ecology, anatomy, and physiology. A technical reference of great value.

PRATT, H. S. 1953. "Manual of the Common Invertebrate Animals." The Blakiston Division, McGraw-Hill Book Company, Inc., New York. This re-issue makes available once again a standard reference work on invertebrates. It covers all groups except insects; treatment is moderately technical.

RICKETTS, E. F., AND JACK CALVIN. 1952. "Between Pacific Tides." 3d ed. Rev. by Joel Hedgpeth. Stanford University Press, Stanford, Calif. Both plants and animals of the Pacific seashore are included in this popular guide. The appendix provides an exceptionally complete list of literature, with notes about each item included.

WARD, H. B., AND G. W. WHIPPLE. 1945. "Fresh-water Biology." John Wiley & Sons, Inc., New York. A strictly technical reference, one of the classics in the field. This modern reprinting has not been brought up to date, but it remains a very useful book. Keys and descriptions are used for identification of specimens. Long a standard reference, it has been to some extent supplanted by more recent publications, but many modern biologists remember it fondly as one of the basic books in the biologist's library.

Protozoa

JAHN, T. L. 1949. "How to Know the Protozoa." William C. Brown Company, Dubuque, Iowa. Because of the extensive use of pictures in the Pictured-Key series, this is one of the few books which the beginner can use with reasonable effectiveness. It includes the more common species of Protozoa found in eastern North America.

Coelenterata

SMITH, F. G. W. 1948. "Atlantic Reef Corals." University of Miami Press, Coral Gables, Fla. There are few popular books on most of the invertebrate groups, but this attractive little guide is of great interest to marine biologists of the eastern United States. Besides discussing corals in general, it includes keys to the Atlantic species and excellent photographs illustrating many of the species.

Parasitic worms

CHANDLER, ASA. 1955. "Introduction to Parasitology." 9th ed. John Wiley & Sons, Inc., New York. Among the most popular texts in parasitology, this book is rather technical. The most recent edition presents up-to-date information which can be read profitably by anyone with a background of college zoology. For more popular treatment, the following book is more suitable.

ROTHSCHILD, MIRIAM, AND TERESA CLAY. 1952. "Fleas, Flukes and Cuckoos." William Collins Sons & Co., Ltd., London. (In U.S., Philosophical Library, Inc., New York.) Despite the incongruous title, this volume covers the subject of parasitology, with special reference to birds, in a most refreshing and interesting manner. The amateur is not burdened with a large number of text references, footnotes, and such items, but an appendix covers the literature very thoroughly for those who wish such information. The illustrations are excellent.

Mollusca

ABBOTT, R. T. 1954. "American Seashells." D. Van Nostrand Company, Inc., Princeton, N.J. One of the New Illustrated Naturalist series, this volume has the beautiful illustrations which are characteristic of the series. More than 1,500 species of marine mollusks are discussed and illustrated.

MORRIS, PERCY. 1939. "What Shell Is That? A Guide to the Shell-bearing Mollusks of Eastern North America." Appleton-Century-Crofts, Inc., New York. This is a popular guide to the more common land and fresh-water mollusks. About seventy-five species are included, with good illustrations.

———. 1951. "Field Guide to the Shells of Our Atlantic and Gulf Coasts." Houghton Mifflin Company, Boston. See entry following.

———. 1952. "Field Guide to the Shells of the Pacific Coast and Hawaii." Houghton Mifflin Company, Boston. These two volumes in the Peterson series permit identification of marine mollusks along our entire coast line. They are beautifully illustrated and authentic.

PILSBRY, HENRY A. 1939–1948. "Land Mollusca of North America." 4 vols. Academy of Natural Sciences, Monograph 3, Philadelphia. A technical work on land mollusks, but with abundant illustrations which may make it useful as a reference for nonprofessionals.

Spiders

COMSTOCK, J. H. 1940. "The Spider Book." 2d ed. Rev. ed. Edited by W. J. Gertsch. Doubleday & Company, Inc., New York. The classic among popular books on spiders, this large and handsome volume is one of the most useful references for this group. It contains a wealth of information about the biology of spiders, as well as serving as an identification manual.

GERTSCH, W. J. 1949. "American Spiders." D. Van Nostrand Company, Inc., Princeton, N.J. This New Illustrated Naturalist volume is a beautifully produced book on the ways of spiders, not specifically designed for identification, but with illustrations which will, nonetheless, permit identification of many species.

KASTON, B. J., AND E. KASTON. 1953. "How to Know the Spiders." William C. Brown Company, Dubuque, Iowa. For the Pictured-Key book on spiders, the authors have done a difficult job well. The more common of the thousands of species of spiders are included, with clear drawings illustrating the technical points of distinction. Because of the tremendous numbers of species and the difficulty of identification, spiders do not lend themselves well to a popular book or a key; in this book, however, the keys are good.

Insects

Among invertebrates, the insects enjoy the same place of popularity which birds have among the vertebrates. For this reason, there is a wealth of material on this group, both popular and technical. Only a few of these works can be included here, but the popular guide by Swain (1948) includes a good list of references for the beginner.

CHU, H. F. 1949. "How to Know the Immature Insects." William C. Brown Company, Dubuque, Iowa. Immature insects are singularly difficult to identify, but this book, by one of the few authorities on this subject, is a very adequate treatment of a difficult field. Most immature insects can be placed in the proper order and family by the use of the well-illustrated keys.

COMSTOCK, J. H. 1940. "Introduction to Entomology." 9th ed. Rev. by Glenn Herrick. Comstock Publishing Associates, Inc., Ithaca, N.Y. Although one of the oldest of entomology references, this book has been revised with enough frequency to make it still useful. The classification is not always in agreement with more modern work, but the excellent keys and the clear illustrations make this a reliable, though technical, book.

HOLLAND, W. J. 1934. "The Moth Book." Doubleday & Company, Inc., New York. See entry following.

———. 1949. "The Butterfly Book." Doubleday & Company, Inc., New York. These two popular classics have been reprinted in several formats, and feature abundant colored plates accompanied by a popularly written text. Both are excellent references.

IMMS, AUGUSTUS DANIEL. 1951. "Insect Natural History." William Collins Sons & Co., Ltd., London. (In U.S., The Blakiston Division, McGraw-Hill Book Company, Inc., New York.) One of the New Naturalist series, this outstanding volume has a most interesting and readable text and some of the most beautiful colored photographs of insects ever published. Not an identification manual, it discusses the lives of insects in an absorbing and well-organized manner.

JAQUES, H. E. 1947. "How to Know the Insects." William C. Brown Company, Dubuque, Iowa. A Pictured-Key book, designed as a key to insect families. Comparatively nontechnical.

KLOTS, A. 1951. "Field Guide to the Butterflies." Houghton Mifflin Company, Boston. A model field guide, with brief but adequate introductory material, beautiful illustrations, and a clear, concise text. One of the Peterson series, this is outstanding.

LUTZ, FRANK. 1935. "Field Book of Insects." 3d ed. G. P. Putnam's Sons, New York. An excellent though old reference. Coverage is more extensive than is usual in popular guides, and the book is interestingly written.

SWAIN, RALPH. 1948. "The Insect Guide." Doubleday & Company, Inc., New York. One or two important species in each of the larger families of insects serve as examples in this beautifully illustrated book. The list of references makes this good field guide even more useful.

FISHES

BREDER, CHARLES M. 1948. "Fieldbook of Marine Fishes." G. P. Putnam's Sons, New York. In the attractive format of the Putnam field guides, this popular book includes line drawings of most species; additional halftones are included in the back of the book. Coverage is the Atlantic and Gulf coasts.

HARLAN, J. R., AND E. B. SPEAKER. 1956. "Iowa Fish and Fishing." 3d ed. Iowa Conservation Commission, Des Moines. Although this is a state publication, it is the most generally useful volume on fishes of the

Midwest. The 3rd edition has ironed out the few faults of the earlier ones, and the colored illustrations of 63 species are outstandingly beautiful. The colored plates are available separately, and are a remarkable example of color reproduction.

HUBBS, CARL, AND KARL LAGLER. 1949. "Fishes of the Great Lakes Region." Cranbrook Institute of Science, Bulletin no. 26, Bloomfield Hills, Michigan. The outstanding guide to eastern fishes; fairly technical, but the terms are described and illustrated in full, so that the keys run fairly easily after the reader gains some experience with them. Clear diagrams of the diagnostic points will help the beginner to learn the necessary technical details. A few good color plates are included, but most species are shown only in halftones from photographs, which vary greatly in quality. Since the book includes all of the waters in the Great Lakes drainage, most of the species which occur in the East are included.

LaMONTE, FRANCESCA. 1945. "North American Game Fishes." Doubleday & Company, Inc., New York. A well-illustrated guide to game fishes, both fresh-water and marine; of special interest to the sportsman are record catches for each species. Many attractive colored plates and a unique key are features of this pocket guide.

NORMAN, J. R., 1951. "A History of Fishes." A. A. Wyn, Inc., New York. A reprint of the 1936 edition, this is perhaps the finest popular book about fishes ever written. All aspects of fish natural history are covered.

ROUNSEFELL, G. A., AND W. H. EVERHART. 1953. "Fishery Science: Its Methods and Applications." John Wiley & Sons, Inc., New York. Designed for the professional worker in fish management, this book contains so much information about techniques in fish study that it is valuable to any naturalist.

SCHRENKHEISEN, RAY. 1938. "Field Book of Freshwater Fishes of North America North of Mexico." G. P. Putnam's Sons, New York. A popular guide to the more common fishes; line drawings of each species. Much good information in an excellent format.

SCHULTZ, L. P., AND EDITH STERN. 1948. "The Ways of Fishes." D. Van Nostrand Company, Inc., Princeton, N.J. Nontechnical treatment of the peculiar habits of fishes, with stress on the strange and unusual. Suitable for younger naturalists.

SCOTT, W. B. 1954. "Freshwater Fishes of Eastern Canada." University of Toronto Press, Toronto. An excellent, semipopular guide for the area covered. Good illustrations.

AMPHIBIANS AND REPTILES

BISHOP, SHERMAN. 1943. "Handbook of Salamanders." Comstock Publishing Associates, Inc., Ithaca, N.Y. One of the Handbooks of American Natural History, this excellent book represents the mature work of one of the great American authorities on salamanders. It is complete, well illustrated, and authoritative, though moderately technical in some respects. Keys to all species occurring in North America north of Mexico are included.

CARR, ARCHIE. 1952. "Handbook of Turtles." Comstock Publishing Associates, Inc., Ithaca, N.Y. This attractive and well-written volume is another of the Handbooks of American Natural History. Carr is among the most readable of present-day natural history writers, as well as an authority on turtles.

DITMARS, RAYMOND. 1949. "Field Book of North American Snakes." Doubleday & Company, Inc., New York. Mr. Ditmars wrote several books about reptiles, and his books are widely read and popular in treatment. This guide for the herpetologist is divided for convenient use according to geographical regions. It depends upon descriptions rather than keys for identification.

LOGIER, E. B. S. 1952. "The Frogs, Toads, and Salamanders of Eastern Canada." Clark, Irwin & Company, Ltd., Toronto. This small but information-packed volume adequately covers the collection and identification of amphibians within its area. The introductory chapters are particularly informative.

NOBLE, G. K. 1931. "The Biology of the Amphibia." McGraw-Hill Book Company, New York. (Reprinted 1954 by Dover Publications, New York.) Long the standard reference for general information about amphibian biology, this book is now again available in a reprint edition. No serious student of amphibia should be without it.

OLIVER, J. A. 1955. "Natural History of North American Amphibians and Reptiles." D. Van Nostrand Company, Inc., Princeton, N.J. For background reading and general information about these groups, this is the most comprehensive and up-to-date book available. It is one of the New Illustrated Naturalist series.

POPE, CLIFFORD. 1939. "Turtles of the United States and Canada." Alfred A. Knopf, Inc., New York. Although supplanted somewhat by Carr's book (see above), this is still a valuable reference, and is perhaps less technical than Carr.

———. 1955. "The Reptile World." Alfred A. Knopf, Inc., New York. This is a beautifully printed volume of up-to-date and pertinent information about reptiles. Pope writes in a most entertaining manner, and the information is authentic.

SCHMIDT, KARL, AND D. D. DAVIS. 1941. "Field Book of Snakes of the United States and Canada." G. P. Putnam's Sons, New York. Almost a model of what a field guide should be, this little book is indispensable to the collector of snakes. The keys are usable, the illustrations good, and the information accurate.

SMITH, HOBART. 1946. "Handbook of Lizards." Comstock Publishing Associates, Inc., Ithaca, N.Y. This is one of the early volumes in the Handbooks of American Natural History series, and one of the best. It is a compendium of information which will permit identification of lizards and will also tell the reader practically everything which is known about them. One valuable feature of this book is the inclusion, after each species or group, of a brief discussion of unsolved problems on which the interested biologist might work.

STEBBINS, ROBERT C. 1954. "Amphibians and Reptiles of Western North America." McGraw-Hill Book Company, Inc., New York. Regional works are often of special value, and this is a good one. Western herpetologists will find it of great interest. Coverage is the United States and Canada, westward from the eastern borders of New Mexico, Colorado, Wyoming, Montana, Saskatchewan, and Mackenzie.

WRIGHT, A. H., AND A. A. WRIGHT. 1949. "Handbook of Frogs and Toads." 3d ed. Comstock Publishing Associates, Inc., Ithaca, N.Y. Dr. Wright is the editor of the Handbooks of American Natural History series and an authority in herpetology. His wife has collaborated with him in producing this valuable book, which has grown increasingly useful with each new edition.

BIRDS

Birds are undoubtedly the most popular group of vertebrates among amateur biologists, and as a result the popular literature of birds is far more extensive than that of most other groups. The list given here is only a sample, but Pettingill (1956) presents a very extensive bibliography of both popular and technical works.

ALLEN, A. A. 1930. "The Book of Bird Life." D. Van Nostrand Company, Inc., Princeton, N.J. This book has served as a textbook for ornithology courses, but it is also suitable for general reading. Illustrations are, for the most part, photographs by the author.

BENT, A. C. 1919 and following. "Life Histories of North American Birds." 19 vols. to date. U.S. National Museum, Washington. This monumental work, when completed, will furnish the most comprehensive reference on natural history of birds ever attempted. Earlier volumes are out of print, although several have been reprinted, and all are available at good libraries.

CAMPBELL, BRUCE. 1953. "Finding Nests." William Collins Sons & Co., Ltd., London. The fine art of finding bird nests is here explained for the benefit of those who have not had the guidance of an expert. Hints are given which will save the beginner many hours.

CHAPMAN, FRANK M. 1932. "Handbook of Birds of Eastern North America." 2d ed. Rev. Appleton-Century-Crofts, Inc., New York. Chapman probably did more to popularize bird study than any other person. This book is semitechnical, with keys to the species and a wealth of other ornithological information.

Griscom, Ludlow. 1945. "Modern Bird Study." Harvard University Press, Cambridge, Mass. The student who does not know how to advance in his studies of birds would do well to read this book. It presents a review of modern concepts and approaches to ornithology and shows how they may be used by the student.

Hickey, J. J. 1953. "A Guide to Bird Watching." Garden City Books, New York. A "how-to" volume for the bird watcher, this book tells about tools and techniques for field study.

Kortright, F. H. 1942. "The Ducks, Geese and Swans of North America." Wildlife Institute, Washington, D.C. Books about particular groups of birds are too numerous to be mentioned here, but this one merits inclusion as a model of its kind. The text is comprehensive and authentic, the illustrations among the best ever printed. Plates of hybrid ducks and downy young and other plumages represent a real contribution to scientific ornithology.

McKenny, Margaret. 1947. "Birds in the Garden and How to Attract Them." University of Minnesota Press, Minneapolis. The easy way to study birds is to attract them to your property as residents or as guests. This handsome book will explain the techniques of attracting by such easy means as feeding trays, or such major operations as landscaping the home grounds.

Peterson, R. T. 1941. "A Field Guide to Western Birds." Houghton Mifflin Company, Boston. The companion volume to the eastern guide listed below, this book covers the area west of the 100th meridian.

———. 1947. "A Field Guide to the Birds." 2d ed. Houghton Mifflin Company, Boston. With this field guide and a pair of binoculars, thousands of Americans have become competent in identification of birds in the field. The Peterson system of identification by quick recognition of diagnostic marks has greatly improved the level of accuracy of field students everywhere.

Pettingill, O. S., Jr. 1956. "A Laboratory and Field Manual of Ornithology." 3d ed., Rev. Burgess Publishing Company, Minneapolis. Although designed for use in ornithology courses, this large and handsome volume is a worthy addition to the library of any student of birds. The bibliography is one of the most useful features of the book.

Pough, R. H. 1946. "Audubon Bird Guide: Eastern Land Birds." See entry following.

———. 1951. "Audubon Water Bird Guide: Water, Game and Large Land Birds." Doubleday & Company, Inc., New York. These two companion volumes represent the entry of the Doubleday Nature Guide series in the bird-book field. They feature excellent colored illustrations and a great deal more general information about each species than can be found in most field guides. The two volumes are available bound as one, but this thick volume is too bulky for convenient carrying in the pocket.

SAUNDERS, A. A. 1951. "A Guide to Bird Songs." Doubleday & Company, Inc., New York. Saunders has long been an active student of bird songs, and his unique system of recording and remembering them is fully explained in this book. The increased availability of bird-song recordings has perhaps made this little book less useful, but it is still very valuable for work in the field.

———. 1954. "The Lives of Wild Birds." Doubleday & Company, Inc., New York. In this little volume, Saunders presents a brief discussion of various aspects of bird life, with special emphasis on the encouragement of further study.

TERRES, J. K. 1953. "Songbirds in Your Garden." Thomas Y. Crowell Company, New York. This book on attracting birds, by the editor of *Audubon Magazine,* is one of the best on the subject.

WALLACE, G. J. 1955. "An Introduction to Ornithology." The Macmillan Company, New York. A textbook for introductory ornithology courses, this book gives a good general survey of modern bird study for the nonprofessional.

WOLFSON, ALBERT. (ed.) 1955. "Recent Advances in Avian Biology." University of Illinois Press, Urbana, Ill. Surveys of this type are of great value in acquainting students with progress in their field. Many of the papers are too technical for the average amateur to understand, but there is much that is useful for the field student who is concerned with the various aspects of ornithological research.

MAMMALS

BOURLIÈRE, FRANCIS. 1954. "The Natural History of Mammals." Alfred A. Knopf, Inc., New York. This translation of a book originally written in French is one of the best general surveys of present knowledge in mammalogy. It is well written in a popular vein and not unduly technical. For the student of mammals who is looking for a challenge, this book is the place to find it.

BURT, WILLIAM. 1952. "A Field Guide to the Mammals." Houghton Mifflin Company, Boston. A well-illustrated modern guide using the Peterson system for the field identification of mammals. It does not concern itself with subspecies but is a handy pocket guide for anyone concerned primarily with recognizing the animals he may see.

CAHALANE, V. H. 1947. "Mammals of North America." The Macmillan Company, New York. A popular survey of American mammals, illustrated with very attractive ink drawings. The writer draws heavily on his extensive field experience with mammals during his travels in the National Parks. The peculiar traits and personalities of the mammals are portrayed in a very interesting manner.

CAMERON, AUSTIN W. 1956. "A Guide to Eastern Canadian Mammals." National Museum of Canada, Ottawa. This little booklet is included as an example of the many local and regional works which are becoming available. Semipopular in treatment, it is especially valuable for its coverage of marine mammals and for its distributional data, which include information on all of Canada.

COCKRUM, E. L. 1955. "Laboratory Manual of Mammalogy." Burgess Publishing Company, Minneapolis. Much more than a laboratory manual, this modern guide for the mammalogist gives extremely valuable information on field techniques, keeping a notebook, field problems, etc.

GLASS, BRYAN. 1951. "A Key to the Skulls of North American Mammals." Burgess Publishing Company, Minneapolis. A technical key, in most cases going only to genera. Abundant line drawings illustrate skull characteristics.

HAMILTON, W. J., JR. 1939. "American Mammals." McGraw-Hill Book Company, Inc., New York. A clearly written and authentic survey of the general natural history of North American mammals. Information on prehistoric mammals is especially good. Each chapter covers a particular aspect of mammalian life, including food, reproduction, homes, classification, etc.

————. 1943. "The Mammals of Eastern United States." Comstock Publishing Associates, Inc., Ithaca, N.Y. An excellent identification guide and general reference to the mammals of this region. Keys to families and genera and good illustrations aid in identification. Coverage of life history is especially extensive. One of the Handbooks of American Natural History, this is indispensable for the student of mammals east of the Mississippi.

MURIE, OLAUS. 1954. "A Field Guide to Animal Tracks." Houghton Mifflin Company, Boston. The title does not fully indicate the tremendous amount of information included in this little volume. A good survey of the use of animal signs in interpreting natural events. One of the Peterson Field Guide series.

PALMER, RALPH S. 1954. "The Mammal Guide." Doubleday & Company, Inc., New York. One of the Doubleday series of nature guides, this is the most information-packed pocket guide to mammals yet produced. The numerous colored illustrations supplement a concise text which covers the habits of mammals in an excellent manner.

SETON, E. T. 1929. "Lives of Game Animals." Doubleday & Company, Inc., New York. Reprinted in 1954, this classic work is now available for a new generation of naturalists. The price of the eight beautifully illustrated volumes is beyond the range of many mammalogists, but it is an outstanding reference and an attractive addition to the naturalist's library. Pure natural history, it is based largely on Seton's own field work, which spanned more than half a century. The outstanding work of one of the last great naturalists.

SOURCES OF BIOLOGICAL LITERATURE
(other than publishing houses)

Books from regular publishers are the main source of biological information for most amateur biologists. The more advanced amateurs and the professional biologists, however, are usually aware of other sources. Many of these sources publish material which is of interest to every naturalist, so we give here a brief summary of the more important publishers of such material.

FEDERAL AGENCIES: All publications of the Federal government can be purchased from the Superintendent of Documents, Washington 25, D.C. Lists of available publications are usually obtainable from the department or branch of government by which they are prepared. Agencies which publish material of interest to biologists include the U.S. Department of Agriculture, U.S. Fish and Wildlife Service (formerly the Bureau of Biological Survey and Bureau of Fisheries), U.S. Forest Service, U.S. Soil Conservation Service, National Park Service, and the National Museum.

STATE AGENCIES: Most state governments engage in some kind of biological study of the state. The work of the agencies which perform these studies is usually published by the state and is given free or sold at cost to interested residents of the state. Among the organizations which may do state biological studies are natural history surveys, state museums, conservation departments, experiment stations, state colleges, or universities. Faunal and floral lists, popular guides to local areas, and sometimes sumptuous volumes on such groups as birds and wildflowers may be available.

MUSEUMS: Many public museums, particularly the larger ones such as those in Chicago and New York, publish a wealth of biological information. Guides to the local plants and animals are often available, and many are directed at the amateur naturalist or even at the beginner. Technical series, based on work in the collections of the museum, are often produced. A list of such publications may usually be secured by writing to the director of the museum.

PUBLIC EDUCATIONAL ORGANIZATIONS: The rise of popular nature study has led to the formation of numerous groups whose interest in nature provides a common bond. Some of these groups include in their activities publication of educational material, which is often of great value to the amateur or beginning naturalist. Among the organizations active in this field are the American Nature Association, National Audubon Society, National Wildlife Federation, Wildflower Preservation Society, Defenders of Furbearers, and the Wilderness Society.

COMMERCIAL ORGANIZATIONS: Business firms whose main sales are biological or scientific materials often publish booklets or pamphlets to aid their customers. Other business organizations sometime publish nature-study information at the popular level for public relations purposes. Biological supply houses (see p. 317) are one of the major sources for this kind of material.

JOURNALS FOR THE FIELD BIOLOGIST

The student who wishes a reasonably complete list of the biological journals of the world may find an up-to-date list in "Biological Sciences Serial Publications, a World List, 1950–1954" by J. H. Richter and C. P. Daly, published by the Library of Congress, 1955. This publication lists about 3,500 biological serials. Shorter lists, adequate for most purposes, may be found for botany in "Taxonomy of Vascular Plants" by G. H. M. Lawrence, The Macmillan Company, New York, 1951, pp. 310–317; for zoology, in "Guide to the Literature of the Zoological Sciences" by Roger Smith, Burgess Publishing Company, Minneapolis, 1952, pp. 72–85.

The list given here makes no pretense to completeness. It is an attempt to cover the major publications in the various branches of field biology, with special reference to those which the nonprofessional biologist may read with understanding. Only American and Canadian journals are included, since it is likely that these are the only ones available to most of our readers, and since they contain a very large proportion of the papers which would interest American field biologists.

AMERICAN FERN JOURNAL. 1910 and following. Published by the American Fern Society. This journal covers ferns and fern allies, and includes much of interest to the nonprofessional.

AMERICAN JOURNAL OF BOTANY. 1914 and following. Published by the Botanical Society of America. One of the biggest and best technical publications in the field of botany, this journal is primarily of interest to the professional.

AMERICAN MIDLAND NATURALIST. 1909 and following. Published by the University of Notre Dame, Notre Dame, Ind. Although this journal specializes in papers about the natural history of the central part of the country (hence the name *Midland*), papers on any aspect of biology are accepted. Unusually long papers are sometimes published as monographs, occupying an entire issue.

AMERICAN NATURALIST. 1867 and following. Journal of the American Society of Naturalists. One of the oldest biological journals in America, the *American Naturalist* is largely concerned with matters of morphology, evolution, and physiology. Occasionally papers of interest to the field student are included.

ANNALS OF THE ENTOMOLOGICAL SOCIETY OF AMERICA. 1908 and following. Published by the Entomological Society of America. This is the most important entomological journal in America, particularly for taxonomic and morphological studies.

THE AUK. 1884 and following. Journal of the American Ornithologists Union. One of the world's great bird journals, *The Auk* succeeded the *Bulletin of the Nuttall Ornithological Club* as the leading journal of American ornithology. Papers of general interest on the ornithology of any section of the world are included, and most of the short notes which fill the back of each issue are field notes.

BIOLOGICAL BULLETIN. 1898 and following. Published by the Marine Biological Laboratory, Woods Hole, Mass. Coverage of this monthly journal is general, with major emphasis on marine biology.

CANADIAN ENTOMOLOGIST. 1868 and following. Journal of the Entomological Society of Canada and the Entomological Society of Ontario. This is a major entomological journal, primarily concerned with the insects of Canada.

CANADIAN FIELD-NATURALIST. 1887 and following. Published by the Ottawa Field-naturalist's Club. (Succeeded the *Ottawa Naturalist.*) Most of the articles in this fine journal are of interest to the field student. Papers on all phases of natural history are accepted.

THE CONDOR. 1899 and following. Journal of the Cooper Ornithological Club. This large and valuable publication is confined to the study of birds, mostly those of the western United States.

COPEIA. 1913 and following. Journal of the American Society of Ichthyologists and Herpetologists. This publication started as a loose serial but now appears quarterly. Any kind of material on fishes, amphibians, or reptiles may appear here. It is the leading American journal in this field.

ECOLOGY. 1920 and following. Journal of the Ecological Society of America. *Ecology* is one of the great ecological journals in the world. Many of the papers are highly technical; others are of interest to the less skilled field worker.

ECOLOGICAL MONOGRAPHS. 1930 and following. Published by the Ecological Society of America. Papers which are too long for inclusion in *Ecology* may be published here. Any phase of ecology may be covered.

EVOLUTION. 1947 and following. Journal of the Society for the Study of Evolution. This relatively new journal has assumed international stature. It includes papers dealing with any phase of evolution in any part of the world.

JOURNAL OF HEREDITY. 1910 and following. Published by the American Genetic Association. Though not concerned with field biology, this leading American genetics journal contains items of interest to all biologists.

JOURNAL OF MAMMALOGY. 1919 and following. Journal of the American Society of Mammalogists. This is the only journal in the English language devoted solely to the study of mammals. Coverage is worldwide, although most of the papers are concerned with North America.

JOURNAL OF PARASITOLOGY. 1914 and following. Journal of the American

Society of Parasitologists. Papers on all aspects of animal parasitism appear in this bimonthly journal. It is one of the leading journals of its kind in the world.

JOURNAL OF WILDLIFE MANAGEMENT. 1937 and following. Journal of the Wildlife Society. This is an excellent quarterly publication devoted to wildlife research and management. Much good natural history material on species of economic importance is included.

QUARTERLY REVIEW OF BIOLOGY. 1926 and following. Although primarily a review journal, offering excellent reviews of biological books, this journal includes one or more technical papers in each issue. Some of these are interesting to the field biologist.

RHODORA. 1899 and following. Journal of the New England Botanical Club. Botany of the Northeast is covered by this small journal.

SCIENCE. 1883 and following. This is perhaps the only weekly journal of science in America. Published by the American Association for the Advancement of Science, it covers the whole field of science, so the number of papers of interest to any one biologist may not be large. Most of the papers are brief reports on discoveries or advances which may be of immediate interest to other workers.

BIBLIOGRAPHIES

BAY, J. C. 1910. "Bibliographies of Botany." *Progressus Rei Botanicae*, 3: 331–456. Although now out of date, this work is valuable for the student who wishes information about publications of the eighteenth and nineteenth centuries.

BIBLIOGRAPHY OF AGRICULTURE. 1942 and following. U.S. Department of Agriculture, Washington. Published monthly, this valuable reference covers a wide variety of biological subjects. It is particularly useful for its coverage of publications of state experiment stations.

BIOLOGICAL ABSTRACTS. 1926 and following. Philadelphia, Pa. The most comprehensive and widely used biological abstracting journal in the country, and probably in the world, this is one of the primary references for the biologist. The inclusion of an abstract (brief summary) of the papers listed is a valuable feature.

BLAKE, S. F., AND ALICE C. ATWOOD. 1942. "Geographical Guide to Floras of the World." Part I, U.S. Department of Agriculture Misc. no. 401. This publication covers Africa, Australia, the Americas, and the islands of the Pacific, Indian, and Atlantic Oceans. Part 2 has not yet been published. In addition to the list of floras, suggestions are given as to the construction of a floral list. Even though incomplete, it is the most useful guide of its kind, and is indispensable to the botanist.

BOTANICAL ABSTRACTS. 1918–1926. Baltimore, Md. This publication was superseded by *Biological Abstracts*, so that its life was relatively short. It is useful for the period which it covers.

DAYTON, WILLIAM. 1952. "United States Tree Books: A Bibliography of Tree Identification." U.S. Department of Agriculture Bibliographical Bulletin 20. The student who needs a local publication on trees may find here a list of those available.

DEAN, BASHFORD. 1916–1923. "Bibliography of Fishes." 3 vols. More than 35,000 references are covered in this great classic of biological bibliographies. It is now badly out of date but still extremely valuable for the period it covers.

HOTCHKISS, NEIL (ed.) 1954. "Wildlife Abstracts, 1935–1951: An Annotated Bibliography of the Publications Abstracted in the Wildlife Review, Nos. 1–66." U.S. Fish and Wildlife Service, Washington. Covering wildlife publications for the very important 15 years during which much of the development of wildlife management has occurred, this very useful volume is a compilation of items from the *Wildlife Review* (see below), and has the same format. Indispensable for the wildlife professional and of great value to all biologists.

INDEX LONDINENSIS TO ILLUSTRATIONS OF FLOWERING PLANTS, FERNS, AND FERN ALLIES. 1920–1931, with supplement, 1941. Oxford University Press, London. This tremendous publication lists the place of publication of illustrations of plants in the groups listed. The years from 1753 to 1935 are covered. For the student who wishes to see a picture of a particular plant, particularly one which has not been shown in many publications, this is a helpful work to have at hand. It may be found in most libraries where botanical research is done.

INDEX TO THE LITERATURE OF ECONOMIC ENTOMOLOGY. 1890 and following. This entomological index, indispensable to the worker in that field, was begun under the Department of Agriculture, and has been sponsored in recent years by the American Association of Economic Entomologists. Because it was for many years prepared by Mabel Colcord, it has become known as the Colcord Index. Numbers appear at three- to five-year intervals. Coverage includes North America and the West Indies, in varying degrees of completeness.

INTERNATIONAL CATALOG OF SCIENTIFIC LITERATURE. 1902–1919. Royal Society, London. This short-lived catalogue is useful for the short period during which it contained biological material, but it is not one of the primary references.

JACKSON, B. D. 1881. "Guide to the Literature of Botany." Longmans, Green & Co., Ltd., London. Although very much out of date, this large volume is often useful for literature of the nineteenth century.

REHDER, A. 1911–1918. "The Bradley Bibliography: A Guide to the Literature of the Woody Plants of the World Published Before the Beginning of the Twentieth Century." 5 vols. Harvard University Press, Cambridge, Mass. The title of this work indicates its coverage and value.

SMITH, ROGER C. 1952. "Guide to the Literature of the Zoological Sciences." 3d ed. Burgess Publishing Company, Minneapolis. For the beginner, adventuring into the field of biological literature, this book is a necessity. For the more advanced student, it is an almost indispensable reference. Although confined to zoological literature, it contains many publications which cover the whole field of biology and also presents valuable information about conducting a literature search, writing a scientific paper, and other matters of interest to the biologist. This is one of the most valuable and least expensive of bibliographic aids.

STRONG, R. M. 1939–1946. "A Bibliography of Birds." 3 vols. Field Museum of Natural History, Zoological Sciences Bulletin 25. Chicago, Ill. The indispensable bibliography for ornithologists; tightly packed with references to the literature about birds.

ULRICH, CAROLYN F. 1951. "Ulrich's Periodicals Directory." 6th ed. R. R. Bowker Company, New York. An annotated list of some ten thousand world periodicals, with information about the content of each one.

UNION LIST OF SERIALS. 1943 and following. The H. W. Wilson Company, New York. This is one of the most valuable publications for the scientist. It lists the holdings of serials in American libraries, so that the worker who wishes to consult a particular publication can readily discover where it is obtainable (see fig. 10-2).

UNITED STATES BOOK CATALOG AND THE CUMULATIVE BOOK INDEX. 1928 and following. The H. W. Wilson Company, New York. A cumulative list of books published and available in the United States, of particular value in determining date of publication and other information about books.

WILDLIFE REVIEW. 1935 and following. U.S. Fish and Wildlife Service, Washington. For workers in the field of wildlife management, this publication is a necessity. For other biologists, it is a very valuable tool. Its coverage is wider than the title would imply, and each article is briefly reviewed. It appears irregularly, about four times each year. Items reviewed prior to 1952 are included in *Wildlife Abstracts* (see above).

WOOD, C. A. 1931. "An Introduction to the Literature of Vertebrate Zoology." Oxford University Press, London. Although now out of print, this book is available in many good libraries and is of great value as an introduction to the field.

ZOOLOGICAL RECORD. 1864 and following. Zoological Society of London. The number-one reference for the zoologist. The length of time covered, and its inclusion of references from the whole world, make this bibliography essential to any literature survey (see p. 249 and fig. 10-4).

SOME TOOLS AND TECHNIQUES OF THE FIELD BIOLOGIST

Even in field biology, machines have been developed to aid man in his work and observations. Particularly in ecology, which is a science of measurement, tools of various kinds assume great importance. A brief survey of some of the more important devices and the ways in which they are used may assist the beginning biologist or anyone who has not had the opportunity to use the tools of this field.

CAMERAS: Almost every field biologist has occasion to use a camera at one time or another. There are dozens of different models, sizes, and degrees of complexity and price. This vast array of cameras is often confusing to the beginner, but the matter can be simplified by breaking them down into four major types most often used in field work.

1. *The single-lens reflex.* These cameras have one lens, which is used as a viewing lens prior to taking the picture. A special mirror flips out of the way automatically as the shutter release is pressed. Such cameras are now available in sizes from the 4- by 5-inch Graflex down to the 35-mm Exakta and its many counterparts. Such a camera is ideal for close-up photos of insects, flowers, and other small objects. Many biologists regard it as the ideal camera for biological work. Good single-lens reflexes are expensive, but satisfactory models without the luxury features of slow shutter speeds and high-speed lenses can be obtained for under $100. Figure 7-1 was taken with a single-lens reflex in the under-$100 class.

2. *The twin-lens reflex.* Most of these cameras take 2¼-inch-square pictures, adequate for sizable enlargements. Sturdy, simple, and convenient, they are available in any price range above $25. Do not confuse the lower-priced cameras, often called "reflexes," with these models. The cheap models are built on the same principle as the ordinary box camera, but with a larger and more brilliant viewer. Twin-lens reflexes have the problem of parallax when used at close range, i. e., the picture seen through the viewing lens is not exactly the same as that taken through the taking lens, for the two lenses are several inches apart. In this respect, they are inferior to single-lens reflexes. Otherwise, this type of camera is very versatile, and the more expensive models are among the most widely used cameras among professional photographers. Figures 1-4 and 8-4 were made with a 2¼- by 2¼-inch twin-lens reflex in the $40 price range.

3. *The view camera and press camera.* These cameras have the advantage of extreme versatility and large negative sizes (from 2¼ by 3¼ inches up to 4 by 5 are popular sizes, although view cameras up to 8 by 10 are available). Because of these features the critical photographer often prefers such cameras. They are, however, relatively expensive, and the large film size increases the cost of use. They are also relatively bulky, which may be a disadvantage for field use. View cameras—the type most often used by professional portrait photographers—require some time to set up and prepare, but press cameras are more convenient. Figure 4-12, of the goshawk, was taken with a view camera, on a 5- by 7-inch plate.

4. *The Leica-type 35-mm camera.* Extremely popular because of its convenience, ease, and economy of use, this is probably the most popular type of camera in America at present. Models are available in every price range, with the Leica, Contax, Nikon, and a few others at the top of the list. The small negative size means that the lens must be extremely good if a fair-sized print is to have high quality. If enlargements are to be made, grain in the film and dust spots on the lens may become critical matters, whereas they are much less significant with larger film. An unlimited variety of accessories for the higher-priced models make these cameras among the most versatile. Figures 1-2 and 9-5 were taken with a $75 camera of this type.

Other popular kinds of cameras are available, including folding cameras, box cameras, etc. Acceptable pictures can be made, even with a box camera, if the user recognizes and accepts the limitations of the camera. Most poor pictures are the result of trying to make the camera do something for which it was not intended, or carelessness in its use. Inability to afford a high-priced camera need not prevent anyone from taking perfectly satisfactory pictures, within a limited range of subject matter and conditions.

CAMERA ACCESSORIES: The biologist who uses a camera will soon find that its usefulness can be greatly increased with a few accessories. The most important of these are the various types of accessory lenses and filters which give added versatility to the camera. Unfortunately, some of these are often very expensive and are not available for lower-priced cameras.

1. *Telephoto lenses.* The function of a telephoto lens is to permit a large image to be recorded from a distance. They are rated as $2\times$, $3\times$, etc., according to the degree of area magnification. The price increases rapidly with increase in power, so that not everyone can afford to equip his camera with these very useful accessories. Recently, binoculars have been adapted to telephoto use with satisfactory results, and the cost of the attachment is not great. The binoculars may, of course, be used for other purposes than photography, thus eliminating the necessity of carrying an additional piece of equipment. Binoculars especially manufactured for this purpose, and the accessory by which they are attached to the camera, may be secured from many camera stores; or information may be obtained by writing to Bushnell, 140 Bushnell Building, Pasadena 1, California.

2. *Close-up lenses.* Biologists often wish to take photographs of small objects, such as flowers, insects, etc., at close range. In single-lens reflex cameras, this is achieved by the use of extension tubes, using the regular camera lens. With view cameras, a double extension bellows permits the same result. For other cameras, inexpensive close-up lenses are available to permit the user to approach within 6 to 36 inches of his subject. They snap on or screw over the camera lens, and are easy to attach and use. Parallax is a major problem in using these lenses,

but this can be overcome by experience or by construction of a frame which exactly covers the area which the picture will cover.

3. *Wide-angle lenses.* In some cases, a photographer is unable to get far enough from a subject to include in the picture as much as he wants. For such occasions, wide-angle lenses are available, which permit coverage of a larger area. Though less expensive than the higher powers of telephoto lenses, they are by no means cheap, and are not so often used in biological work as the other types of accessories mentioned here.

4. *Filters.* Filters of tinted glass or plastic may be placed over the lens of the camera to secure special effects. In most cases their use is artistic rather than scientific, but they greatly enhance the effect of scenic shots by showing clouds in true contrast, by cutting down glare, or by rendering more accurate tonal relationships in the picture. Figure 6-22 shows the dramatic effect which can be obtained by proper use of a filter. Filters are so inexpensive that the photographer can readily afford to own the three or four most commonly used types.

FILMS: Standard films are of two types: orthochromatic and panchromatic. Orthochromatic (or ortho) film is insensitive to light at the red end of the visible spectrum, while panchromatic (or pan) film is more sensitive in that area. The latter is most widely used for scientific purposes.

Films vary greatly in such characteristics as speed, i.e., the amount of light needed to secure an adequate image; grain, i.e., the size of particles built up during the developing process; the degree of contrast between black and white; and other ways. The beginner should secure one of the books listed below from a photographic store or book store, rather than experiment with different films.

Special films are available for copying, for taking pictures through haze, and for many other specific needs. Indeed, the film industry is developing so rapidly that new products appear constantly to fill the varied needs of the photographer.

BINOCULARS: Observers of birds and mammals need binoculars for almost all of their field work, while other biologists have only occasional use for them. There are two major variables, other than quality of the lenses, in binoculars. First is *magnification.* Six- to eight-power glasses are the most popular. At higher magnifications it is difficult to hold binoculars steady in the hand; they become heavy and bulky. For greater magnification a telescope is needed (see below). The second variable is *diameter of objective (front) lens.* In order to allow for adequate light transmission, the diameter of the objective lens should be at least five times the magnification. Thus 6-power glasses with a 30-mm objective lens (6 × 30) are quite satisfactory, while an 8-power glass with the same objective lens would be usable only in bright light. For observation in dim light, as at dawn or twilight, or in dense forests, 7 × 50 glasses are the most popular type. These are sometimes known as night glasses.

Binoculars are available with *center focusing*, or with *individual eyepiece focusing*. Preference in this matter is largely a matter of personal taste; with practice, anyone can use either with perfect satisfaction. Individual-focusing glasses are thought to be somewhat more durable. Practically all binoculars today are made with *coated lenses*. A thin chemical coating is put over certain of the lenses to increase the light transmission by about 25 per cent. A purplish reflection from the objective lenses indicates that they are coated.

Price of binoculars is extremely variable and is not an adequate indication of quality. Whenever possible, binoculars should be tried out thoroughly before purchasing, or should be bought on a 30-day-trial guarantee. Common faults of binoculars include *chromatic aberration* —appearance of a rainbow of colors around objects seen through the glasses; *poor alignment*—divergence of one of the oculars from exactly the same field as the other, causing a distortion which will result in severe eyestrain if it is not corrected; *poor construction*—allowing lenses to become unglued under field use, dust to get inside the lenses, eyepieces to crack. The best guard against this is to secure a guarantee. Some manufacturers use a relative-brightness figure to indicate the light-transmitting ability of their binoculars. For comparative purposes this is helpful, but in the final analysis only use in the field under varied conditions will tell you whether a pair of binoculars will fit your needs.

TELESCOPES: For long-range observation of big-game animals, waterfowl, and various other animals, a telescope is necessary. Relatively inexpensive models are available which will give magnifications of 30 to 40 power, which is adequate for most biological uses. Most of the so-called "spotting scopes" are fitted with a tripod mount so that any camera tripod can be used to hold them steady. As with binoculars, actual use in the field is the best guarantee of satisfaction. Foreign-made telescopes, particularly from Japan, may be cheaper than American brands, and some of them are excellent, but care must be exercised in purchasing one.

HAND LENSES: The hand lens is the trademark of the botanist, as the bird glass is of the ornithologist and the insect net of the entomologist. Doublet (two-lens) and triplet (three-lens) models are available, the latter more expensive and better. Good hand lenses can be secured from biological supply houses at $10 to $15. All biologists will find them essential for examining small objects in the field.

MICROSCOPES: Most biologists do not own a microscope because of the high price involved. A good modern microscope, suitable for research use, may cost from $500 to $1500. For the amateur, however, who merely wants to look at the little things of nature, small and cheap microscopes, mostly of Japanese make, are available at prices ranging from $5 to $50. The worst fault of these models is the very small field. Finding organisms in a culture is difficult, and often only the smallest organisms can be seen entirely in one field. Student microscopes, suitable for some uses, are sold at prices around $100, but these lack the refinements which are needed by the person who uses a microscope extensively.

Suggested Reading

BAILEY, A. M. 1951. "Nature Photography with Miniature Cameras." Denver Museum of Natural History, Museum Pictorial no. 1, Denver, Colo. For the devotee of the 35-mm camera, this book tells how to use such cameras in nature photography. Bailey is one of today's outstanding nature photographers.

KODAK DATA BOOK. Eastman Kodak Company, Rochester, N.Y. A compendium of photographic information, much of it technical, and mostly directly related to Kodak products. Available in most photo stores.

SHUMWAY, HERBERT D. 1956. "Nature Photography Guide." Greenberg: Publisher, Inc., New York. Everything from insects to elephants is covered in this guide for the beginner in nature photography. It is well illustrated with photos taken by the author.

YEATES, G. K. 1946. "Bird Photography." Faber & Faber, Ltd., London. Yeates is one of England's outstanding bird photographers, and his point of view is the opposite of that of Bailey (above), in that he insists that the view camera is the only adequate instrument for nature photography. This is an excellent book for the student who is interested in bird photography.

Ecological Tools and Instruments

Ecological data must be quantitative; that is, scientific study requires taking actual measurements, rather than depending upon subjective judgments. In chaps. 4 and 8, the methods of sampling biological factors in the environment are treated in some detail. Physical factors of the environment are equally important, and ecologists have devised or adapted a variety of instruments and tools to measure these factors. We will list here some of the more important ones.

INSTRUMENTS FOR MEASURING ATMOSPHERIC CONDITIONS:

1. *Light.* An ordinary photoelectric meter, such as an exposure meter, may be used for this purpose. The meter measures only light intensity, of course, but this is usually adequate. More refined data on the heating effects of light and other factors of light may be obtained with more specialized instruments, but these are not usually required.

2. *Temperature.* A standard mercury thermometer is suitable for most temperature readings, provided it is checked for accuracy. If the instrument can be left in place, a maximum-minimum thermometer will give measurements of the highest and lowest temperatures over a given period of time. If continuous records are needed, and the area is not disturbed, a thermograph may be placed there. This device records temperatures during a time span on a paper attached to a revolving drum.

3. *Evaporation and transpiration rates.* Rate of evaporation at a given site is most often determined by the use of the Livingston atmometer. This is a porous clay sphere made to precise specifications and attached to a water container. When water evaporates from the atmometer, more water is drawn in through the connecting tube, and the rate of evaporation can be determined by the decrease of water in the container. Plant transpiration rates are often roughly determined by the use of cobalt chloride–treated paper. The paper is blue when dry and turns pink when it takes up moisture. A piece of this paper is attached to a leaf between glass plates. The time required for the paper to turn completely pink gives a guide to relative rate of transpiration.

4. *Relative humidity.* Most ecological studies of humidity are made with a sling psychrometer. This is an instrument which has a dry-bulb and a wet-bulb thermometer, and which is whirled through the air by a sling attachment at one end. The wet bulb is cooled because of evaporation of its water. The amount of evaporation—and hence the temperature of the bulb—is determined by the amount of water vapor in the air. The temperature of the wet bulb, therefore, in relation to the temperature of the dry bulb, indicates relative humidity. Standard tables are used to convert the readings. In smaller spaces, where it is impossible to whirl the instrument, models have been devised which pass air over the bulbs in a different manner. One works more or less on the principle of an egg beater. Another, known as the dewpoint apparatus, is operated by forcing air from a rubber bulb through a silver-lined vessel containing a) ether, b) a protruding, open-ended glass tube through which the air escapes, and c) a thermometer. Evaporation of the ether lowers the temperature of the metal, and when it reaches a given point, dew condenses on the outside of the vessel. The dew point depends on the humidity. Through temperature readings and the use of tables, relative humidity can be determined.

5. *Precipitation.* Rain gauges of standard types are used to measure rainfall. Many different shapes and sizes are used. Snow is more difficult to measure accurately because of variation in weight and water content, so that depth alone means little. Sampling of accumulated snow with tubes which draw out a core are often used to determine

depth and to give a sample from which water content can be determined.

6. *Wind.* The anemometer is a standard weather instrument which can be adapted for ecological use. Some anemometers have automatic recorders for long-term use. The cup anemometer is the most widely used type. The movement of air currents in a confined area may be measured with the katathermometer, based on cooling of a column of alcohol; which process is facilitated by air currents.

INSTRUMENTS FOR MEASURING SOIL CONDITIONS:

1. *Temperature.* Soil temperature is measured with ordinary mercury thermometers, often with special attachments which permit them to be forced into the soil to various depths. For permanent or long-term installations a metal tube may be installed, into which a thermometer is lowered. If continuous records are needed, a thermograph may be set up just as for measuring air temperature, but with the instrument set to record temperatures underground.

2. *Moisture.* Several factors are concerned in soil moisture. If we need only to know the moisture content of a particular soil at a particular time, this can be determined by drying a weighed sample of soil and then reweighing it. The difference between the weight before and after drying is due, of course, to water removal. A simpler method is the soil point, a porcelain cone of standard size and porosity. When inserted into the soil, this cone will absorb water, the amount of which is relative to the water content of the soil, and is readily determinable by weighing the cone. Comparisons are thus easily made in different places. For more detailed studies, we may wish to determine water-holding capacity and other factors, but these are of greater importance to the agronomist than to the field biologist.

3. *Aeration.* The air space in the soil may be roughly determined by calculating the amount of water the soil will hold at saturation, since water will fill most of the air space. This is close enough to fulfill the usual requirements of an ecological study.

4. *pH.* Several methods are used for measuring pH. Colored papers and indicator chemicals are the most convenient, and field kits adequate for general use are available at low cost. For precise determination, ecologists use electric measuring devices, such as the pH meter.

5. *Structure.* Soil scientists classify soil according to the size of the particles, gravel having the largest particles and clay the smallest. Size of the particles may be determined by examination of a sample under a microscope, or more often by differential settling of the particles in water. Amount of humus in the soil may also be of great significance, and is often roughly determined by heating the soil sample to a high temperature so as to burn off the organic matter.

6. *Soil profile.* For some studies it is desirable to study the depth of topsoil and its various characteristics. This may be done by digging

into the soil to expose a section to the necessary depth. A larger number of samples can be taken by a core sampler, which removes a cylinder of soil to the desired depth. In sampling peat bogs to study pollen at various depths, thus determining vegetational patterns over hundreds of years, samples of the peat must be taken at varying depths. A core sampler has been devised which, when closed, can be forced into the bog and then opened and locked at the desired depth. Then it is driven down again and picks up a sample at that point.

INSTRUMENTS FOR MEASURING AQUATIC CONDITIONS:

1. *Light.* Light penetration into water has an important effect on life at any depth. To determine this factor, limnologists use the Secchi disk. This is a white disk 20 centimeters in diameter, which is let down on a rope. The depth at which it disappears from view is noted. Then it is drawn up, and the depth at which it reappears is noted. The average of these two depths gives a rough relative figure of light penetration. For more precise data, photoelectric recorders have been devised.

2. *Temperature.* Since temperature varies greatly from top to bottom of a body of water, it is often necessary to determine temperature at different depths. Electrical recording devices have been made which will give a continuous record of temperature as the depth increases. A simpler device is the reversing thermometer. This is a device inside which a thermometer is lowered on a wire to the desired depth. A metal messenger is then sent down the wire to release a catch which quickly inverts the thermometer. This sudden reversal permits some of the mercury to leave the main reservoir and enter a subsidiary reservoir. The amount of mercury which has left the main reservoir is correlated with the temperature of the water at the point of reversal. The thermometer can be raised to the surface and read.

3. *Bottom type.* Dredges and core samplers are used to draw up bottom samples for study, and are similar to the soil samplers discussed above.

4. *Water movement.* Stream velocity is most often measured by timing a floating object over a measured course. With this technique, care must be taken to measure velocity in different places, since velocity is decreased around the edges and bottom of streams because of friction.

5. *Chemical conditions.* Many chemical factors have an effect on the productivity of fresh water. These include oxygen content, pH, free carbon dioxide, amount of carbonates, bicarbonates, and other chemicals, and content of dead organic matter. Samples of water are taken by a sampler which works on much the same principle as the peat sampler. An open cylinder is lowered into the water to the desired depth and closed by a metal messenger which is dropped down the wire. The details of the determination of these chemical factors are beyond the scope of this book, but further information may be obtained from the books by Welch, listed below.

SUGGESTED READING

OOSTING, HENRY J. 1956. "The Study of Plant Communities." 2d ed. W. H. Freeman and Co., San Francisco.

WELCH, PAUL S. 1952. "Limnology." 2d ed. McGraw-Hill Book Company, Inc., New York.

———. 1948. "Limnological Methods." The Blakiston Division, McGraw-Hill Book Company, Inc., New York.

THE USE OF STATISTICS IN BIOLOGICAL STUDIES

In the study of natural history, many observations are made which are not subject to experimental proof. Science, however, demands that we be as certain as possible of our facts, and in recent years many workers have come to depend upon statistics to provide evidence. This trend has been called by some a fad, but there can be no doubt that statistical analysis of data is an extremely valuable tool in many studies. The biologist with little mathematical training must know when his work requires the use of statistics, and he must know enough about the subject to read with understanding the work of his colleagues. The more abstruse elements of statistics may well be left to competent mathematicians, and these facts are in any case too lengthy to be included here. This brief summary is intended to indicate some of the field projects in which statistical analysis is needed, as well as some of the more important methods which are used. The interested reader may further his knowledge by consulting the references which are listed at the end of this section.

Statistical analysis is restricted to data which can be expressed in numerical terms. Such data are said to be *quantitative* or *meristic*. Thus the number of feathers on the bodies of members of a particular species of bird can, if one has the patience, be counted, producing meristic data which can be statistically analyzed. The numerous instruments available to the biologist today make meristic or quantitative data obtainable in a great number of biological studies.

The basis of statistical analysis is the population which is being analyzed. This may be the trees in a forest, the animals in a field, the organisms which belong to a particular species, or any other discrete population. (It should be noted here that this is not the same usage of the word "population" as in chap. 8.)

It is rarely possible to study an entire population. If you could do so, you would know that your facts were absolutely reliable and covered the entire range of variation within that population. Since we cannot study the whole group, we usually depend upon samples. Some of the difficulties and problems of sampling are discussed in chap. 4 and chap. 8. An adequate sample must be chosen in a random manner and must be large enough to include most of the range of variation of the characteristics which we are going to measure. Complete randomness would require that every member of the population had as much chance of being included in the sample as any other member. This is, of course, very difficult to achieve, but the biologist should make every effort to approach it as closely as possible.

From our sample, we derive data about the specimens included in it, and from these data we want to derive other data about the population as a whole. The most commonly derived statistics are the *range*, the *mean*, the *mode*, the *median*, and the *standard deviation*.

The *range* includes all the integers in a sample, from the smallest measurement to the greatest; it reflects the variability of the characteristic being studied.

The *mean* is the arithmetic average of the counts or measurements, derived by adding all the measurements together and dividing by the number of specimens in the sample.

The *mode* is the count or measurement which occurs most frequently in a given sample; it may or may not be close to the mean.

The *median* is the exact middle score of the distribution, and this too may or may not closely approximate the mean.

Standard deviation is a measure of variation from the mean of individual counts in the sample. It is derived by a rather easy mathematical process and is useful in determining the expected range of the population, among other things.

The usual way of setting up quantitative data is in the form of a frequency distribution. Each member of the sample is assigned to a class, whose members have the same measurement. For example, if you were measuring the total length of a sample of deer mice, you might divide the sample into classes with millimeter lengths of 150–154, 155–159, 160–164, 165–169, etc., to the largest measurement. Each of these divisions is known as a *class interval*.

In some cases, a frequency distribution will give all the information needed when presented in the form of a graph. Graphic presentations are readily understood if they are properly devised, and may express data which are difficult to understand in the form of tables.

When a characteristic is distributed at random throughout a population, a graph of its frequency distribution would take the form of a *normal* curve. This term has a precise mathematical meaning, but for our purposes we may say that the curve is bell-shaped, with the highest point at the middle, curving off in the same manner in both directions. Thus the distribution of height in American men, if plotted on a graph, would be expected to produce a normal curve. If the highest point of the curve is nearer one end than the other, we call this a *skewed* curve. Such a curve would be obtained by plotting the age at which American men marry, since a large percentage of them would fall into the class interval between 20 and 30, near the bottom of the curve. A curve which has two well-separated high points is called a *bimodal* curve, and such a curve indicates that the sample includes individuals from two distinctly different groups. For example, if you plotted the height of Americans on a single graph without regard to sex, you would probably have a bimodal curve, with one high point representing the class into which the largest group of women fell, and another high point representing the class into which the largest group of men fell.

Frequency distributions are often used to derive other data. One common use is that of comparing two or more populations with regard to meristic characteristics. Two groups in which the ranges of the counts or measurements do not overlap would probably be regarded as two distinct species. If the ranges are essentially similar, the two samples were no doubt drawn from the same natural population. When the ranges differ in a marked way, but still overlap, we are faced with the problem of deciding whether the data indicate that the populations are different, or that individual variation can account for the differences. By applying certain statistical tests to the data, we can show that our hypothesis is either probably right or probably wrong, and can state mathematically the degree of probability. A simple example may help to explain this.

Suppose that the wing measurements of a sample of 50 birds of a species which occurs in New England range from 70 to 90, with a mean of 81. A similar sample from Newfoundland shows a range from 76 to 98, with a mean of 87. Obviously there is a difference, but is it statistically significant? Or, in other words, is it probable that the two samples could not have been drawn from a single homogeneous population?

There are several ways of arriving at this information, and they are too complex to be treated in detail here. The results are usually expressed in terms of percentage; e.g., the results are said to be significant at the 95 per cent or 99 per cent level. At the 95 per cent level, this means that the odds are 95 to 5—or 19 to 1—that the hypothesis is correct; although this is not proof, it is strong evidence.

The many uses of statistics in biological research are too varied and complex to consider here. Perhaps the best way to introduce the student to such uses is to indicate some studies in which statistics have played a part, and which will serve to demonstrate some of the methods commonly used and some of the types of research which profit by statistical treatment. The papers listed in the Suggested Reading which present a cross section of biological statistics are marked (S).

These studies vary a great deal in the complexity of the statistics employed, some being very simple and some rather complicated. Simple statistics, such as graphs and frequency distributions, are used in a large percentage of biological studies. The more complex statistical operations are used less often, but in ecology and taxonomy particularly they have become important. For the biologist who has some doubts as to the needs of a particular study, it would be wise to consult a statistician before the experiments are set up. Often experiments can be designed to give satisfactory results from the statistical viewpoint, whereas if a statistician were consulted after the performance of the experiments, he might find that they were not set up to yield data suitable for statistical analysis.

SUGGESTED READING

BARTHOLOMEW, GEORGE A., JR., AND WILLIAM R. DAWSON. 1954. Temperature regulation in young pelicans, herons, and gulls. *Ecol.*, 35:466–472. Certain physiological and morphological data are subject to statistical analysis. This paper uses statistics in analyzing the development of temperature regulation. (S)

CAZIER, M. A., AND A. BACON. 1949. Introduction to quantitative systematics. *Bull. Amer. Mus. Nat. Hist.*, 93:347–388.

HAYNE, DON W. 1950. Apparent home range of *Microtus* in relation to distance between traps. *J. Mammal.*, 31:26–39. A statistical study of the determination of home range. (S)

KEMPTHORNE, O., ET AL. 1954. "Statistics and Mathematics in Biology." Iowa State College Press, Ames, Iowa.

MACLULICH, D. A. 1951. A new technique of animal census, with examples. *J. Mammal.*, 32:318–328. A statistical approach to the counting problem. (S)

MATHER, K. 1947. "Statistical Analysis in Biology." Interscience Publishers, Inc., New York.

MOORE, P. G. 1954. Spacing in plant populations. *Ecol.*, 35:222–227. The use of statistics in vegetational analysis. (S)

RAND, A. L., AND M. A. TRAYLOR. 1951. Variation in *Dumetella carolinensis*. *The Auk*, 66:25–28. Analysis of differences among members of a single species over its entire range. (S)

SIMPSON, GEORGE G., AND ANNE ROE. 1939. "Quantitative Zoology." McGraw-Hill Book Company, Inc., New York.

WOHLSCHLAG, DONALD E. 1954. Mortality rates of whitefish in an arctic lake. *Ecol.*, 35:388–396. Management of wildlife is dependent upon knowledge of all phases of life history. Statistics can often be employed to advantage in securing information of this type. (S)

BOOKS ON NATURE-STUDY ACTIVITIES AND TECHNIQUES

ANDERSON, R. M. 1948. "Methods of Collecting and Preserving Vertebrate Animals." National Museum of Canada, Bulletin 69, Ottawa. Although designed for the professional biologist, this little book contains a wealth of information for the person who has occasion to preserve biological material. The information on where and how to capture animals is of value even to those who want live animals for study.

BROWN, VINSON. 1954. "How to Make a Home Nature Museum." Little, Brown & Company, Boston. For the teacher of biology who wishes to improve the appearance of his classroom, or for the amateur who wants a display to attract and educate children, this book provides the necessary information.

———. 1948. "The Amateur Naturalist's Handbook." Little, Brown & Company, Boston. Although this little pocket-sized book is a veritable hodgepodge of miscellaneous information about nature study, much of its contents deal with the aims and the techniques of the field naturalist. It has special appeal for the younger naturalist.

HEADSTROM, B. R. 1941. "Adventures with a Microscope." J. B. Lippincott Company, Philadelphia. For the explorer in the microscopic world, this book will give guidance and encouragement. The young naturalist with a low-priced microscope will find it especially helpful.

HILLCOURT, WILLIAM. 1950. "Field Book of Nature Activities." G. P. Putnam's Sons, New York. One of the Putnam field book series, this excellent volume gives a tremendous quantity of information about techniques for the field naturalist. Small and compact enough to carry in the field, it is probably the best nontechnical resumé of the subject.

JAEGER, ELLSWORTH. 1948. "Tracks and Trailcraft." The Macmillan Company, New York. The young reader of trails and signs will find here the techniques of trail reading and track identification. It is aimed at a younger group than is the book by Murie (see below).

———. 1950. "Nature Crafts." The Macmillan Company, New York. A book for the young naturalists with artistic or handicraft leanings.

MILLER, DAVID F., AND GLENN W. BLAYDES. 1938. "Methods and Materials for Teaching Biological Sciences." McGraw-Hill Book Company, Inc., New York. The first part is concerned with teaching methods in science, and is thus of interest only to teachers. Most of the book, however, is a gold mine of information about techniques, collecting, and other aspects of biology, much of which is of value in field work.

MOORE, CLIFFORD. 1954. "Book of Wild Pets." G. P. Putnam's Sons, New York. Whether you are keeping a pet or maintaining captive animals for study, this book gives information about the requirements of all kinds of wild animals in captivity, which will help you keep your animals alive, healthy, and comfortable.

MURIE, OLAUS. 1954. "Field Guide to Animal Tracks." Houghton Mifflin Company, Boston. See review under the list of books about mammals.

NEEDHAM, J. G. (ed.) 1937. "Culture Methods for Invertebrate Animals." Comstock Publishing Associates, Inc., Ithaca, N.Y. A compendium of techniques, this book draws on the experience of hundreds of biologists. It would be difficult to name an invertebrate group which is not included.

PETERSON, A. M. 1953. "A Manual of Entomological Techniques." 7th ed. Published by the author, Ohio State University, Columbus, O. Every phase of entomological technique is covered in this book. Information on collecting, rearing, experimental setups, and many other aspects of entomological work is given, with abundant illustrations of the necessary equipment.

OMAN, P. W., AND A. D. CUSHMAN. 1948. "Collection and Preservation of Insects." U.S. Department of Agriculture Misc. no. 60. An inexpensive and authoritative guide to techniques in collecting insects and preparing them for study.

PRAY, LEON. 1943. "Taxidermy." The Macmillan Company, New York. Though small, this book gives an adequate introduction to the subject. It is well illustrated and simply written, so that even the younger naturalist will find it useful.

SMITHSONIAN INSTITUTION. 1944. "A Field Collector's Manual in Natural History." Smithsonian Institution, Publ. no. 3766. Designed for the field workers of the Smithsonian Institution, this book contains a wealth of valuable information for the field biologist.

WAGSTAFFE, R. J., and J. H. FIDLER. 1955. "The Preservation of Natural History Specimens." vol. 1, "The Invertebrates." Philosophical Library, Inc., New York. The first volume of what should eventually be the most exhaustive survey of techniques for the collector.

WING, LEONARD. 1951. "Practices of Wildlife Conservation." John Wiley & Sons, Inc., New York. Two chapters of this book are devoted to techniques of wildlife study and management. These chapters warrant the inclusion of the book in this list, for they cover a wide variety of techniques which have extensive application in field biology.

SOURCES OF MAPS

Maps of various kinds are essential to any biological study. The accompanying list may be of value to the student who is unfamiliar with the kinds of maps used for particular purposes, and with the places where such maps may be secured. The list progresses from maps on a relatively small scale, covering large areas, to maps which give detailed coverage of a small area.

ATLASES AND GAZETEERS: Such books cover the entire world, but the maps are so small as to be of limited value. Good atlases are published by Mc-Graw-Hill Book Company, Inc., New York; J. B. Lippincott Company, Philadelphia; Rand McNally & Company, Chicago; and many other publishing houses. Any good library is likely to have a selection of atlases on its reference shelves.

FOLDING MAPS OF COUNTRIES AND CONTINENTS: Larger in scale than the maps in atlases, these maps are still of value only in a general survey of an area. Many such maps are available from the National Geographic Association, Washington, D.C.; C. S. Hammond & Co., Inc., New York; and from many other sources.

STATE MAPS: In preparing distributional studies, and for many other purposes, the biologist may need state maps with county lines and other important geographical features clearly demarcated. Such maps are available in various scales from companies which specialize in geographical material, including the McKinley Publishing Co., Philadelphia, and the National Survey Co., Chester, Vermont.

STATE ROAD MAPS: Gasoline companies are the most convenient source of these maps, which vary a great deal in usefulness and accuracy. Some companies publish atlases which include all the states and the provinces of Canada.

COUNTY HIGHWAY MAPS: Ordinary road maps do not include secondary or dirt and gravel roads, which are often of great interest to the biologist. County highway departments, located at the county seat, usually can provide maps which are brought up to date each year, showing the entire county highway system with notes on the condition of the various roads.

TOPOGRAPHIC MAPS: The U.S. Geological Survey has prepared numerous maps covering most of the country, which are the most valuable maps the biologist can secure. These "top-sheets" are of different scales, but the two most generally available scales are the 15-minute series, most of which are not modern, and the 7½-minute series, many of which are based on surveys made recently. An index map for each state, and for Alaska, Hawaii, and Puerto Rico, can be secured free of charge by writing to the Director, Geological Survey, Washington 25, D.C. From those index maps, individual sheets can be ordered at 30 cents each. For the beginner, an instruction sheet on topographic symbols can be obtained free. These maps show topography by means of contour lines, which can be easily interpreted with a little practice. The newer maps in the 7½-minute series may show wooded areas in green, a feature of great value to biologists.

SOILS MAPS: The U.S. Department of Agriculture has published large-scale soils maps of many counties. A list of these maps can be secured from the Department. For the biologist who is concerned with the ecology of an area, these maps are useful.

COASTAL MAPS: The U.S. Coast and Geodetic Survey publishes numerous maps of the shore line and adjacent areas, similar to the topographic sheets mentioned above. Such maps are also available for overseas possessions and dependencies of the United States (see below).

AERIAL PHOTOGRAPHS: For certain purposes, large-scale aerial photographs are more useful than maps. Vegetation, condition and extent of bodies of water, and certain other features can be seen clearly on these photographs. Since it requires a good deal of time to prepare maps, aerial photographs may be considerably more up to date than maps of comparable scope. The armed forces may have restrictions on the availability of maps of some areas, but aerial photographs of many areas may be obtained through the Soil Conservation Service, which uses them in planning conservation measures for farmers. The county soil conservation agent or Farm Bureau agent can help in securing these photographs if they are available for your area.

Foreign Maps: The traveler to foreign lands may not be content with the continental or country maps in an ordinary atlas. Maps of a scale similar to topographic maps are available for many countries. More complete information than can be given here may be obtained from Olson and Whitmarsh (see below).

1. *Canada*. Numerous maps similar to U.S. Geological Survey topographic sheets may be obtained from Canada Topographical Survey, Ottawa.

2. *Latin America*. Maps of Mexico in scale of 1:100,000 may be secured from Comision Geografica de Guerra y Fomento, Mexico City. Many of these are out of date. Maps of most parts of Latin America in the scale of 1:1,000,000 have been issued by the American Geographical Society.

3. *United States Possessions and Dependencies*. The U.S. Coast and Geodetic Survey has produced some shore-line maps of Alaska, Guam, Hawaii, the Philippines, and Samoa, which cover most of the areas usually visited.

4. *Other countries*. Road maps of many countries, which may now be somewhat out of date but which are useful in planning itineraries, are included in Atlante Internazionale del Touring Club d'Italiano, available in many libraries.

5. *List of map sources*. Olson, E. C., and Agnes Whitmarsh. 1944. "Foreign Maps." Harper & Brothers, New York. This publication lists major sources of maps for all countries.

SOURCES OF BIOLOGICAL SUPPLIES

Although this is not an exhaustive list, it should permit the reader to secure almost any type of standard biological equipment and supplies.

Carolina Biological Supply Company
Elon College, Elon, North Carolina

Cambosco Scientific Company
37 Antwerp Street
Brighton Sta., Boston, Massachusetts

General Biological Supply House
8200 South Hoyne Avenue
Chicago 20, Illinois

Nature Lab
12 Prospect Street
Bloomfield, New Jersey

Quivira Specialties Company
4204 West 21st Street
Topeka, Kansas

W. M. Welch Manufacturing Co.
1515 Sedgwick Street
Chicago 10, Illinois

Ward's Natural Science Establishment
3000 Ridge Road East
Rochester 9, New York

INDEX

Page references in **boldface** type indicate illustrations

Date Due